INTERNATIONAL SERIES OF MONOGRAPHS ON
BIOMETRY
GENERAL EDITOR: M. J. R. HEALY

INTERNATIONAL UNION OF BIOLOGICAL SCIENCES
UNION INTERNATIONALE DES SCIENCES BIOLOGIQUES
Series B (Colloquia) N° 38

BIOMETRICAL GENETICS

Published with the assistance of U.N.E.S.C.O

International Symposium on

Biometrical Genetics

Proceedings of an International Symposium held at Ottawa, August 1958, sponsored by the Biometrics Society and the International Union of Biological Sciences

Edited by

OSCAR KEMPTHORNE

Professor of Statistics
Iowa State University of Science and Technology

Published by
SYMPOSIUM PUBLICATIONS DIVISION

PERGAMON PRESS

NEW YORK · LONDON · OXFORD · PARIS
1960

PERGAMON PRESS INC.
122 East 55th Street, New York 22, N.Y.
140A New York Avenue, N.W., Washington 5, D.C.
P.O. Box 47715, Los Angeles, California

PERGAMON PRESS LTD
4 & 5 Fitzroy Square, London, W.1
Headington Hill Hall, Oxford

PERGAMON PRESS S.A.R.L.
24 Rue des Ecoles, Paris Ve

PERGAMON PRESS G.m.b.H.
Kaiserstrasse 75, Frankfurt-am-Main

Library of Congress Card No. 59–13096

PRINTED IN GREAT BRITAIN BY ROBERT MACLEHOSE AND CO. LTD
THE UNIVERSITY PRESS, GLASGOW

CONTENTS

EXPERIMENTAL RESULTS

PREFACE

GENETICS is a young subject in the history of science but is already pervading the whole of biological science in a similar way to the pervasion of physics through physical science. The reasons for this are many, but probably one should pick out two: on the one hand, it is a beautiful subject from a purely aesthetic viewpoint and on the other hand it has impact on the whole range of human activity from the study of what is life itself to the utilization of economic plants and animals. It is a branch of science which must be consulted whenever any problem of living matter is under investigation.

The rapid growth of genetics is undoubtedly in part attributable to the growing use of stochastic representations of phenomena and to the development in the past 60 years of procedures for drawing uncertain inferences. No doubt is possible concerning the role of the growth of statistical inference on the growth of genetics, and this is particularly so because the basic genetic mechanism is probabilistic.

It would be rash to attempt a definitive partition of the subject matter of genetics, but it has become apparent in the last 30 or 40 years that there are complementary areas each of which has status in its own right, even though all stem back to classical Mendelian genetics. Perhaps a good way of representing what is happening is to distinguish two approaches requiring somewhat different talents. One approach is the biological one including chemical and physical aspects, and the other is mathematical, including ordinary mathematics, probability and statistics.

One can also make a partition of the subject matter of genetics on the basis of whether it is directed to the identification and understanding of genotypes or whether it is directed to the situation in which genotypes are not identifiable. Text books of genetics abound in examples of the former and text books on animal or plant breeding abound in examples of the latter. It is the latter which is the subject of this volume.

If we consider attributes like milk production of a cow, growth rates of swine, yield of grain of a cereal, or endocrine activity of mice, we can certainly envisage the possibility of identifying genetic factors which are influential and should always be aware of this possibility, but we should also be aware of the fact that there are undoubtedly many different genotypes which give essentially the same value of the attribute. Also we must take account of the fact that such attributes are affected to varying degrees by variations in the environment, in contrast to (say) wrinkled peas which are wrinkled providing one has any reasonable environment.

These two facts, non-identifiability of genotypes and dependence on environment even within a restricted class of environments such as the soil and climatic conditions of the Corn Belt of the United States of America,or South-East England or what you will, have led to the development of a branch of genetics to which the name biometrical genetics is frequently applied. The branch is also referred to sometimes as population genetics, though this is hardly appropriate because population genetics also includes the mathematical theory of population dynamics with specified Mendelian systems and the purely biological examination of natural populations. It is also referred to sometimes as the theory of quantitative inheritance. It seems rather likely that the term ' biometrical genetics ', which is due, it is believed, to K. Mather, will emerge as the generally accepted name for the area.

That there should be deep general interest in biometrical genetics is not surprising because the two main tools for genetic improvement of economic species are the identification of genotypes and what methodology we have for unidentifiable genotypes. It is also not surprising that the interest in biometrical genetics among biometricians is both widespread and deep, because the tools of biometrical genetics are mathematics and biometry.

It was with this background that the organizers of the Third International Biometrics Congress decided to open the congress with an International Symposium on Biometrical Genetics.

The program of the symposium was arranged by a committee consisting of R. E. Comstock, J. F. Crow, C. R. Henderson, O. Kempthorne (Chairman), J. L. Lush and K. Mather. The general arrangements were under the supervision of the secretary of the Biometrics Society, M. J. R. Healy. Excellent local arrangements at Ottawa were made by Canadian groups specifically those associated with G. B. Oakland and J. W. Hopkins. The International Union of Biological Sciences made a grant towards the publication of the proceedings of the Symposium. The great bulk of editorial work and the preparation of the index have been done by Mr. Neeti Ranjan Bohidar, to whom considerable gratitude is due. The cooperation of the Pergamon Press is most gratefully acknowledged.

It only remains to hope that this volume of papers presented at the Symposium will be useful to workers in the field and will stimulate further development in the area of biometrical genetics.

OSCAR KEMPTHORNE

THEORETICAL GENETICS

DOMINANCE, GENOTYPE–ENVIRONMENT INTERACTION, AND HOMEOSTASIS

By R. E. Comstock
University of Minnesota

A formidable operational problem in the study of variance patterns of quantitative characters arises because the environments pertinent to a genetic population are not distributed randomly in time and space. Instead, the environments associated with a specific point or region in the time-space habitat of a population comprise a unique stratum or sub-set that can never be fully representative of the totality of environments that have had to do with the evolution of the population or will have to do with its future.

Because genotype and environment have interacting (not independent) effects on phenotype, the data from any finite experiment pertain unambiguously to the genetic variance of the population with reference only to the sub-set(s) of environment actually sampled by the experiment. In theory, and to a degree in practice, the difficulty can be overcome by replication of the experiment at different points within the pertinent regions of time and space. However, this is expensive business, subject ordinarily to severe restriction.

For the sake of a specific point of reference and to remain on ground familiar to me, what follows will be related to work with corn. During my association with the quantitative genetics research program at North Carolina State College, a major objective was estimation of the total and relative magnitudes of components of the total variance in grain yield of corn populations. By now, the procedures used can be referred to as routine. They consisted of replicated comparisons of random families from populations being studied. Inclusion of two types of families (full-sib and half-sib) in the same experiment allowed estimation of two components of the genetic variance. At North Carolina such experiments were designed to yield simultaneous estimates of the additive and dominance portions of the genetic variance (see Robinson *et al*, 1955). Primary interests were (1) magnitude of the additive component and (2) the relative magnitudes of the additive and dominance components.

The problems involved in getting estimates (unbiased by variance of genotype–environment interaction effects) of variance in genetic effects defined as averages for the totality of environments pertinent to the destiny of a genetic population have become familiar to workers in the field. They were noted by Comstock and Robinson (1952) and reviewed in greater detail by

Comstock (1955). Attention here will be confined to relative magnitudes of estimates of different sorts of genetic variance.

From the beginning of the North Carolina work, we recognized that, to avoid bias in estimates of the absolute size of genetic variances in which we were interested, contributing data would need to be collected in two or more years and two or more locations. At the same time I argued (wishfully, perhaps) that estimates from experiments not meeting this requirement would be satisfactory for evaluating relative magnitudes, e.g. that

$$\frac{V_g}{V_d}=\frac{B_g}{B_d}$$

where V_g = additive genetic variance
V_d = dominance variance
B_g = bias in the estimate of V_g, and
B_d = bias in the estimate of V_d.

The reasoning behind this argument was that the definition of genetic variance components is not related to the physiology of gene action, that the various kinds of genetic effects (statistically defined) involve comparable sorts of physiological pathways and hence should not differ in sensitivity to varying environment.

Lerner (1954) proposed that greater developmental homeostasis is associated with more heterozygous genotypes; that, on the average, phenotypes associated with a heterozygous genotype vary less as a consequence of environment than those associated with a more homozygous genotype. He reviewed pertinent evidence and other evidence has since been reported (e.g. Dobzhansky and Levene, 1955). There is no need here to review all that has been written concerning Lerner's proposal or to debate its merits. More pertinent is examination of what ' homeostasis of heterozygotes ' could mean with respect to biases of variance component estimates.

For illustration, let us consider what happens if one or the other homozygote (at any locus) is superior to the heterozygote in almost all sub-sets of environments but the heterozygote, on the average for all pertinent sub-sets of environments, is superior to both homozygotes. (For simplicity two alleles are assumed per locus.) In such a situation, it is obvious that the ratio of expectations of additive genetic and dominance variance estimates from experiments confined to one sub-set of environments would be characteristic of partial to complete dominance, while the same ratio in an adequate experiment would be characteristic of overdominance. Symbolically this can be stated as follows:

$$\frac{V_d+B_d}{V_g+B_g}<\frac{V_d}{V_g}$$

which means that

$$\frac{B_d}{B_g} < \frac{V_d}{V_g} \quad \text{and} \quad \frac{B_d}{V_d} < \frac{B_g}{V_g}.$$

Bias in experiments that fail to sample the whole of the pertinent environment distribution arise from genotype–environment interaction, i.e.

$$B_d = V_{dE} \quad \text{and} \quad V_g = V_{gE}.$$

Here V_{dE} and V_{gE} are portions of the genotype–environment interaction variance that get confounded with V_d and V_g, respectively, in results from experiments conducted within one stratum (sub-set) of environments.

Now let us look at the problem in terms of a simple genetic model, which will not serve for comprehensive analysis, but will provide enough insight for present purposes. Consider one locus with segregation of two alleles. In any sub-set of environments (the ith) let the average phenotypic difference between *AA* and *aa* homozygotes be $Y_{2.i} - Y_{0.i} = 2x_i$ which may be positive or negative. Let the deviation of the average for heterozygotes from the mean of homozygote averages be

$$Y_{1.i} - \frac{Y_{2.i} + Y_{0.i}}{2} = h_i.$$

Then expectations of contributions of this locus to estimates from an experiment confined to one sub-set of environments will be

$$V_{gi} = 2pq[x_i - (p-q)h_i]^2$$

and

$$V_{di} = 4p^2q^2h_i^2$$

where $p = 1 - q =$ frequency of allele, *A*.

Corresponding averages over all possible sub-sets of environments are

$$\bar{V}_g = 2pq[(\bar{x}^2 + \sigma_x^2) - 2(p-q)(\bar{x}\bar{h} + \sigma_{xh}) + (p-q)^2(\bar{h}^2 + \sigma_h^2)]$$
$$\bar{V}_d = 4p^2q^2(\bar{h}^2 + \sigma_h^2).$$

Here $\bar{x}$ and $\bar{h}$ represent means over all environment sub-sets; σ_x^2, σ_h^2 and σ_{xh}, the variances and covariance of x and h.

Contributions to the variances (for genetic effects defined as averages over the totality of environments) which were the real objects of interest in the North Carolina studies would in this case be

$$V_g = 2pq[\bar{x}^2 - 2(p-q)\bar{x}\bar{h} + (p-q)^2\bar{h}^2]$$
$$V_d = 4p^2q^2\bar{h}^2$$

$\overline{V}_g$ and $\overline{V}_d$ are V_g and V_d plus genotype–environment interaction components, i.e.

$$\overline{V}_g = V_g + V_{gE} \qquad \overline{V}_d = V_d + V_{dE}.$$

Hence

$$V_{gE} = \overline{V}_g - V_g = 2pq[\sigma_x^2 - 2(p-q)\sigma_{xh} + (p-q)^2\sigma_h^2]$$
$$V_{dE} = \overline{V}_d - V_d = 4p^2q^2\sigma_h^2.$$

The ratios of bias to variance are

$$\frac{V_{gE}}{V_g} = \frac{\sigma_x^2 - 2(p-q)\sigma_{xh} + (p-q)^2\sigma_h^2}{\bar{x}^2 - 2(p-q)\bar{x}\bar{h} + (p-q)^2\bar{h}^2}$$

and $$\frac{V_{dE}}{V_d} = \frac{\sigma_h^2}{\bar{h}^2}.$$

Of concern to us are conditions that lead to equality or inequality of the two ratios.

Consider, first, a special case. Given $\bar{h} > \bar{x}$, i.e. over dominance in average effects of the genotypes, and $p = (\bar{x}+\bar{h})/2\bar{h}$, the denominator of V_{gE}/V_g would be zero. The ratio itself would go to infinity and would obviously exceed V_{dE}/V_d.

For more general treatment let

$$a = \bar{h}/\bar{x} \quad \text{and} \quad b = \sigma_h/\sigma_x.$$

Then $\dfrac{V_{gE}}{V_g} \gtreqless \dfrac{V_{dE}}{V_d}$ when

$$(a^2 - b^2) \gtreqless 2(p-q)ab(ar-b)$$

where r is the correlation between x and h. There is no loss of generality if $\bar{x}$ is limited to positive values. This amounts only to deciding that the allele which in homozygous state has the higher average phenotype shall be designated as A. It is reasonable also to consider only positive values of h; because in characters related to fitness the regression of phenotype on heterozygosity is ordinarily positive. Under these conditions, a will always be positive; as will b, since standard deviations are always positive. Then

$$\frac{V_{gE}}{V_g} > \frac{V_{dE}}{V_d}$$

when

(1) $a > b$, $p = q$ or $r = b/a$

(2) $a > b$, $p > q$ and $r < b/a$

(3) $a > b$ $p < q$ and $r > b/a$.

The reverse will be true when

(4) $a<b$ and $p\leqq q$

(5) $1-a^2/b^2>2(p-q)a$ and $a<b$.

These sets of conditions are, of course, sufficient rather than necessary. The intent is merely to demonstrate that inequality of V_{gE}/V_g and V_{dE}/V_d, in either direction, is possible.

It is proper to inquire next whether any of the conditions that make $V_{gE}/V_g>V_{dE}/V_d$, and vice-versa, are, on biological grounds, at all probable. First, consider case (2). Given overdominance a is greater than 1.0 and might easily be greater than b. The frequency, p, of the more favorable allele would often be larger than q, frequency of the less favorable allele. Finally, r might easily be smaller than b/a. This situation is of special interest in connection with inference concerning level of dominance from the ratio of estimates of dominance and additive genetic variance. It is easily seen that upward bias in the estimate of dominance variance could be less than in the estimate of additive genetic variance when estimates are based on data from a single sub-set of environments. Then interpretation assuming equal bias would under-evaluate the true level of dominance.

On the other side of the picture, consider case (5). Given a character for which affecting genes exhibit little dominance, a rather small and considerably less than b is not improbable. In this case condition (5) could easily be met. However, the chance of critical misinterpretation as a consequence of disproportion in biases appears less likely here than in case (2).

The prime issue is that for biases under discussion the ratio,

$$\frac{\text{Bias}}{\text{Variance estimated}}$$

is not necessarily the same for all kinds of genetic variance. Hence ratios of genetic variance components cannot be inferred with complete assurance from data collected in one sub-set of environments, say, in one year at one location.

Experimental evidence on biases actually encountered is scanty. Rojas and Sprague (1952) estimated V_g, V_d and components of genotype–environment interaction variance in corn yield. They reported that interaction variance associated with dominance effects was larger relative to dominance variance than interaction variance associated with additive effects relative to additive genetic variance. Somewhat different results were reported by Comstock *et al.* (1957) in a summary of data then available from the North Carolina studies. Their data were also on corn yield but did not allow complete separation of genotype–environment interaction variances from genetic variances. In one series of experiments, replicated over years but not over places, V_g+V_{gp}, $V_{gy}+V_{gpy}$, V_d+V_{dp} and $V_{dy}+V_{dpy}$ could be estimated. In another series, replicated in some instances over years but not over places and in other instances over places but not over years, the quantities listed above or the quantities, $V_g + V_{gy}$, $V_{gp} + V_{gpy}$, $V_d + V_{dy}$ and $V_{dp} + V_{dpy}$ could be estimated. Here

V_{gy} is variance due to interaction of additive genetic effects with year,
V_{gp} is variance due to interaction of additive effects with places,
V_{gpy} is variance due to second order interaction of additive effects with year and place,

and V_{dy}, V_{dp} and V_{dpy} have analogous meaning in terms of dominance effects. Averaging over experiments the ratios of the purely interaction variance estimate to the estimate of the quantity including V_g or V_d, e.g. estimate of $V_{gy} + V_{gpy}$ divided by estimate of $V_g + V_{gp}$, were as follows:

	Estimates involving additive effects	Estimates involving dominance effects
Series 1	0.73	0.50
Series 2	0.73	0.16

In contrast to results reported by Rojas and Sprague, the North Carolina data suggested greatest bias from genotype–environment interaction variance in estimates of V_g. This contrast could be interpreted in two ways: (1) as indicating that the ratio of interaction to genetic variance is sometimes higher for one kind of genetic effects and in other cases higher for another kind, or (2) as the result of high sampling error of the estimates involved. The nature of the sampling errors is such that their magnitude can only be approximated in terms of the observed variation of a series of estimates of the quantities (ratios) in question. In this respect the evidence cited does not suffice for confident interpretation.

The foregoing and its implications may be summarized as follows:

1. If estimates of genetic variances and ratios among them are to be useful in analysis of forces responsible for the present status of populations and in prediction of future changes, they must pertain to genetic effects defined meaningfully in terms of the totality of environments having to do with the history and destiny of the population.
2. At best such variances are elusive quantities. A reasonable approach to unbiased estimates of their absolute magnitudes requires data from experiments replicated in both time and space. Places employed should of course be properly related to the normal ‘ habitat ’ of the population.
3. Inferences from relative magnitudes of estimates of different kinds of genetic variances could be based on biased estimates if it were safe to assume, for all genetic variances, a constant ratio of bias to variance estimated.
4. The notion that developmental homeostasis is a function of hetero-

zygosity suggests that this is not a safe assumption. The analysis presented here demonstrates, if that were necessary, that the ratio of bias to variance estimated may conceivably be either higher or lower for dominance variance than for additive genetic variance. Of special interest is the fact that inequality of this ratio might have a critical bearing on inference concerning level of dominance based on the relative magnitude of estimates of dominance and additive genetic variance.

5. The prime implication is that information about the relative magnitude of different sorts of genetic variance obtained from an experiment confined to one stratum of the totality of pertinent environments needs to be supplemented by at least some information on magnitude of bias from genotype–environment interaction variance.
6. Replication (of the whole experiment providing estimates of two or more genetic variances) in time and place is desirable but often impossible due to cost considerations. A supplementary experiment providing information on magnitude of bias in estimation of only one genetic variance will sometimes suffice. For example, in the work of Robinson *et al.* (1955) the smallness of the ratio of the estimate of dominance variance to that of additive genetic variance was the critical finding. The critical feature of the result could have been the result of estimation bias only through greater upward bias in additive genetic variance than in dominance variance. Adjusting the original estimate of additive genetic variance downward in accord with later information on bias in the estimate of that component and accepting the original estimate of dominance variance as unbiased provides a severe test of the original interpretation. When this is done, the ratio of the estimate of dominance variance to the estimate of additive genetic variance is still small enough so that interpretation of the finding is unchanged, though the force of the evidence is a little less.

REFERENCES

COMSTOCK, R. E. (1955) Theory of quantitative genetics: synthesis, *Cold Spring Harbor Symposia on Quant. Biol.* **20**, 93–102.

COMSTOCK, R. E. & ROBINSON, H. F. (1952) Genetic parameters, their estimation and significance. *Proc. 6th International Grasslands Congress*, **1**, 284–291.

COMSTOCK, R. E., ROBINSON, H. F. & COCKERHAM, C. C. (1957) Quantitative Genetics Project Report (mimeo.), 98 pp.

DOBZHANSKY, TH. & LEVENE, HOWARD (1955) Genetics of natural populations. XXIV. Developmental homeostasis in natural populations of *Drosophila pseudoobscura*, *Genetics* **40**, 797–808.

LERNER, I. MICHAEL (1954) *Genetic Homeostasis*, 134 pp., Wiley, New York.

ROBINSON, H. F., COMSTOCK, R. E. & HARVEY, P. H. (1955) Genetic variances in open-pollinated varieties of corn, *Genetics* **40**, 45–60.

ROJAS, BASILIO A. & SPRAGUE, G. F. (1952) A comparison of variance components in corn yield trials. III. General and specific combining ability and their interaction with locations and years, *Agronomy J.* **44**, 462–466.

THE BALANCE-SHEET OF VARIABILITY

By K. MATHER
University of Birmingham

PROVIDED that there has been no selection and in the absence of interactions between non-allelic genes, the genetic variability in the segregating generations descended from a cross between two homozygous lines appears in three components. First, there is the D component, depending on differences between individuals homozygous for allelic genes, and second, there is the H component, depending on departures of heterozygotes from the average of the two corresponding homozygotes. Both of these contribute to the variation within each generation, measured round its own mean. Thirdly, there is the departure of the generation mean from the mid-parent value, found as the average of the two parental homozygous lines, and this is a function of $S(h)$, the notation being that of Mather (1949a). Since genetic variation measured round the mid-parent value is the sum of the variance round the generation mean and the squared deviation of this mean from the mid-parent, it may be written in terms of D, H and $S^2(h)$ each component taking a coefficient appropriate to the generation. These coefficients must sum to unity (Mather, 1949b). Thus if we write the variation of any generation as $xD+yH+zS^2(h)$, then $x+y+z = 1$. For example in the F_1, $x = y = 0$ and $z = 1$, while in the F_2 generation $x = \frac{1}{2}$, $y = \frac{1}{4}$ and $z = \frac{1}{2}^2 = \frac{1}{4}$. In F_3, we must add $V_{1F2} = \frac{1}{2}D+\frac{1}{16}H$ and $V_{2F3} = \frac{1}{4}D+\frac{1}{8}H$, these being the genetic variances between and within families, to obtain the genetic variance round the generation mean, which is itself $\frac{1}{4}S(h)$. Then $x = \frac{1}{2}+\frac{1}{4} = \frac{3}{4}$, $y = \frac{1}{16}+\frac{1}{8} = \frac{3}{16}$ and $z = \frac{1}{4}^2 = \frac{1}{16}$. Similarly for the S_3 generation obtained by sibmating in F_2, $x = \frac{1}{4}+\frac{1}{4} = \frac{1}{2}$, $y = \frac{1}{16}+\frac{3}{16} = \frac{1}{4}$, and $z = \frac{1}{2}^2 = \frac{1}{4}$.

The total variability as measured from the phenotypes will vary with the generation according to the relative magnitudes of D, H and $S^2(h)$. But in a deeper sense the differences are no more than a redistribution among the components. Genetically the total variability is constant, as is indeed required by the permanence of genetic differences. A similar relation holds for the components of variation depending on genotype–environment interactions, and a similar balance sheet may be struck for them (Mather and Morley Jones, 1958).

The situation is changed in detail, though not in principle, if selection is practised. Some of the gene differences will then be lost because certain alleles will be fixed in the sense that every member of the population will become homozygous for them. This will be reflected in a corresponding and permanent departure of the mean from the mid-parent, and this departure will thus come to contain a further component depending on the d increments of the fixed genes as well as the h increments of those still unfixed.

Returning, however, to the case where selection is absent, the visible variability as measured by $xD+yH+zS^2(h)$ is not the total of the variability contained in the cross. Indeed it may be only a small part of it. Let us consider a very simple example where the two parent lines differ in k unlinked genes, each contributing the same d increment and all with $h = 0$. The maximum difference obtainable is where all the increasing alleles are associated in one line and all the decreasing alleles in another. Each line then departs by $S(d)$ from the mid-parent so that the total variation is $S^2(d) = (kd)^2 = kD$. Now in the F_2 from crossing two such lines, half the variation is present in the heterozygous state and will be reflected in the H and $S^2(h)$ components. The other half is present in differences between homozygotes and is measured by the D component. But half the total variability is $\frac{1}{2}kD$ of which $\frac{1}{2}D$ constitutes only the fraction $1/k$. The fraction $(k-1)/k$ of the variability is concealed, obviously as a result of balancing combinations of homozygous genes of the type $AAbb$ etc. The more genes there are the greater will be this concealed fraction $(k-1)/k$. This concealed fraction is the homozygotic potential variability of Mather (1943). With linkage the concealed fraction is increased where the repulsion phase is preponderant and decreased where coupling relations preponderate. It is not difficult to accommodate inequality of the k values of d in the calculation, but the simple case outlined will serve to illustrate the point.

Two balance sheets of variability may thus be struck. The first relates to the immediately measureable variability which may be redistributed among the three components and this may be represented by the relation $x+y+z = 1$ in the expression $xD+yH+zS^2(h)$. The second balance sheet goes deeper, for it covers all the variability, potential as well as free, in the cross and it depends on the additional parameter k. In principle, k can be estimated in various ways by quantities generally denotable as K, the number of effective factors (Mather, 1949a). Such estimates are, however, difficult to arrive at reliably, and little attention has so far been paid to their calculation. Nevertheless without reliable estimation of the number of effective factors the balance of potential and free variability cannot be struck and the magnitude of ultimate response to selection cannot be calculated. The derivation of reliable methods of estimation is long overdue.

REFERENCES

Mather, K. (1943) Polygenic inheritance and natural selection *Biol. Revs.* **18**, 32–64.

Mather, K. (1949a) *Biometrical Genetics*, Methuen, London.

Mather, K. (1949b) The genetical theory of continuous variation, *Proc. 8th Int. Congr. Genetics. Hereditas* (*Suppl. Vol*) 376–401.

Mather, K. & Morley Jones. (1958) Interactions of genotype and environment in continuous variation I Description, *Biometrics* **14**, 343–359.

BIOMETRICAL RELATIONS BETWEEN RELATIVES AND SELECTION THEORY*

By Oscar Kempthorne
Statistical Laboratory, Iowa State College

INTRODUCTION

For several years I have been concerned about the status of the theory of genetic selection in the case of polygenic inheritance. I take the book by Lush (1937) and the recent book by Lerner (1958) to be definitive accounts of our present knowledge, and it appears to me that what mathematical or statistical theory we have is based on the assumption that the genes act additively. It would be comforting if we could assume, without proof, that the theory based on additive gene action would predict what would happen to the additive genetic values. It is obvious, however, that no such result can be proved because the additive genetic value of a genotype is a statistical abstraction and is not a biological fact peculiar to the genotype and the environment or population of environments, but is a property of a genotype, which may well not change, but also of all other genotypes and the genotypic frequencies in a population which certainly do change. The additive genetic values of genotypes will change as the population structure changes and we do not even have a theory to the effect that they change less slowly under selection than does the population structure. It is for reasons such as these that the theory initiated by Fisher, Immer and Tedin (1932) and carried forward so effectively by Mather and his co-workers has appeal. For this is based on a model for genotypic values remain unchanged. This theory, however, is restricted largely to populations derived from homozygous lines.

We have fairly extensive results on what may perhaps be termed the economic efficiency of various combined testing and selection schemes taking into account generation interval and breeding and testing facilities available (e.g. Lush, 1937; Lerner, 1958). This line of work is exemplified in Robertson's (1957) paper on the optimum number of progeny. As far as I know all this work is based on a model in which these gene effects are additive. Just how useful such selection theory is, in my opinion, is a moot point with any of our economic animals.

In the present state of development of genetic selection for economic plants and animals it seems that we must make a partition of situations into at least two classes. With many plants the situation is that we may be able

* Journal Paper No. J–3579 of the Iowa Agricultural and Home Economics Experiment Station, Ames, Iowa. Project No. 890.

to develop stocks which breed true and which may be mated to give material of superior merit. In other cases, and this appears to be very much the case with animals, we have to select parents from each generation of a continuing population to provide the individuals of the next generation. It is this situation that I am concerned with. For here the problem is quite unambiguously to predict which matings in a particular generation will give offspring of superior merit. Indeed, it is appropriate to ask whether there are matings which throw superior offspring. The amount of theory available on this question is pathetically little.

The aim of the present paper is to attempt a review of our present knowledge of the biometrical relationships among relatives and to discuss the relevance of these to what may be termed the purely statistical theory of mass genetic selection. The main idea is to consider the accuracy with which we can predict the phenotypes of individuals from knowledge of their relatives. I call this the purely statistical theory to distinguish it from the economic theory in which the cost of obtaining observations and the amount of resources available must also be taken into account. In other words the statistical theory plus cost and time considerations lead to measures of economic efficiency of procedures. It seems that a useful economic theory must be preceded by what I call the statistical theory.

INGREDIENTS OF A THEORY OF QUANTITATIVE INHERITANCE

Development of a theory of quantitative inheritance and application of the theory to real problems requires unambiguous statement of the assumptions of the theory. This corresponds rather closely to the accepted view that exact descriptions of experimental technique are necessary for assessment of experimental evidence. But in the field of mass selection no such standards seem to be general.

The ingredients which I regard as essential for a theory of quantitative inheritance applicable say to farm animals are:

1. That there is an arbitrary number of loci for each of which there is an arbitrary number of alleles.
2. That there are no assumptions with regard to the magnitude of gene effects, such as for instance that individual gene substitutions have small effects. Such a theory I have termed an infinitesimal theory, the most complete, even to the present time, being that of Fisher (1918). It seems to me that the theory should envisage a full spectrum of gene effects from small to large, possibly with greater frequency of small effects, though assumptions as to these frequencies should be avoided.
3. That there should be no assumptions as regards the nature of gene effects, with regard to the non-existence of dominance or epistacy of any form.

If the theory is to be applicable to selection in a dairy herd for example, it should take some account of:

4. Non-random mating.
5. Differential viabilities and fecundities.

Here the difficulty is that a formal statement requires the specification of a large number of parameters and no one has yet discovered a useful way of doing this. The absence of a theory of some generality with regard to linkage is a deficiency which should be susceptible to correction because the problem can be specified fairly precisely on the basis of formal genetic knowledge and can be set up, using for example Kosambi's formula (1943) without the requirement of specifying a large number of parameters. Even in this case, however, I suppose one should visualize tight linkage of genetic factors with complementary roles, and any such model presents considerable difficulties.

In addition to the above ingredients, one can also list the following:

6. Sex-linked factors.
7. Maternal effects either genetic or non-genetic.

and 8. Genotype environmental interactions.

The difficulty with these is not at all conceptual, but merely that they increase the size of the problem, particularly with regard to the number of symbols that must be carried along.

I deemed it worth while to set the above views down, because I am sure there is a considerable lack of appreciation of what one means by ' a theory of quantitative inheritance ' or ' a theory of mass selection ', to the extent that considerable effort is being put into large breeding projects on the basis of inadequate if not fallacious theory, with at the same time no appreciation of the complementary roles of theoretical and experimental research.

As an example of what I mean, theoretical workers, including myself, have examined the mathematical nature of additive genetic variance in non-random mating populations which does no harm because theoretical people will devote some of their activities to purely intellectual problems. At the same time experimental people talk about the additive genetic variance in non-random mating populations. But has anyone considered how one obtains from observations on unidentified genotypes an estimate of the additive genetic variance of a non-random mating population? As far as I know no one has, and I know of no procedure of taking observations and making computations from them which will give an estimate of the mathematically defined additive genetic variance of the non-random mating population. Even the calculation of inbreeding coefficients may be misleading in a population under selection.

THE GENERAL BASIS FOR PREDICTING AN INDIVIDUAL'S PERFORMANCE FROM THOSE OF RELATIVES

The ensuing section contains a formulation first put in the literature by Czekanowski (1933), though it is felt that another presentation may be helpful to students. If we consider predictors which are linear, then the formula for predicting an individual X from relatives R_1, R_2, ... R_k is, ignoring population mean,

$$X = \alpha_1 R_1 + \alpha_2 R_2 + \ldots + \alpha_k R_k$$

where α_1, α_2, ... α_k are given by the equations

$$\begin{aligned}
\alpha_1 V(R_1) + \alpha_2 \operatorname{Cov}(R_1, R_2) + \ldots + \alpha_k \operatorname{Cov}(R_1, R_k) &= \operatorname{Cov}(X, R_1) \\
\alpha_1 \operatorname{Cov}(R_1, R_2) + \alpha_2 V(R_2) + \ldots + \alpha_k \operatorname{Cov}(R_2, R_k) &= \operatorname{Cov}(X, R_2) \\
\cdot \quad \cdot \quad \cdot \quad \cdot \quad \cdot \quad \cdot \quad \cdot \quad \cdot \quad \cdot \quad \cdot \quad \cdot & \quad \cdot \\
\alpha_1 \operatorname{Cov}(R_1, R_k) + \alpha_2 \operatorname{Cov}(R_2, R_k) + \ldots + \alpha_k V(R_k) &= \operatorname{Cov}(X, R_k) \qquad (1)
\end{aligned}$$

I shall assume that there is additivity of genotypic and environmental forces and that the environmental variance is constant. I shall also deal with the case in which the individuals X, R_1 ... R_k are random members of the population subject only to the particular relationships among them, and correlated only because of the genetic relationship. The prediction equation is of course easily modified to take care of environmental correlations but to include these would take me away from my present point of interest. All populations will be taken to be in equilibrium under random mating.

The attributes may be standardized so that the variances are all unity and the covariances become correlations. The equations determining the α's then become

$$\begin{aligned}
\alpha_1 + \alpha_2 \rho_{12} + \ldots + \alpha_k \rho_{1k} &= \rho_{x1} \\
\alpha_1 \rho_{12} + \alpha_2 + \ldots + \alpha_k \rho_{2k} &= \rho_{x2} \\
\cdot \quad \cdot \quad \cdot \quad \cdot \quad \cdot \quad \cdot & \quad \cdot \\
\alpha_1 \rho_{1k} + \alpha_2 \rho_{2k} + \ldots + \alpha_k &= \rho_{xk} \qquad (2)
\end{aligned}$$

and the variability in X removed by the predictor is

$$\sum_i \alpha_i \rho_{xi}$$

The residual variability is

$$1 - \sum_i \alpha_i \rho_{xi}$$

There are no hard and fast rules by which one should compare predictors. From the point of view of assessing the gain in information on an individual arising from knowledge of relatives, we could consider the amount of variance accounted for by the prediction or the amount of variance around the predicted value.

In considering the use of possible biometric relations among relatives in selection the appropriate basis for comparison is as follows. This is developed by considering the predictor as an index I for selecting individuals. The expected gain from truncation selection of X on the basis of I is

$$\rho_{XI}\frac{\Delta I}{\sigma_I},$$

where ρ_{XI} is the correlation of X and I, ΔI is the selection differential in I and σ_I is the standard deviation of I. With a particular amount of selection the gain is proportional to ρ_{XI}.

Also

$$\begin{aligned}
\text{Cov}(X, I) &= \text{Cov}(X, \textstyle\sum \alpha_i R_i) \\
&= \sum_i \alpha_i \text{Cov}(X, R_i) \\
&= \text{Sum of squares removed by regression of } X \text{ on } R_1, R_2, \ldots \\
\text{V}(X) &= 1 \\
\text{V}(I) &= \sum_{ij} \alpha_i\alpha_j \text{Cov}(R_i, R_j) \\
&= \sum_i \alpha_i \text{Cov}(X, R_i) \text{ from the normal equations.}
\end{aligned}$$

Hence

$$\rho_{XI}^2 = \text{Sum of squares removed by regression.}$$

Therefore in comparing predictors for mass selection purposes, the appropriate measure is the square root of the sum of squares removed by the predictor evaluated in standardized variables, or the square root of the proportion of the sum of squares removed by the predictor. This will be called the efficiency of the predictor.

In what follows we need various correlations among relatives. In view of the general formula which takes account of dominance and epistacy (which can be modified to take care of an inbred parental generation with random mating)

$$\sigma_p^2\rho_{xy} = 2r_{xy}\sigma_A^2 + u_{xy}\sigma_D^2 + (2r_{xy})^2\sigma_{AA}^2 + (2r_{xy})u_{xy}\sigma_{AD}^2 + u_{xy}^2\sigma_{DD}^2 + \ldots$$

where σ_p^2 is the phenotypic variance
σ_A^2 is the additive variance
σ_D^2 is the dominance variance
σ_{AA}^2 is the additive × additive variance

etc.,
we may designate a correlation by

$$\rho(s, t)$$

where $s = 2r_{xy}$ = twice the coefficient of parentage of the two relatives
= twice the probability that two genes at a locus, one from each of the two related individuals, are identical by descent.

and $t = u_{xy}$ = the probability that the two genes at a locus of one individual are identical by descent to the two genes at the same locus of the related individual.

PREDICTION FROM ONE PARENT

If we are predicting an offspring (O) of a parent (P) by the use of a linear predictor

$$O = \alpha P,$$

then the normal equation is

$$\alpha = \rho(\tfrac{1}{2}, 0),$$

the variability removed is $\rho^2(\frac{1}{2}, 0)$ and the efficiency is $\rho(\frac{1}{2}, 0)$.

We could consider the use of various other relatives on one side of the lineage but before doing so it is worth noting that if we have a predictor which includes Z, say, where Z is the mean of an infinite array of offspring of the parent, which will in a large population be half sibs, then the predictor will be Z. This fact, which is rather obvious intuitively, can be seen from the normal equations (1) by letting X equal O, R_1 equal Z, and $R_2, \ldots R_k$ equal phenotypic values for other relatives, and noting that

$$V(Z) = \text{Cov}\,(HS) = \text{Cov}\,(X, Z)$$

and

$$\text{Cov}\,(Z, R_k) = \text{Cov}\,(X, R_k)$$

so that $\alpha_1 = 1$. The amount of variability removed is $\rho(\frac{1}{4}, 0)$.

The maximum possible efficiency is therefore $\sqrt{[\rho(\frac{1}{4}, 0)]}$. It seems rather pointless to assess any predictor by its overall efficiency and more appropriate to assess it relative to the best predictor we can find with infinite data. It seems appropriate therefore to introduce a concept of relative efficiency exemplified as follows.

The overall relative efficiency of predicting from one parent alone is

$$\frac{\rho(\frac{1}{2}, 0)}{\sqrt{[\rho(\frac{1}{4}, 0)]}}.$$

If the only variability were genotypic and this were additive in gene effects this ratio would be unity. In general the ratio is

$$\frac{1}{2}\frac{\sigma_A^2}{\sigma_P^2} \Big/ \sqrt{\left(\frac{1}{4}\frac{\sigma_A^2}{\sigma_P^2}\right)} = \sqrt{\left(\frac{\sigma_A^2}{\sigma_P^2}\right)}$$

and if we denote σ_A^2/σ_P^2 by h^2, the relative efficiency is h.

I have been interested in the extent to which utilization of information on the one parent and his relatives of the same or previous generations can approach the maximal possible efficiency. This is equivalent to posing the question: knowing a parent in one generation and any relatives of that parent, how well can one predict an offspring of the parent? Rather as one might imagine I.Q. scores on all humans and then wish to predict the I.Q. of an offspring of a particular individual (though of course with a human population we would not be able to do so because of homogamy and association of environmental and genotypic effects). It is easily seen that the best predictor X from the phenotypic value of a parent and of its two parents GP_1, and GP_2 is by the equation

$$X = \frac{(\rho-2\rho\rho')}{1-2\rho^2}P+\frac{(\rho'-\rho^2)}{1-2\rho^2}(GP_1+GP_2)$$

where ρ is $\rho(\frac{1}{2}, 0)$ and ρ' is $\rho(\frac{1}{4}, 0)$. The variability removed by this predictor is

$$\frac{\rho^2+2\rho'^2-4\rho^2\rho'}{1-2\rho^2}.$$

If ρ is $\frac{1}{4}$ and ρ' is $\frac{1}{8}$, this works out to be 1/14 as opposed to a maximum amount possible with one side of the lineage equal to 1/8 and to 1/16 with a predictor utilizing only the parental value. The relative efficiency using the parent only is for this case 0.5 with parental value only and 0.536 with parent and grandparental values.

As another example I considered the prediction of an individual from knowledge of one parent, the two parents of that parent and the average of an infinite array of full sibs of the parent. There is no point in cluttering up this paper with formulae but some computations I performed are relevant to the type of problem I am considering. For the case $\sigma_A^2 = \frac{1}{2}$, $\sigma_D^2 = \frac{1}{4}$, epistatic variance $= 0$, $\sigma_P^2 = 1$, I found that the predictor was

$$\frac{2}{11}\text{(parent)}+\frac{11}{264}\text{(total of 2 grandparents)}+\frac{5}{33}\text{(mean of full sibs of parent)}$$

and that this prediction equation accounted for 79/1056 of the variability. This is to be compared with the predictor based on parent alone accounting for 66/1056 and the optimal predictor based on the mean of an infinite array of half-sibs of the individual to be predicted accounting for 132/1056 of the variability. The gain over the use of the parent alone is sizeable and I wonder what is the best possible predictor assuming information on the parent and infinite arrays of all possible collateral or ancestral relatives. The question is academic to be sure (it is interesting that the same question was posed but not solved by Czekanowski, 1933), but I think it is relevant to our understanding of selection formulae. I do not have the answer to the question or I would give it here.

LINEARITY OF BIOMETRIC RELATIONSHIPS

It is a common pedagogic example of linear regression to present the case when a dependent variable y, say, is exactly a quadratic function of x but the range of x is such that the linear regression of y on x is zero. This ' horrible ' example is completely relevant to the use of biometric relationships as formulae for selection. The regression of offspring on parent which seems to be one of the main tools of selection theory is nothing more or less than a mean square linear regression. At risk of repeating knowledge well known in statistical literature, but because, despite the existence of this knowledge in the statistical literature, the concepts appear not to be fully understood by applied geneticists, the mean square linear regression of y on x is defined to be the function $\alpha+\beta x$ such that

$$E(y-\alpha-\beta x)^2,$$

where E denotes averaging over the population, is a minimum (see for example Cramer 1945). The regression of y on x however is the relationship of the expected value of y given x to x, and tells us the mean y in any x-array. These two regressions are by no means the same as in the ' horrible ' example quoted above. They are the same if regression of y on x is linear and this will happen, for example, if the joint distribution of y and x is bivariate normal. In general, however, a mean square regression tells us what linear function of x is the best predictor of y averaging over the whole population of y and x values. We are not entitled to use this regression to obtain an indication of the phenotypic value of offspring arising from a selected parent unless we have some evidence that the regression is linear throughout its range. This prompts immediately three questions:

(*a*) Is the regression of offspring on parent linear or essentially linear?

(*b*) Does the curvature of the regression of offspring on parent have any significance with regard to biometrical genetics?

and (*c*) How much would we gain by using a predictor of offspring which is quadratic in the parental value?

Perhaps some workers have thought and written about these questions, but I am aware of no published theoretical consideration of the questions. One observation to be made in connection with these questions is that if we designate the parental value by P, then P^2, $\log P$, $\sqrt{P}$ and indeed any function of P which can be defined (and is not necessarily continuous) are also attributes which can be considered as being determined by polygenic inheritance. This suggests immediately that the questions posed above are intimately related to the use of correlations within and between different animals of different attributes in selection for one attribute. This point, however, is offhand confusing also because, in selecting for P for instance, we are also selecting for P^2 or $\log P$ or against $1/P$ and so on.

On the question of linearity of regression of offspring on parent, my deliberations lead me to two conclusions:

1. That if there are no environmental effects and the genes are additive in their effects there will be linearity of regression (a well-known conclusion of little value because the premises hold so rarely).
2. That even if the genes are additive in their effects but there is environmental variability the regression of offspring on parent will be non-linear in general.

The second remark is to be modified if one can assume a very large number of loci with infinitesimal effects, when normality of joint distributions of offspring and parent may well obtain. This serves, I think, to lead us to the view that normality of the joint distribution is a property to be sought after by transformation if the selection theory is to be appropriate.

On the question of whether the curvature of regression of offspring on parent has any biometrical genetic significance I have no answer after considerable deliberation. I am impressed however by the fact that even if we exclude epistacy, our currently popular description of the situation is given by the representation

$$\text{phenotype deviation} = A+D+E$$

in which A is the additive (or breeding value)
D is the sum of dominance deviations
and E is the environmental contribution

and that we estimate only (denoting average over the population by ‘ ave ’)

$$\text{ave}\,(A^2), \quad \text{ave}\,(D^2), \quad \text{ave}\,(E^2)$$

assuming ave (AE), ave (DE), to be zero and with ave (AD) equal to zero by definition. This impresses me as a most primitive description which we can surely improve on. I have examined ways of estimating

$$\text{ave}\,(A^3), \quad \text{ave}\,(A^2D), \quad \text{ave}\,(AD^2) \quad \text{and} \quad \text{ave}\,(D^3)$$

as well as fourth moments of the quantities A and D. I find for instance that

$$\text{Cov}\,(P, 0^2) = \text{Cov}\,(P^2, 0) = \tfrac{1}{2}\,\text{ave}\,(A^3)+\text{ave}\,(A^2D)+\tfrac{1}{2}\,\text{ave}\,(AD^2)$$

There is therefore the possibility of exploring the relationship of A to D. It could happen for instance that individuals with large positive or negative values of A have D values which are large in absolute magnitude. The occurrence of large positive D values in superior animals could explain difficulty in making genetic advance. In the case of F_2 populations there appears to be the possibility of constructing and evaluating several measures of degree of dominance. This is of course possible also using the methods of Fisher, Immer and Tedin (1932).

On the question of how much we would gain by in predicting an offspring using the square of the parental value as well as the parental value, I have only been able to get messy formulae, and wonder what examination of real data would show. One study I know of (Beardsley *et al.*, 1950) is somewhat inconclusive. A question I have not been able to get a neat answer for is the extent to which one can approach the maximal efficiency of predicting an offspring which uses the mean of an infinite array of half-sibs by using a polynomial in the parental value.

PREDICTION OF THE OFFSPRING OF A MATING

It is easily seen that if we have random mating the predictor of offspring from the two parents is

$$O = \alpha(P_1+P_2)$$

where

$$\alpha = \rho(\tfrac{1}{2}, 0)$$

and the amount of variability removed is $2\rho^2(\frac{1}{2}, 0)$. Also the best possible predictor of the offspring of a mating is the mean of an infinite array of offspring of the mating, which accounts for a proportion $\rho(\frac{1}{2}, \frac{1}{4})$ of the variability. If the only genetic variability were additive and it comprised 50% of the total the relative efficiency of prediction by the two parental values would be about 71%.

The best predictor using the two parental values and the four grand-parental values is

$$0 = \frac{(\rho-4\rho\rho')}{(2-4\rho^2)}(P_1+P_2)+\frac{(2\rho'-\rho^2)}{(2-4\rho^2)}(GP_1+GP_2+GP_3+GP_4)$$

where $\rho = \rho(\frac{1}{2}, 0)$ and $\rho' = \rho(\frac{1}{4}, 0)$. The amount of variability removed is equal to

$$\frac{(\rho-4\rho\rho')}{(2-4\rho^2)}2\rho+\frac{(2\rho'-\rho^2)}{(2-4\rho^2)}4\rho'$$

$$=\frac{\rho^2-8\rho^2\rho'+4\rho'^2}{(1-2\rho^2)}$$

I next considered the extent to which non-linear predictors from the two parental values could be useful and felt optimistic about the use of a predictor based on the parental values P_1 and P_2 and the product of the two P_1P_2.

It is not to be surprised at that this sort of regression was used by Fisher (Fisher, 1930, and Fisher, Immer and Tedin, 1932). It is related also to the constant parent regression technique of Hull (1952; see also Griffing, 1950). Under random mating P_1 and P_2 are independent and the predictor

$$O = \alpha P_1 + \beta P_2 + \gamma P_1 P_2$$

has coefficients α, β, γ which are given by the equations

$$\begin{aligned}
\alpha \mathrm{V}(P_1) + \quad 0 \quad + \gamma \operatorname{Cov}(P_1, P_1P_2) &= \operatorname{Cov}(O, P_1)\\
0 \quad + \beta \mathrm{V}(P_2) + \gamma \operatorname{Cov}(P_2, P_1P_2) &= \operatorname{Cov}(O, P_2)\\
\alpha \operatorname{Cov}(P_1, P_1P_2) + \beta \operatorname{Cov}(P_2, P_1P_2) + \gamma \mathrm{V}(P_1P_2) &= \operatorname{Cov}(O, P_1P_2)
\end{aligned}$$

Also using standardized variables

$$\begin{aligned}
\mathrm{V}(P_1) = 1 = \mathrm{V}(P_2) &= \mathrm{V}(P_1P_2)\\
\operatorname{Cov}(P_1, P_1P_2) = \operatorname{Cov}(P_2, P_1P_2) &= 0\\
\operatorname{Cov}(O, P_1) = \operatorname{Cov}(O, P_2) &= \rho(\tfrac{1}{2}, 0)
\end{aligned}$$

so that we need to find $\operatorname{Cov}(O, P_1P_2)$. This is easily obtained for the case of one segregating locus (or many independently segregating loci among which there is no epistacy). With one locus it is

$$\begin{aligned}
&\operatorname{Cov}\left[\{\tfrac{1}{2}(\alpha_i+\alpha_j+\alpha_k+\alpha_m)+\tfrac{1}{4}(d_{ik}+d_{im}+d_{jk}+d_{jm})\}\right.\\
&\qquad \left.\{(\alpha_i+\alpha_j+d_{ij})(\alpha_k+\alpha_m+d_{km})\}\right]\\
&= E(\alpha_i\alpha_k d_{ik})
\end{aligned}$$

This can also be written as $E[\frac{1}{2}(\alpha_i+\alpha_k)^2 d_{ik}]$ or as $\frac{1}{2}E(A^2D)$.
We have therefore in the case of independently segregating loci with no epistacy

$$\begin{aligned}
\alpha = \beta &= \tfrac{1}{2}E(A^2)\\
\gamma &= \tfrac{1}{2}E(A^2D)
\end{aligned}$$

and the total variability removed by the predictor is

$$\alpha^2+\beta^2+\gamma^2.$$

This line of argument indicates that the expectations of powers of A and D, the additive value and the dominance deviation respectively play a role which may of course be slight above that of $E(A^2)$ and $E(D^2)$ in determining regressions among relatives. In the case of the F_2 population with the following structure at the ith locus

$$\tfrac{1}{4}(AA)_i+\tfrac{1}{2}(Aa)_i+\tfrac{1}{4}(aa)_i$$

with genotypic values for $(AA)_i$, $(Aa)_i$ and $(aa)_i$ equal respectively to u_i, a_iu_i and $-u_i$, it is seen that

$$F_1-\tfrac{1}{2}(P_1+P_2) = \sum_i a_iu_i$$

$$\frac{AA-aa}{2} = \sum_i u_i$$

$$E(A^2) = \sigma_A^2 = \tfrac{1}{2}\sum_i u_i^2$$

$$E(D^2) = \sigma_D^2 = \tfrac{1}{4}\sum_i a_i^2 u_i^2$$

$$E(A^2D) = -\tfrac{1}{4}\sum_i a_i u_i^3.$$

With these and other relationships that can be developed it is possible to examine the relationship of a_i to u_i. For instance, even without looking into quantities like $E(A^2D)$, the mean square regression of a_i on u_i is given by

$$\frac{F_1 - \frac{1}{2}(P_1+P_2)}{2\sigma_A^2}$$

a quantity which could be revealing.

CONCLUDING REMARKS

In this paper I have endeavored to give an account of the status and deficiencies of our present knowledge of the theory of mass selection. I have raised questions which strike me as being relevant and needing solution, on the theory that unless we know where we are now we do not know where we want to go. I have mentioned a few lines of investigation which seem to me to merit attack, and shall be happy if they interest others to the point of working on them. I shall have succeeded in my endeavor if I have convinced the reader that our present knowledge is very limited. I think that some highly original and novel approach to the whole problem is in order, of dimensions like the break-through of Fisher's (1918) paper.

REFERENCES

BEARDSLEY, JOHN P., BRATTON, R. W., & SALISBURY, G. W. (1950) The curvilinearity of heritability of butter fat production, *J. Dairy Sci.*, **33**, 93–97.

CRAMER, H. (1945) *Mathematical Methods of Statistics*, Princeton University Press, Princeton, N.J.

CZEKANOWSKI, JAN. (1933) Mendelistiches 'Laws of ancestral heredity'. *Z. indukt. Abstamm-u. Vererb. Lehre* **64**, 154–168.

FISHER, R. A. (1918) On the correlation between relatives on the supposition of Mendelian inheritance, *Trans. Roy. Soc. Edinburgh* **52**, 399–433.

FISHER, R. A., IMMER, F. R., TEDIN, O., (1932) The genetical interpretation of statistics of the third degree in the study of quantitative inheritance, *Genetics* **17**, 107–124.

GRIFFING, BRUCE (1950) Analysis of quantitative gene action by constant parent regression and related techniques, *Genetics* **35**, 303–321

HULL, F. H. (1952) Overdominance and recurrent selection. Chapter 28 of *Heterosis*, (Ed. by J. W. GOWEN), Iowa State College Press, Ames.

KOSAMBI, D. D. (1943) The estimation of map distances from recombination values, *Ann. Eugen., Lond.* **12**, 172–175.

LERNER, I. M. (1958) *The Genetic Basis of Selection*, Wiley, New York.

LUSH, J. L. (1937) *Animal Breeding Plans*, Iowa State College Press, Ames.

THE EFFECTS OF INBREEDING WHEN SELECTION ACTS AGAINST HOMOZYGOSIS AT ONE OR MORE LOCI

By E. C. R. Reeve

A.R.C. Unit of Animal Genetics,
Institute of Animal Genetics, Edinburgh

and J. C. Gower

Rothamsted Experimental Station,
Harpenden, Herts.

In view of the particulate nature of the units of heredity, the effects of systematic inbreeding invite mathematical analysis, and this led to the early studies of Robbins (1917) and others, to the classical path-coefficient analysis of all the main systems of inbreeding by Sewall Wright (1921), and to the later more detailed analyses of these systems by Haldane (1937) and Fisher (1949), using matrix methods.

In all this work it was tacitly assumed that ' all genetic particles are equal ', in the sense that all alleles at each locus, in all combinations, give genotypes with equal survival value—an assumption which is mathematically very convenient and is, in fact, essential for applying the elegant method of path coefficients. But such an assumption seems a little unrealistic, in view of the general tendency for inbreeding of a normally outbred species to lead to a marked decline in vigour, fertility, etc., and there is little doubt that selection against homozygosis occurs at certain loci during inbreeding. It has, in fact, been suggested that selection of this kind will tend to increase in severity as inbreeding progresses, and there is some indirect evidence in support of this conclusion (Reeve, 1955; Tantawy and Reeve, 1956).

To approach a more realistic inbreeding theory, we must explore the effects of selection against homozygosis. There are, in fact, a bewildering variety of situations to be examined, since selection may act with different intensities on the homozygotes of different alleles, while there may be selection within lines only, or also selection between lines (i.e. the more homozygous lines may tend to be discarded because of their lower fertility). Moreover, selection at one locus will have both direct effects on that locus and also indirect effects on neighbouring loci through linkage, and both types of effect must be taken into account. Finally, apart from the probability that selection intensities will change as inbreeding progresses, there is likely to be selection against homozygosity at several points on the same chromosome.

Unfortunately, mathematical results obtained from analysing these situations cannot be checked experimentally, since we cannot determine what selection is acting on the different loci while a population is being inbred. (The experimental studies relevant to this problem are discussed by Tantawy and Reeve, 1956). But it is still worth while to examine those cases whose analysis is mathematically feasible, and from these to attempt to draw a rough general picture.

The mathematical difficulties are well illustrated in Table 1, which shows the size of the generation matrix for the simplest one-lcous and two-locus cases in which selection acts at one locus.

TABLE 1. SIZE OF GENERATION MATRIX UNDER DIFFERENT CONDITIONS

Conditions (2 alleles per locus)	Selfing	Sib-mating	½-sib-mating	D.F.C. mating
One locus: equal selection*	2 × 2	4 × 4	9 × 9	13 × 13
One locus: unequal selection	3 × 3	6 × 6	15 × 15	21 × 21
Unselected locus linked to:				
(*a*) one pair of lethal alleles	2 × 2	5 × 5	13 × 13	22 × 22
(*b*) two pairs ,, ,, ,,	2 × 2	10 × 10	46 × 46	118 × 118
(*c*) one selected locus with				
(i) equal selection*	4 × 4	19 × 19	156 × 156	424 × 424
(ii) unequal ,,	6 × 6	29 × 29	?	?

* Both alternative homozygotes have equal survival rates.

Selfing, full-sib mating, half-sib mating (a male mated to two of his half-sisters who are full sisters of each other) and double-first-cousin (D.F.C.) mating are compared; and the top line shows the case of a single two-allele locus (*A*, *B*) with equal selection against *AA* and *BB*. This matrix is the same size as when selection is absent, but it has to be expanded appreciably to take account of different survival values for *AA* and *BB*, as shown in the second line of the table, and when a second locus is introduced the matrix soon looks unmanageable (last two rows).

Hayman and Mather (1953), who were the first to examine the effects of selection against homozygosity, studied the equilibrium conditions at a single locus when there is equal selection within and between lines, and found that more than 50% loss of both homozygotes under selfing, 23.7% loss under sib-mating, or 14.5% under double-first-cousin mating, completely prevents fixation of the locus during the inbreeding of a large population of lines. This indicates the power of moderate selection against homozygosity to combat the effects of inbreeding, provided that selection between lines is allowed.

In species producing large numbers of progeny, most of the between-line selection can be eliminated, and Reeve (1955) has examined the effects of within-line selection on a single locus in the four inbreeding systems. Here we always reach full homozygosity in the end, with finite selection pressures, but the different inbreeding systems make an interesting comparison, as we see from Fig. 1, taken from Reeve (1955). This shows the rate of inbreeding

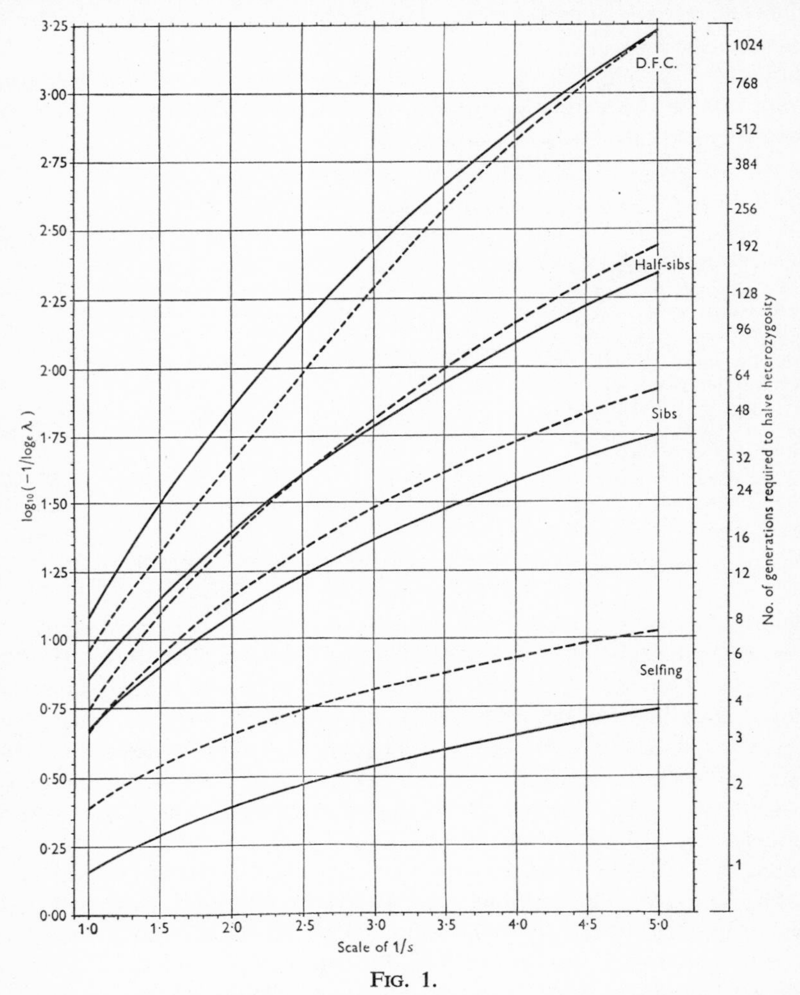

FIG. 1.

progress, on a logarithmic scale, plotted against the reciprocal of the survival value (s) of the homozygotes (solid lines), or of one homozygote when the other is lethal (dashed lines).

As selection intensifies, the reduction in relative speed of inbreeding is much greater in the milder than in the more intense inbreeding systems. Thus, with equal survival of the two homozygotes, when s changes from 1.0 to 0.2, we multiply the number of generations necessary to halve the level of heterozygosity by 3.8 for selfing, 14 for sib-mating, 30 for half-sib mating and 142 for double-first-cousin mating. Some cases of differential survival are also discussed in this paper.

Selection at one point will slow down inbreeding progress at neighbouring points on the chromosome, through linkage, and this problem has been ignored until recently, apart from a study of the effects of enforced heterozygosity at one locus by Bartlett and Haldane (1935). It is clearly important, particularly if appreciable selection may act at several points on the same chromosome, as seems likely. Reeve (1957) has given a general solution for unequal selection pressures both within and between lines and against the two alleles at one locus, and its effects through linkage on another locus (not itself under direct selection) for the case of selfing. This leads to a 6×6 matrix which is easily solved. (See also Haldane, 1956, and Hayman and Mather, 1956, for discussions of the one-locus case under selfing).

But to go further than this soon leads to difficulties, as Table 1 makes clear. Taking the general case of the effects of selection at one locus (A, B) on a linked locus (a, b) not under direct selection, when the survival of AA and BB is equal sib-mating requires a generation matrix of 19×19, half-sib mating of 156×156 and double-first-cousin mating of 424×424. On giving unequal survival values to AA and BB the sib-mating matrix rises to 29×29, and the other matrices doubtless increase correspondingly. Clearly the even more interesting case of the effects which selection acting at loci on each side of (a, b) has on progress at this locus, with the milder inbreeding systems, would defy analysis.

With the help of a desk calculator and Aitken's ingenious methods of analysis (Aitken, 1937), it is just about possible to tackle a 13×13 matrix, but digital computers enable us to analyse much larger matrices. With really large matrices it becomes very tedious even to work out the details of the matrix itself, let alone to build it into a programme for the computer. It should be possible, however, for a digital computer to be programmed so that it receives the basic structure of the inbreeding process and then calculates the elements of the corresponding generation matrix, as functions of the variables (recombination frequencies and survival values) involved. This possibility is being examined.

Looking forward, one might even imagine the time when a general programme can be fed into a large digital computer which enables it first to calculate the generation matrix and then to analyse it for sets of values of the variables.

Meanwhile, we have been analysing the modest 19×19 matrix for sib-mating on the Elliott 401 digital computer at Rothamsted Experimental Station, and propose to summarise some of the results here and to compare them with the same situation under selfing. A detailed study of the 19×19 matrix is in the press (Reeve and Gower, 1958).

To recapitulate, we are interested in the rate of progress towards homozygosity of a locus (a, b) not itself under selection, which is linked with recombination frequency y to a locus (A, B) under selection such that fractions x of AA and BB survive.

The full matrix and its derivation are given in the paper referred to above, and need not be repeated here. But Table 2 shows the different mating types (i.e., phases of the two alleles in a pair of mates) for each locus, and the corresponding distinct mating types for the two loci combined, which may be encountered. By distinct mating types we mean, of course, that each leads to a different array of mating types in the next generation of sib-mating. Two mating types are identical, from this point of view, if one is converted into the other by interchange of a with b, of A with B, or of both, throughout.

Table 2. Sib-mating with two linked loci: mating types

Unselected locus (a, b)	Selected locus (A, B)
$t=\frac{a}{a}\times\frac{a}{a}$	$T=\frac{A}{A}\times\frac{A}{A}$
$u=\frac{a}{a}\times\frac{a}{b}$	$U_1=\frac{A}{A}\times\frac{A}{B}$, $U_2=\frac{A}{A}\times\frac{B}{A}$, $U_3=\frac{A}{B}\times\frac{A}{A}$
$v=\frac{a}{b}\times\frac{a}{b}$	$V_1=\frac{A}{B}\times\frac{A}{B}$, $V_2=\frac{A}{B}\times\frac{B}{A}$
$w=\frac{a}{a}\times\frac{b}{b}$	$W=\frac{A}{A}\times\frac{B}{B}$

Distinct combinations of both loci

(tT), (tU, tV, tW), (uT, vT, wT),
$(uU_1, uU_2, uU_3, uV, uW, vU, vV_1, vV_2, vW, wU, wV, wW)$

A fraction x of AA and BB survive.

The full 19×19 generation matrix, when written out in the order of Table 2 so that a parent mating type heads each column and a progeny type each row, contains the four sub-matrices indicated by brackets in the table, situated along the leading diagonal, with only zeros below, so that the roots of the full matrix are the roots of these sub-matrices. The four sub-matrices represent the following situations:

$A_1 = (tT)$: both loci fixed
$A_2 = (tU, tV, tW)$: (a, b) but not (A, B) fixed
$A_3 = (uT, vT, wT)$: (A, B) but not (a, b) fixed
$A_4 =$ remaining 12×12 : neither locus fixed.

It turns out that the rate of change in heterozygosity at the (a, b) locus, once the system has settled down to a steady state, is a function of the largest latent roots (which we will call μ_1, μ_2, μ_3 and μ_4) of these four sub-matrices.

The two cases we shall consider are

Case I: selection acts within lines only, so that all columns of the generation matrix add to unity;

Case II: selection acts equally within and between lines. This requires that all T columns should add to x, all U and V columns to $\frac{1}{2}(1+x)$, and all W columns to unity.

The first three sub-matrices are all in effect single-locus cases and their largest roots are known. In fact, μ_1 and μ_3 are 1.0 and 0.809017 in case I, and x and $0.809017x$ in case II, while μ_2 is the largest root of a cubic in μ:

$$(1+x)^4\mu^3-(1+x)^2(1+2x)\mu^2-\tfrac{1}{2}x^2(1+x)^2\mu+x^3 = 0 \text{ in case I,}$$
$$4(1+x)^2\mu^3-2(1+x)(1+2x)\mu^2-x^2(1+x)\mu+x^3 = 0 \text{ in case II.}$$

The largest root of A_4 is a function of x and y, the survival and recombination values, and has to be determined by computation for different (x, y).

Let h_n be the proportion of heterozygotes at the (a, b) locus after n generations of sib-mating, starting say with a population of double heterozygotes aA/bB.

Let
$$\lambda = \lim_{n\to\infty} (h_n/h_{n-1}).$$

Then $(1-\lambda)$ is the eventual rate of loss of heterozygosity and λ is equivalent to the maximum latent root (less than unity) of an inbreeding matrix referring to a single locus.

It may be shown (Reeve and Gower, 1958) that λ has the following values in cases I and II, (it should be remembered that the roots of the four sub-matrices are generally different in the two cases):

Case I: = largest of μ_3 and μ_4

Case II: = (largest of μ_3 and μ_4)/(largest of μ_1 and μ_2).

In interpreting these results it is easiest to think in terms of speed of inbreeding $(-\log_e \lambda)$, which may be converted into a percentage of the speed when selection is absent by multiplying by $100/(-\log_e 0.809017)$. Then a speed of 50% means that two generations are needed to make as much progress as one generation in the absence of selection.

Fig. 2 gives the final speed of inbreeding measured in this way, in cases I and II, for various recombination frequencies (y) plotted against survival x of homozygotes at the (A, B) locus.

The solid lines (case I) generally reach 100% (i.e. $\mu_4>\mu_3$) for values of x well below unity, so that a combination of fairly strong selection and close linkage is necessary before the final speed of inbreeding is reduced below 100%. This is an unexpected result, but it should be noted that the speed is at first always less than normal for x and $y<1$, so that the total amount of heterozygosity remaining at any stage is always less than in the absence of selection. Another surprising point is that the minimum final speed for

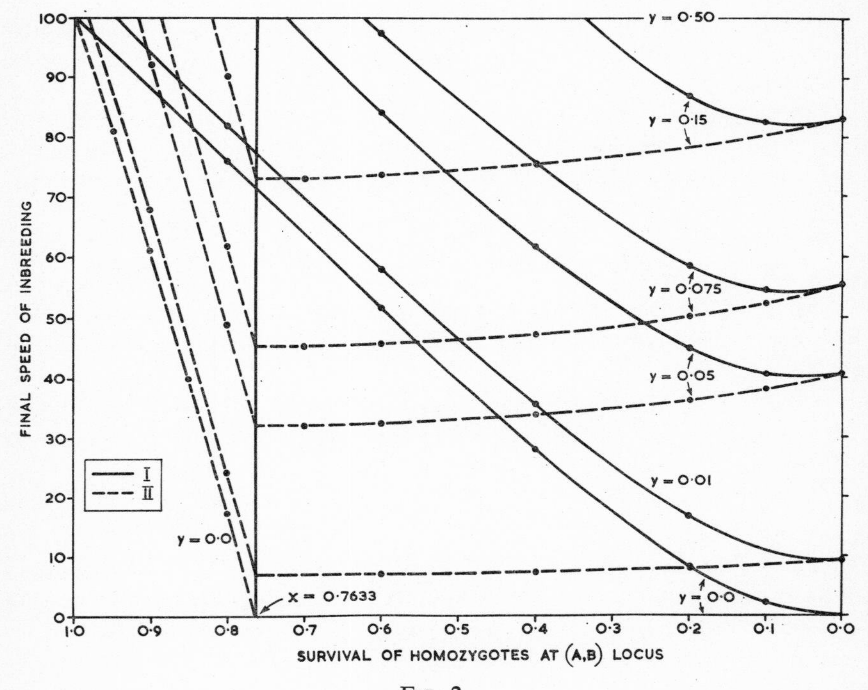

FIG. 2.

constant y ($y>0$) evidently occurs with x slightly greater than 0 instead of at $x=0$, as one might have expected. μ_4 in case I must have a maximum with $x>0$ for constant y.

In case II the picture is rather different. As x declines below unity with y constant, the speed at first remains at 100%, then declines sharply to a minimum at $x=0.7633$, and afterwards rises slowly until it reaches the same value as in case I (and in fact touches the case I curve) at $x=0$. $x=0.7633$ is the value of x below which fixation at the (A, B) locus never occurs, and this gives the minimum final speed for a point situated on the same chromosome at any distance from (A, B). More intense selection speeds up the rate of inbreeding progress a little at the linked locus, instead of further reducing it. Again, we should point out that during the earlier generations of selection the picture is a little different, the curves falling smoothly to a minimum with x in the neighbourhood of 0.6. This is illustrated in some detail by Reeve and Gower (1958).

A graph of the four latent roots for constant y against x, in case II (Fig. 3), helps to make the nature of the two discontinuities in Fig. 2 clearer. Here

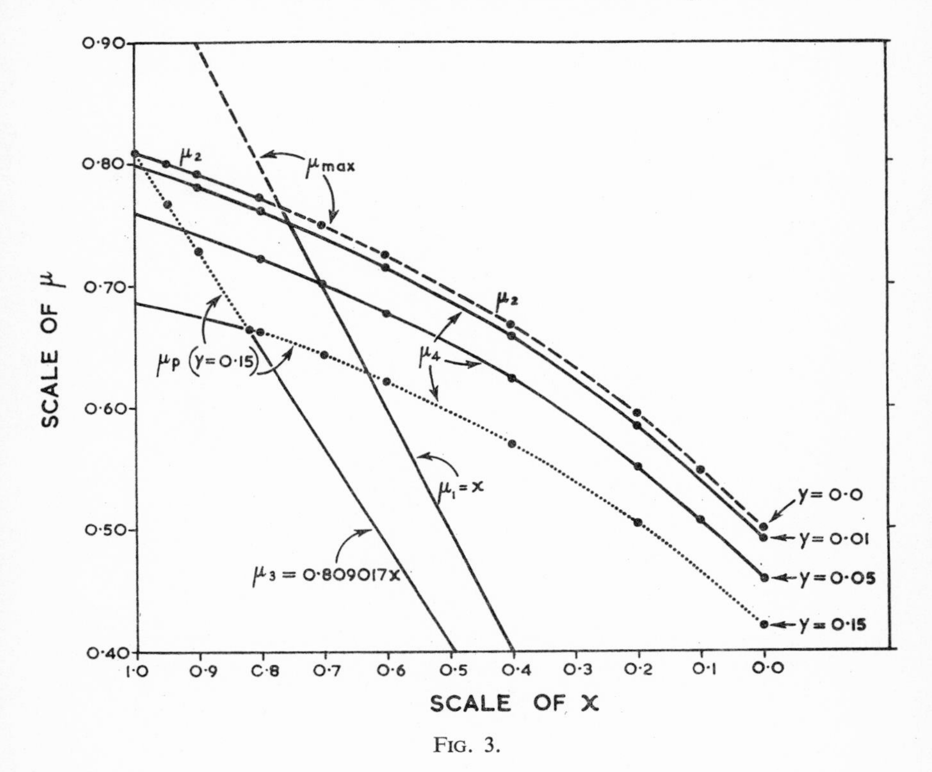

FIG. 3.

we have plotted μ_1, μ_2 and μ_3 (which are all independent of y) against x, and also μ_4 for several values of y. The dashed line labelled μ_{max} gives the largest of μ_1 and μ_2, the former being the largest when $x > 0.7633$. The dotted line labelled μ_p gives the largest of μ_3 and μ_4 for $y = 0.15$. Our measure of inbreeding progress is $\lambda = \mu_p/\mu_{max}$, and, on plotting this against x, we obtain two discontinuities, since its numerator and denominator have discontinuities at different values of x.

In these graphs we have held the recombination frequency y constant and considered the effect of varying the selection intensity x. It is perhaps of even more interest to consider the effects of a given selection intensity at one locus on points at different distances from it along the chromosome, since this shows what selection against homozygosity at one point will actually achieve, and to compare the results in different inbreeding systems.

Fig. 4 compares the effects of different selection pressures at the (A, B) locus on the rest of the chromosome, under selfing and sib-mating, when selection acts within lines only. The abscissa shows the number of cross-over units distant from (A, B), and the ordinate gives the relative speed compared with the absence of selection under the same inbreeding system. The absolute speeds are, of course, very different for the two systems, since normal progress under selfing is about $3\frac{1}{4}$ times as fast as under sib-mating.

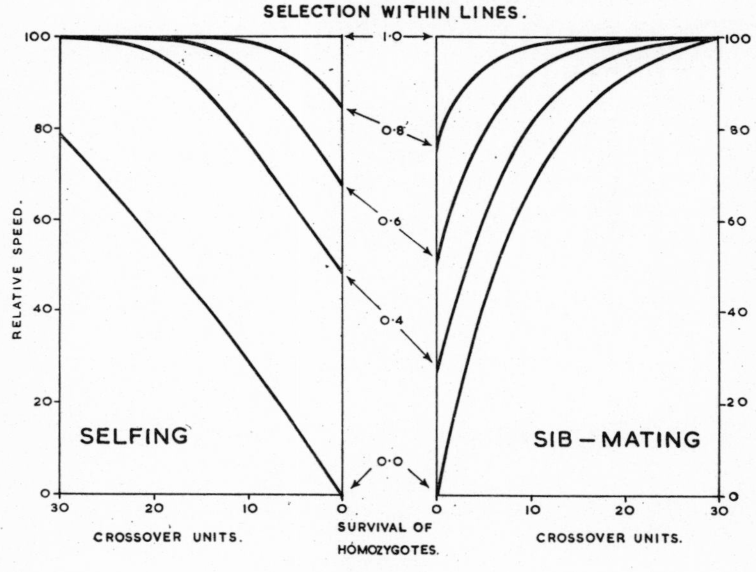

FIG. 4.

This graph brings out an interesting contrast between the two systems. A given selection pressure causes substantially less reduction in speed under selfing than under sib-mating, at the locus directly affected (i.e. at abscissa 0), but as we move away along the chromosome the effect of selection is dissipated much more slowly under selfing. Thus 40% survival of homozygotes gives a relative speed of 44% under selfing compared with only 24% under sib-mating at the locus selected. But at a point 6 cross-over units away the relative speeds are the same (about 63%) with both systems, and for points further away the relative speed is greater under sib-mating. In other words, while the local effects of selection against homozygosity are relatively greater under sib-mating, they are also more localized in terms of the length of chromosome affected.

One might guess that the same trend would be continued in the milder inbreeding systems—half-sib mating and double-first-cousin mating. We know that selection at one locus causes a relatively greater delay in progress at this locus with the milder systems (Fig. 1), and one can be almost certain that the localization of the effect will be correspondingly greater. Thus, one generalization we can make is that the pattern of effects of selection against homozygosity at one point on the whole chromosome is different under the different standard inbreeding systems—the milder the inbreeding system, the sharper and more localized will be the effect.

The next stage in the analysis is to consider the effects of selection against homozygosity, acting at two loci on the same chromosome, on points in between them. The general statement of this situation requires very large matrices, but they become quite manageable for the more rapid inbreeding systems in the special case where all homozygotes at the two loci under selection are lethal (see Table 1); and this at least gives us limiting values for the effects of selection at two points. Reeve (1957) gave the formula for selfing, and we have analysed the 10×10 matrix for sib-mating with the help of the Rothamsted digital computer.

Some typical cases under selfing and sib-mating, when only within-line selection occurs, are given in Fig. 5. Here the abscissa measures the distance from the mid-point between the two loci under selection, and the ordinate gives the relative speed as a percentage of the normal speed for the same inbreeding system. Curves which start and end at 20 cross-over units refer

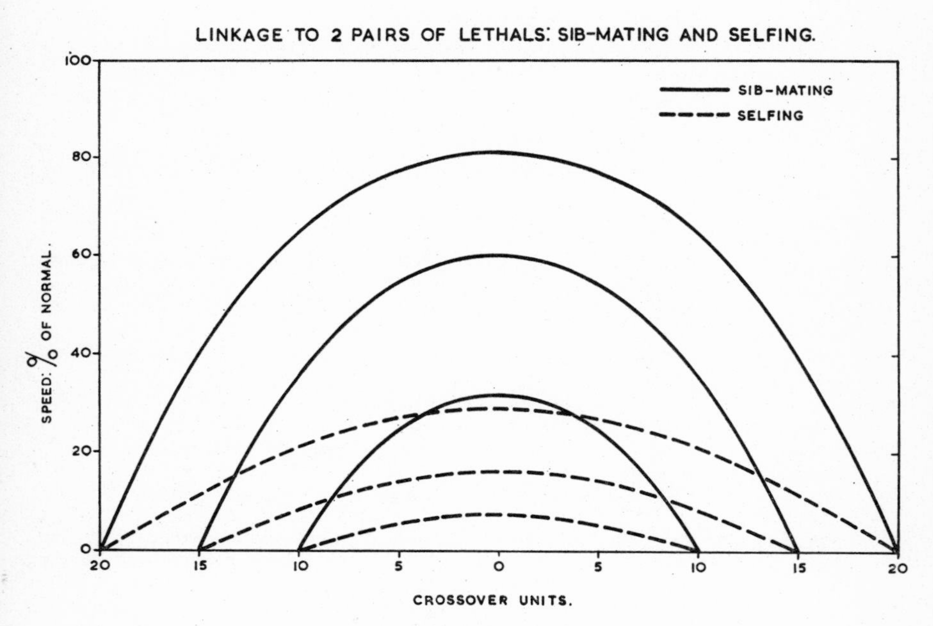

FIG. 5.

to the effects of two selected loci 40 units apart, and so on. There is assumed to be no chiasma interference throughout the region.

These graphs, then, show the relative speed of inbreeding throughout a whole region of the chromosome bounded by the two loci carrying only recessive lethals. We see at once that there is a very great difference between selfing and sib-mating. When the two pairs of lethals are 20 units apart, selfing gives a maximum speed of only about 8%, compared with 32% for sib-mating; and when the two points are 40 units apart the speed at the half-way mark is still under 30% for selfing but over 80% for sib-mating. Thus the whole region of the chromosome is affected much more dramatically under selfing than under sib-mating—though, of course, it must be emphasised that the absolute speed of inbreeding is always greater under selfing.

The same kind of difference doubtless occurs when the selection against homozygosity at the two ends of the region is not so extreme, although we then have the complication that the speed of inbreeding will be reduced more, near these end-points, under sib-mating.

Combining the information provided by Figs. 1, 4 and 5, we may conclude that selection against homozygosity acting at several points on a single chromosome will tend to sharpen the differences in speed between different inbreeding systems in the neighbourhood of these points and to lessen the differences in speed at loci in intermediate regions.

REFERENCES

Aitken, A. C. (1937) Studies in practical mathematics. II. The evaluation of the latent roots and latent vectors of a matrix, *Proc. Roy. Soc., Edinburgh* **57,** 269–304.

Bartlett, M. S. & Haldane, J. B. S. (1935) The theory of inbreeding with forced heterozygosis, *J. Genet.* **31,** 327–40.

Fisher, R. A. (1949) *The Theory of Inbreeding*, Oliver & Boyd, Edinburgh.

Haldane, J. B. S. (1937) Some theoretical results of continued brother-sister mating. *J. Genet.* **34,** 265–74.

Haldane, J. B. S. (1956) The conflict between inbreeding and selection. I. Self-fertilisation, *J. Genet.* **54,** 56–63.

Hayman, B. I. & Mather, K. (1953) The progress of inbreeding when the homozygotes are at a disadvantage, *Heredity* **7,** 165–83.

Hayman, B. I. & Mather, K. (1956) Inbreeding when homozygotes are at a disadvantage: a reply, *Heredity* **10,** 271–4.

Reeve, E. C. R. (1955) Inbreeding with the homozygotes at a disadvantage, *Ann. Hum. Genet., Lond.* **19,** 332–46.

Reeve, E. C. R. (1957) Inbreeding with selection and linkage. I. Selfing, *Ann. Hum. Genet., Lond.* **21,** 277–88.

Reeve, E. C. R. & Gower, J. C. (1958) Inbreeding with selection and linkage. II. Sib-mating, *Ann. Hum. Genet. Lond.*, **23,** 36–49.

Robbins, R. B. (1917) Some applications of mathematics to breeding problems. *Genetics* **2,** 489–504.

Tantawy, A. O. & Reeve, E. C. R. (1956) Studies in quantitative inheritance. IX. The effects of inbreeding at different rates in *Drosophila melanogaster*. *Z. indukt. Abstamm-u. Vererb. Lehre* **86,** 439–58.

Wright, S. (1921) Systems of mating, I–V, *Genetics* **6,** 111–78.

HIGH SPEED SELECTION STUDIES*

By Frank G. Martin, Jr.† and C. Clark Cockerham
North Carolina State College, Raleigh, North Carolina

An empirical approach, making use of high speed computers, to problems in population genetics is being explored. A program mimicking a population evolving under mass selection has been written for the IBM 650. Results have been obtained for various situations, and primarily directed at the effects of linkage on the progress from mass selection in small populations.

The program and the results represent the efforts of the senior author in partial preparation of a doctoral thesis. The results and their interpretation must be regarded at this stage as preliminary.

THE PROGRAM

It is not the purpose here to describe in detail the method of programming a genetic system and its modification for various electronic computers. Each machine has its own special operations. In any case, a detail set of rules of operation must be translated into machine language and checked.

This particular program is determined by eight parameters:

1. The number of loci for a single chromosome, $m = 1, 2, \ldots, 25$.
2. The number of individuals (offspring) of each sex available for selection, $N = 1, 2, 3 \ldots$.
3. The number of individuals of each sex selected, $n = 1, 2, \ldots, 47$.
4. Arbitrary scores for each of the three genotypes of a locus which are constant for all loci and additive between loci.
5. The number of generations of selection, $g = 1, 2, 3, \ldots$.
6. The initial gene frequency for the unfavorable one of two alleles which is the same for all loci, $p = 0.00, 0.01, \ldots, 1.00$.
7. The recombination fraction which is the same between every pair of consecutive loci, $\alpha = 0.00, 0.01, \ldots, 0.50$.
8. An environmental variate with variance $\sigma^2 = 0.00, 0.01, 0.02, \ldots$.

Parameters 6, 7 and 8 are expected values of variates which are stochastically determined while the other parameters are constants. Selection intensity is

* This research was supported in part by a grant from the Rockefeller Foundation. Contribution from the Departments of Experimental Statistics and Genetics, North Carolina Agricultural Experiment Station, Raleigh, N. C. Published with the approval of the Director of Research as Paper No. 996 of the Journal Series.

† Present address, Westinghouse Electric Corporation, Pittsburgh, Pennsylvania.

given by the fraction n/N. The expected value of the initial heritability is given by the joint consideration of parameters 1, 4, 6 and 8.

The procedure is best understood in two parts, the initial generation and one of the successive generations. For the initial generation the genotypes for N individuals of each sex are generated by a random process such that at each locus the expected frequency of the unfavorable allele is p. The alleles are represented by one of two symbols. Each genotype consists of two sequences of m symbols. These two sequences represent the homologous chromosome pair, and the position of the symbols in the sequence specifies the locus. For each individual three scores or values are calculated. The genotypic score is computed by employing the scoring rule for each locus and summing all the values for the loci. Another score, called the environmental variate, is really a binomial variate but generated in such a manner that for all practical purposes it may be considered a normal variate with variance σ^2. The genotypic and environmental scores are added to form the phenotypic score of the individual. From each of these two groups of N phenotypic scores, one group for each sex, the top n is selected to be parents of the next generation. Thus, selection is by truncation.

The procedure is modified only slightly for all generations after the initial generation in order to include the phenomena of segregation and recombination. For each progeny to be generated a male and a female parent are chosen at random from the individuals just previously selected. From each parent a modified sequence is formed by first selecting one of the original sequences at random. Beginning with the first position of the chosen sequence the new sequence is formed so that the allele (symbol) at the jth position has the probability $1-\alpha$ of being chosen from the same sequence as the allele (symbol) in the $(j-1)^{\text{th}}$ position and probability α of being chosen from the other sequence. The two modified sequences, one from each parent, form the offspring. The genotypic and environmental scores are calculated in the same way as in the initial generation to form the phenotypic score. As before the top n of each sex are selected as parents of the next generation. This process is repeated until either (1) all selected individuals have the same homozygous genotype, or (2) there have been a predetermined number of generations of selection.

The output from this process is of two forms. One output is of the $2N$ initial or offspring individuals which contain each individual's genotype, its genotypic and environmental scores and identification numbers. The second output is of the $2n$ selected individuals and contains the same information as for the offspring.

It is possible to by-pass the initial generation and selection step and to load the machine with an initial set of parents. This gives additional flexibility in that any type of initial population can be studied.

The generation of genotypes, pairing of mates, segregation and recombination, and the environmental variate employ random numbers. The generation of these numbers is accomplished by a method described by Moshman (1954). His method is based upon taking successive powers of the number

$$\delta = 7^{4k+1}$$

and reducing its modulus 10^s, where k is a positive integer less than five and s is the number length. Hence the ith random number is obtained by using

$$\delta_i = \delta_{i-1}.\delta \qquad (\text{mod } 10^s)$$

with

$$\delta_0 = \delta.$$

The values of k and s used in this program are 4 and 15, respectively. This results in the generation of a repeating sequence of fifteen uniformly distributed random numbers with a period of 5×10^{12}. No more than the first ten digits are ever used from any generated number.

To summarize, the genetic situation that is being mimicked should be apparent at this point. Selection is based on the individual's phenotype and is of the truncation type. Selected parents are mated at random with replacement. Such a scheme for a long time has been called mass selection. Any degree of dominance with two alleles may be called upon, but there is no epistasis and the loci all have equal effects. The results of segregation and recombination of diploids is truly mimicked except that the recombination fraction is the same between all adjacent loci and no interference is allowed for. Equal effects of loci and equal recombination are not considered to be drawbacks for any useful purposes of the program. The genotypic values and environmental values are additive and uncorrelated.

RESULTS

The choice of values for the parameters was somewhat arbitrary. Results of some of the initial runs influenced later choices. The results are best visualized by means of graphs and reference is made to Fig. 1 for format. Each line in the graph is a plot of the genotypic mean of the offspring against time in generations. Each line represents the average of all the runs for that combination of parameters and is designated by n/N, α. Hence, 2/20, 0.01 denotes the selection of 2 out of 20 for each sex with the recombination value of 0.01. The other parameters common to all lines in the graph are given in the legend for the figure, as also are the number of runs that are averaged. No line is carried beyond the generation in which the longest individual run reached fixation.

All runs were started by generating the initial individuals with expected gene frequencies of 0.5 and in linkage equilibrium except when distinguished as *loaded repulsion*. In the case of loaded repulsion the initial individuals were loaded into the machine and all had the genotype *AbCdE*/*aBcDe*, or were in maximum repulsion.

For an additive model the genotypes *AA*, *Aa* and *aa* were scored as 2, 1 and 0 respectively. For dominance the corresponding scores were 2, 2 and 0. The environmental variance, when other than zero, was made equal to the expected additive genetic variance in the initial generation.

Generation zero corresponds to the initial population of 2*N* individuals generated by the machine, or when the parents were loaded, to the 2*N* offspring derived from random mating the loaded parents.

Initial Population in Linkage Equilibrium with Five Loci

The results for the additive model are presented in Figs. 1 and 2. In the first figure with no environmental variance progress is more rapid with the more intense selection, 2/20, and there is a suggestion of an effect of linkage.

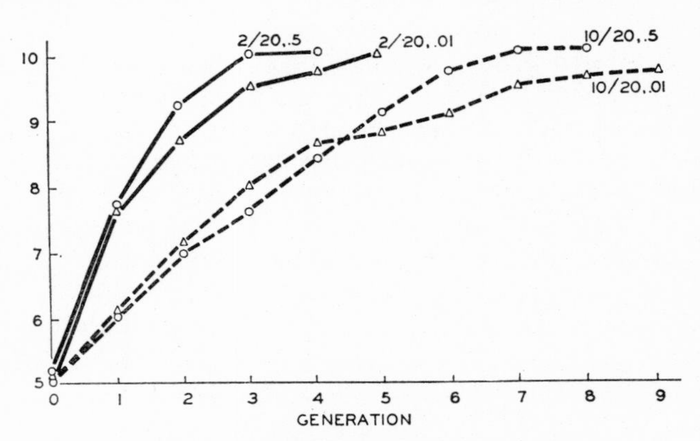

FIG. 1. $m=5$, additive model, $\sigma^2=0$, 5 runs.

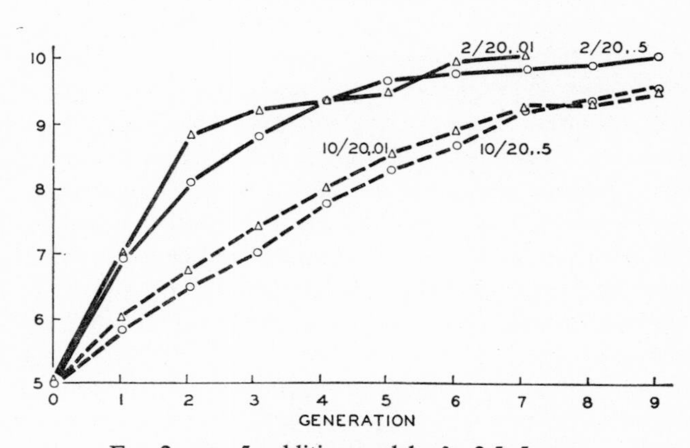

FIG. 2. $m=5$, additive model, $\sigma^2=2.5$, 5 runs.

Inclusion of an environmental variate, Fig. 2, slowed down the rate of progress. No linkage effects were suggested, otherwise the results were the same.

For the dominance model, Figs. 3 and 4, no effect of linkage is apparent. Even the environment and selection intensity had only small effects and these only in the early generations. The alternative number of parents showed no appreciable differences in the results. None of the parameter sets reached fixation.

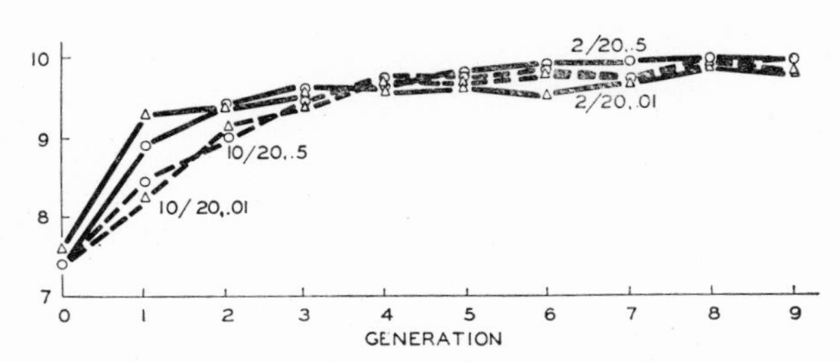

FIG. 3. $m=5$, dominance model, $\sigma^2=0$, 6 runs.

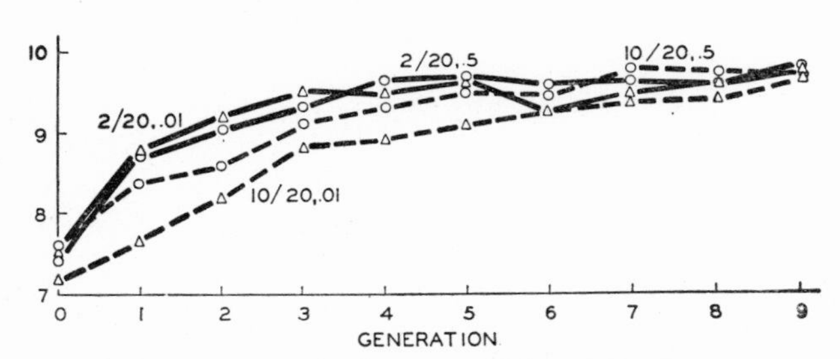

FIG. 4. $m=5$, dominance model, $\sigma^2=2.5$, 6 runs.

Initial Population in Repulsion with Five Loci

The primary difference between these results, Figs. 5 through 8, from corresponding results for an initial population in linkage equilibrium, given just previously, is the very large and apparent effect of linkage when the initial parents are in repulsion. As before, more intense selection gave more rapid progress and environmental variance slowed down the rate of progress for the additive model but not appreciably for the dominance model.

Additional results were obtained for five loci by substituting 5/50 for 2/20 and 25/50 for 10/20. Thus the number of offspring of each sex was increased to 50 and selection intensities were maintained the same. With these substitutions all the combinations of parameters in Figs. 1 through 8 were run. The results were almost duplicates of those for twenty offspring of each sex and will not be presented. Progress was some faster in the larger population for the additive model, and fixation at the best genotype was reached on the average one generation sooner.

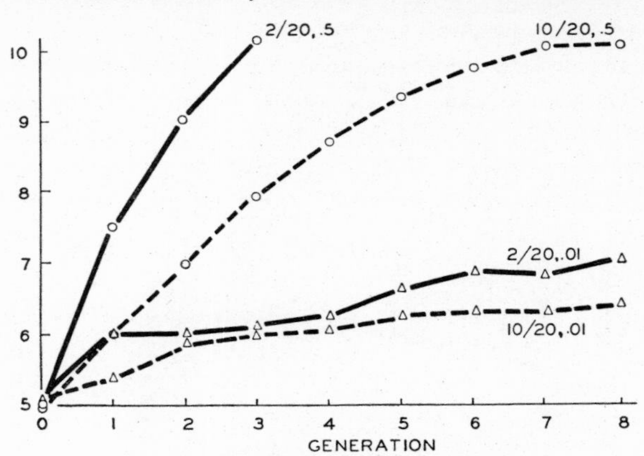

FIG. 5. $m=5$, additive model, $\sigma^2=0$, 4 runs, loaded repulsion.

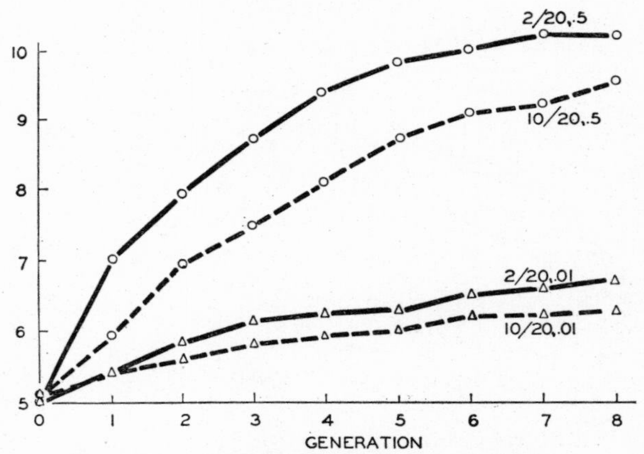

FIG. 6. $m=5$, additive model, $\sigma^2=2.5$, 4 runs, loaded repulsion.

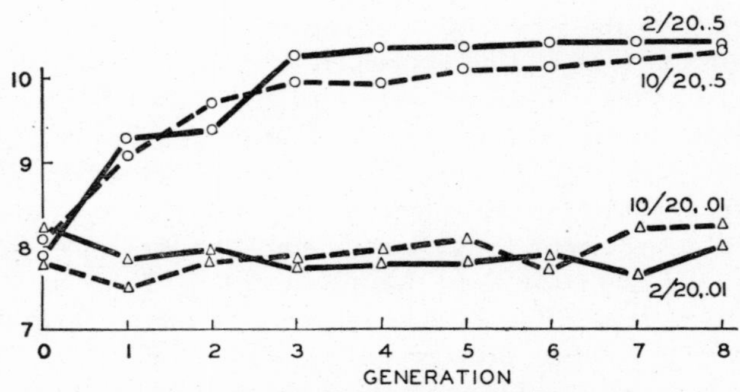

FIG. 7. $m=5$, dominance model, $\sigma^2=0$, 3 runs, loaded repulsion.

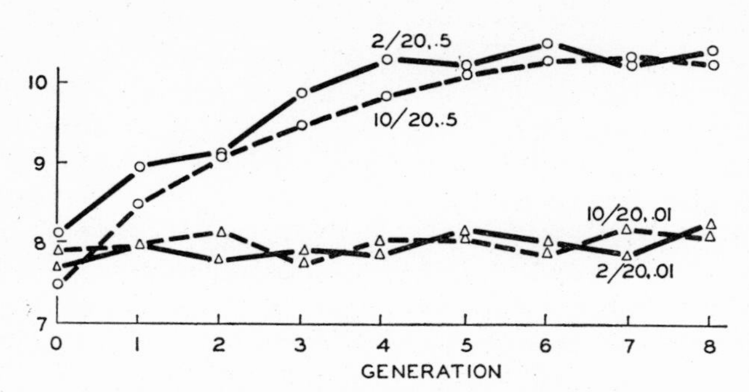

FIG. 8. $m=5$, dominance model, $\sigma^2=2.5$, 3 runs, loaded repulsion.

Initial Population in Linkage Equilibrium with Twenty Loci

While there was little suggestion of an effect of linkage for five loci, such an effect, if any, should be magnified by the inclusion of more loci. Thus, the number of loci was increased to twenty and the additive and dominance models were first run without environmental variance with the results given in Figs. 9 and 10. For the additive model (Fig. 9) and free recombination

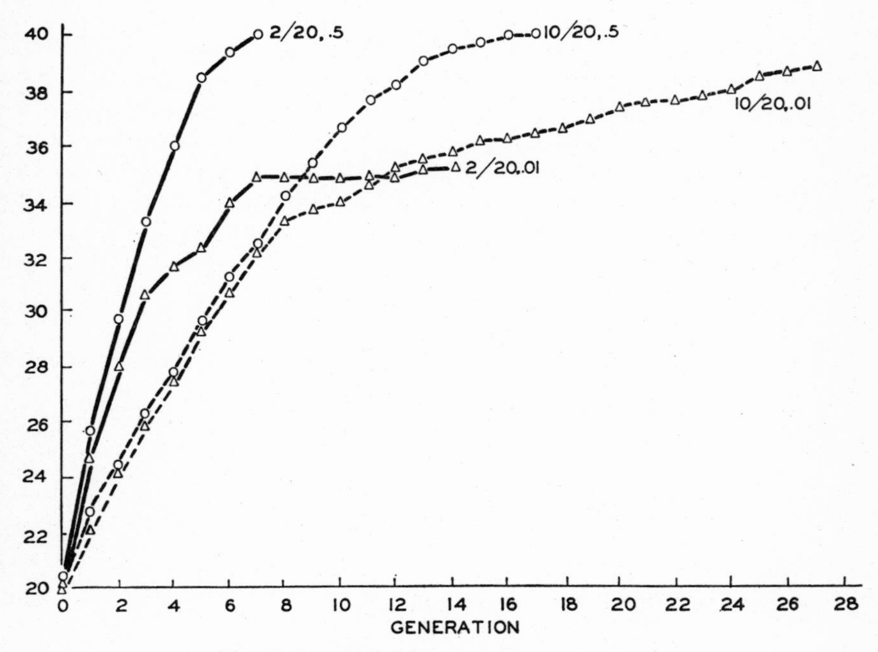

FIG. 9. $m=20$, additive model, $\sigma^2=0$, 3 runs.

there was an effect of selection intensities as there was for five loci. With tight linkage the whole complex changed. The more intensely selected populations progressed more rapidly at first but were passed by the less intensely selected populations. Tight linkage slowed down the progress in all populations, and in the intensely selected populations all three runs were fixed for less than the maximum genotype. Thus, lack of enough recombination caused the intense selection to drag some poor alleles into fixation.

Essentially the same effect of tight linkage, except manifested earlier, was found for the dominance model and no environmental variance in Fig. 10. The intensely selected populations had not become fixed after 28 generations, however. With free recombination the advantage of the intensely selected populations disappeared by the 14th generation.

Environmental variance (Figs. 11 and 12) generally slowed down the progress from selection and reduced some of the effects of selection intensities as expected, but qualitatively the effects of linkage were the same as those without environmental variance.

A notion of how progress from selection varies with the recombination fraction can be obtained from Fig. 13 where runs for recombination fractions of 0.3 and 0.1 were included with those of 0.5 and 0.01 for the additive model and no environmental variance. The decrease in linkage effect is suggested to be quadric. Progress is slowed down only slightly by the recombination fraction of 0.3.

It should be apparent at this point, however, that the availability of better genotypes, necessary for progress from selection, is a joint function of selection intensity, population size and the recombination fraction. By increasing the number of offspring of each sex to 100 and selecting the top tenth, i.e. 10/100, 0.01, progress is much more rapid with tight linkage than with 2/20, 0.01 as shown in Fig. 14. With free recombination the larger number of offspring gave only slightly more rapid progress.

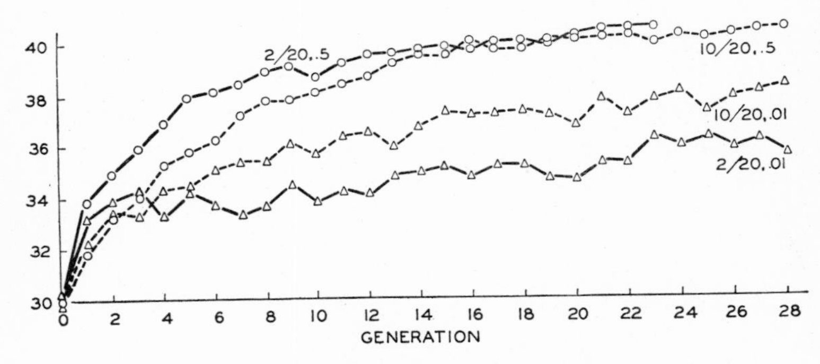

FIG. 10. $m=20$, dominance model, $\sigma^2=0$, 3 runs.

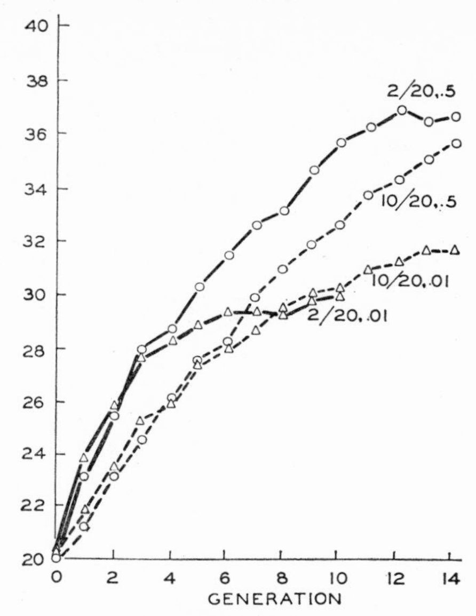

FIG. 11. $m=20$, additive model, $\sigma^2=10$, 3 runs.

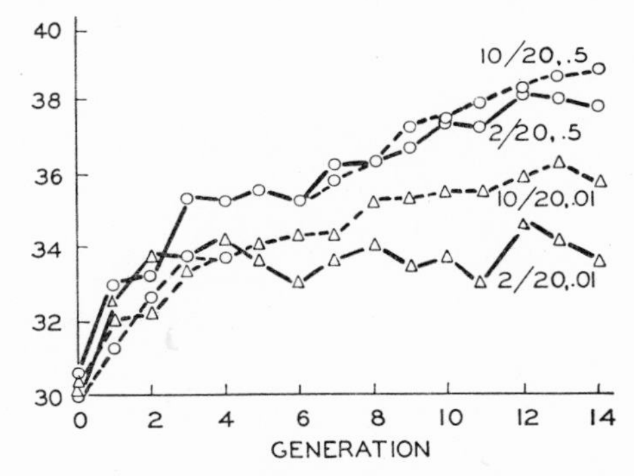

FIG. 12. $m=20$, dominance model, $\sigma^2=10$, 3 runs.

DISCUSSION

The deductive treatment of the theory of natural selection has been largely developed by Fisher, Wright and Haldane. Population size, linkage, mutation, selection intensity, gene action and others have received attention but in limitated combinations and in restricted situations. Recent interest in the use of stochastic processes may lead to the solution of some of the problems involved in finding distributions in more complex situations. However, the joint consideration of selection and linkage in small populations so far has defied elucidation.

This study represents another method of attacking some of the complicated

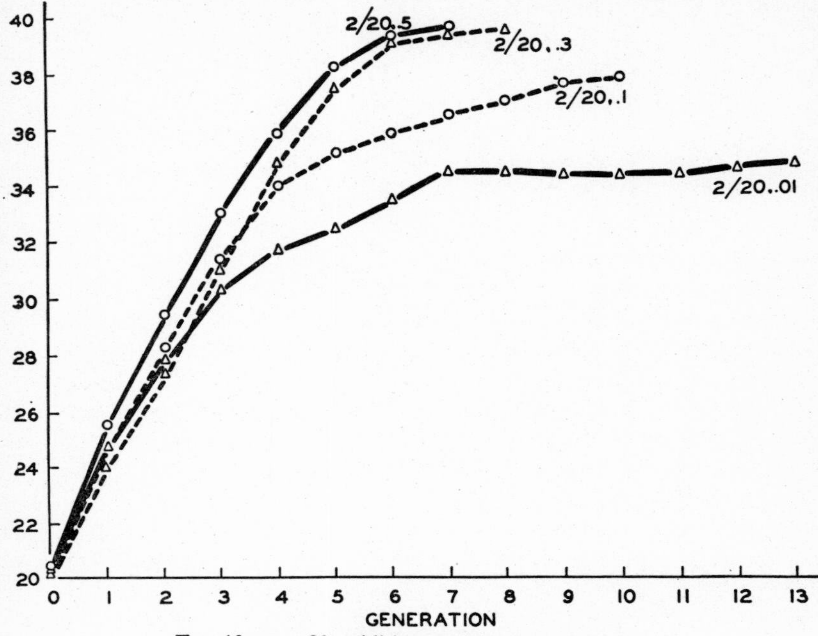

FIG. 13. $m=20$, additive model, $\sigma^2=0$, 3 runs.

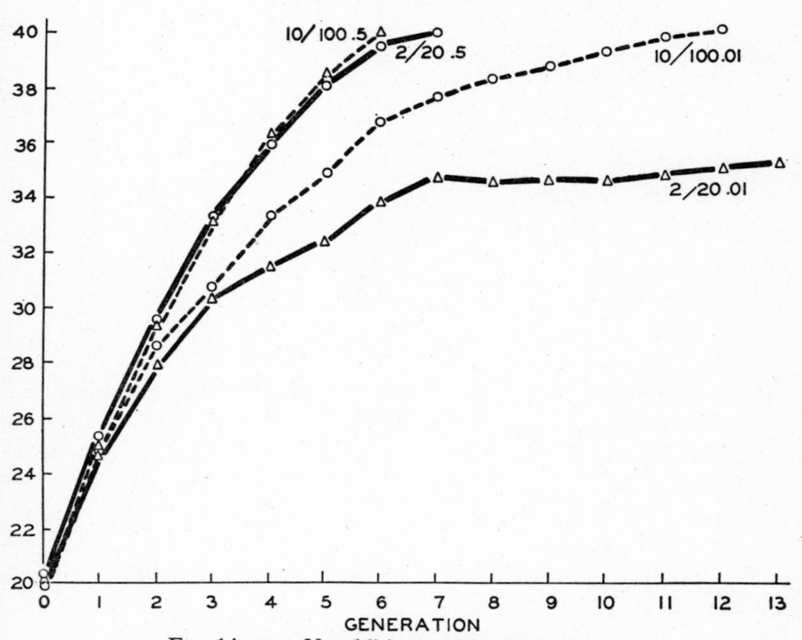

FIG. 14. $m=20$ additive model, $\sigma^2=0$, 3 runs.

problems with which the population geneticist is faced. While the complexity of the genetic situation incorporated into the program is very modest compared to that probably prevalent in biological material, much more complex situations can be handled with the large machines now available.

A program similar in objective to the one of this study, but different in many details and procedures, was reported by Fraser (1957, I), and in a subsequent paper Fraser (1957, II) gave some results. He found that tight linkages slowed down the progress from selection in populations which were in maximum repulsion initially with gene frequencies of 1/3 in one case and 2/3 in another case. He also found the effect to be much greater in small populations with intense selection, 4/40, than in larger populations with less intense selection, 50/100. When translated into n and N of this study the corresponding values are 2/20 and 25/50, respectively.

The results of this study show that tight linkages can also slow down progress from selection when the populations are initially in linkage equilibrium. The results also show that the effect is a joint function of n, N, m and α. In some cases less intense selection can lead to more progress (Figs. 9–12). While many results have been obtained, they still leave a vacancy as to exactly how these various parameters are interacting. It does not seem likely that this vacancy will be filled by the wholesale accumulation of additional results on other variations of the parameters.

It is worth while then to reflect on the utility of empirical machine studies. The authors have come to view the procedure as one of detection and suggestion. It is an excellent method of detecting where present theory breaks down or of detecting effects of variations in parameters, providing of course that one has some luck and judgement in the proper choice of values of the parameters. It can also suggest how the parameters operate. However, a thorough understanding requires a formulated theory. It is believed that the empirical procedure is properly a tool to this end and is not to be used to generate the end product or total response surface.

It is tempting to extrapolate from the present results that the animal and plant breeders should either use larger populations or select less intensely than is often found in practice. However, it is probably advisable to await a better understanding of the situation. Efforts are now being directed not just on a summarization of the results but on the formulation of a quantitative theory which will encompass the results.

REFERENCES

FRASER, A. S. (1957) Simulation of genetic systems by automatic digital computers I. Introduction. II. Effects of linkage on rates of advance under selection. *Austral. J. Biol. Sci.* **10,** 484–491, 492–499.

MOSHMAN, J. (1954) The generation of pseudo-random numbers on a decimal calculator. *J. Assoc. Computing Machinery* **1,** 88–91.

FRASER, A. S. (1958). Monte Carlo simulation of genetic systems. This volume.

GENETIC AND STATISTICAL THEORY FOR QUANTITATIVE INHERITANCE STUDIES OF HAPLOIDS*

By D. S. Robson †
Cornell University

INTRODUCTION

Haploid organisms, which have been acclaimed as nearly ideal subjects for genetic study, offer very real advantages for the study of quantitative inheritance. Neurospora, in particular, may be grown in large numbers under well controlled laboratory conditions, and individuals may be replicated by asexual means to permit the direct measurement of interaction between genetic and environmental factors. The recent developments in the statistical theory of quantitative inheritance, however, have not explicitly covered the haploid case and are therefore not immediately available to Neurospora geneticists. An earlier paper (Robson, 1957) described the partitioning method of quantitative inheritance analysis of haploid systems derived from two parents, and the present paper discusses the genetic variance component method as applied to haploids.

A RANDOM-EFFECTS MODEL FOR HAPLOID POPULATIONS AT EQUILIBRIUM UNDER RANDOM MATING

The quantitative phenotypes generated by a haploid system at equilibrium under random mating form a population which is identical in concept to the population structure underlying the ordinary random-effects, N-factor linear statistical model. In the usual statistical case, the ' yield ' of an individual unit randomly selected from the population is a function of N independent chance variables $X_1, \ldots, X_N$ representing the levels of the N different factors controlling yield; in the present case, ' yield ' is phenotype and the N factors are the N segregating genetic factors controlling phenotype, with the ' levels ' of each factor represented by the different alleles of each gene present in the system. If alleles are considered countable then X_i is a discrete chance variable which indexes the alleles at the ith locus, and because of the equilibrium assumption,

$$\Pr\{X_1, \ldots, X_N\} = \Pr\{X_1\} \ldots \Pr\{X_N\}; \tag{1}$$

* Paper number 364 of the Department of Plant Breeding, Cornell University, and paper number SS489 of Colorado A and M College.

† This paper was prepared, in part, while the author was serving as Visiting Professor at Colorado A and M College.

i.e. the frequency of any given genotype is equal to the product of the corresponding gene frequencies.

The population average 'yield' associated with any given combination $x_1, \ldots, x_N$ of levels of the N factors becomes, in the present case, the average phenotype, called the *genotypic value* $g(x_1, \ldots, x_N)$ of the genotype indexed by $x_1, \ldots, x_N$. The usual linear model for yield then becomes

$$g(x_1, \ldots, x_N) = \mu + \sum_{i=1}^{N} \alpha_{x_i} + \sum_{i_1 \neq i_2} \alpha_{x_{i_1}, x_{i_2}} + \ldots + \alpha_{x_1, x_2, \ldots, x_N}$$

where μ is the population mean,

$$\mu = \mathscr{E}[g(X_1, \ldots, X_N)],$$

$\alpha_{x_1}, \ldots, \alpha_{x_N}$ are the 'main effects', or additive effects,

$$\alpha_{x_i} = \mathscr{E}[g(X_1, \ldots, X_N) \mid X_i = x_i] - \mu,$$

$\alpha_{x_1, x_2}, \ldots, \alpha_{x_{N-1}, x_N}$ are the 'first order interaction effects', or additive $\times$ additive effects,

$$\alpha_{x_i, x_j} = \mathscr{E}[g(X_1, \ldots, X_N) \mid X_i = x_i, X_j = x_j] - \alpha_{x_i} - \alpha_{x_j} + \mu,$$

and so on in the usual manner.

The chance variables $\alpha_{X_1}, \ldots, \alpha_{X_1, \ldots, X_N}$ defined in this way are known to be uncorrelated under the assumption (1), so the total genetic variance σ_G^2 may be expressed as

$$\mathscr{E}[g(X_1, \ldots, X_N) - \mu]^2 = \sum_{i=1}^{N} \mathscr{E}(\alpha_{x_i}^2) + \sum_{i_1 \neq i_2} \mathscr{E}(\alpha_{X_{i_1}, X_{i_2}}^2) + \ldots + \mathscr{E}(\alpha_{x_1, \ldots, x_N}^2)$$

or

$$\sigma_G^2 = \sigma_1^2 + \sigma_2^2 + \ldots + \sigma_N^2$$

where

$$\sigma_k^2 = \sum_{i_1 \neq \ldots \neq i_k} \mathscr{E}(\alpha_{X_{i_1}, \ldots, X_{i_k}}^2).$$

RELATION OF THE HAPLOID RANDOM-EFFECTS MODEL TO THE KEMPTHORNE MODEL FOR AUTOPOLYPLOIDS

The random-effects model described here for haploids represents a direct application of the well known N-factor variance component Model II, so no mathematical proofs were required. The Kempthorne (1955) variance component model for simple autopolyploid populations at equilibrium under random mating may also be regarded mathematically as a special case of Model II, the haploid model. For the haploid case, the chance variables $X_1, \ldots, X_N$ indexing the alleles at the N loci are independently distributed; the additional restrictions which characterize a simple auto-r-ploid population at equilibrium are $N = rM$, where r and M are integers, and the chance variables $X_i, X_{M+i}, \ldots, X_{(r-1)M+1}$ indexing the alleles at the ith locus in the first, second,

..., and r^{th} set of chromosomes, respectively, are identically distributed for each i, $1 \leqq i \leqq M$. The genotypic value $g(x_1, \ldots, x_{N=rM})$ must also be assumed invariant under permutations of the arguments $x_{(i}, x_{M+i}, \ldots, x_{r-1)M+i}$ for all i; that is, the genotypic value depends only upon the unordered set of alleles present at each locus. Since assumption (1) is fulfilled it follows that

$$\sigma_G^2 = \sum_{i=1}^{N} \mathscr{E}(\alpha_{x_i}^2) + \sum_{i_1 \neq i_2} \mathscr{E}(\alpha_{X_{i_1}, X_{i_2}}^2) + \ldots + \mathscr{E}(\alpha_{x_1, \ldots, x_N}^2);$$

however, under these additional restrictions the collection of independent chance variables $\alpha_{X_{i_1}, \ldots, X_{i_v}}$ becomes partitioned into subsets of identically distributed chance variables. For example, the collection of additive effects $(\alpha_{X_1}, \ldots, \alpha_{X_N})$ becomes partitioned into the subsets

$$\{(\alpha_{X_1}, \alpha_{X_{M+1}}, \ldots, \alpha_{X_{(r-1)M+1}}), \ldots, (\alpha_{X_M}, \alpha_{X_{2M}}, \ldots, \alpha_{x_{rM}})\}$$

where the r chance variables within each subset are identically distributed;

consequently, $$\sum_{i=1}^{N=rM} \mathscr{E}(\alpha_{X_i}^2)$$

may be written $$\sum_{i=1}^{N} \mathscr{E}(\alpha_{X_i}^2) = r \sum_{j=1}^{M} \mathscr{E}(\alpha_{X_j}^2).$$

The set of first order interaction effects, $(\alpha_{X_1, X_2}, \ldots, \alpha_{X_{N-1}, X_N})$ becomes partitioned into two kinds of subsets, one kind typified by the subset

$$(\alpha_{X_1, X_2}, \alpha_{X_1, X_{M+2}}, \ldots, \alpha_{X_{(r-1)M+1}, X_{(r-1)M+2}})$$

containing the r^2 chance variables having the same distribution as the additive $\times$ additive effect α_{X_1, X_2}, and the other kind typified by the subset

$$(\alpha_{X_1, X_{M+1}}, \alpha_{X_1, X_{2M+1}}, \ldots, \alpha_{X_{(r-2)M+1}, X_{(r-1)M+1}})$$

containing the $r(r-1)/2$ chance variables having the same distribution as the dominance effect $\alpha_{X_1, X_{M+1}}$. Thus, the first order interaction component of genetic variance may be written as the sum of an additive $\times$ additive component and a dominance component,

$$\sum_{i_1 \neq i_2}^{N=rM} \mathscr{E}(\alpha_{X_{i_1}, X_{i_2}}^2) = r^2 \sum_{j_1 \neq j_2}^{M} \mathscr{E}(\alpha_{X_{j_1}, X_{j_2}}^2) + \frac{r(r-1)}{2} \sum_{j=1}^{M} \mathscr{E}(\alpha_{X_j, X_{M+j}}^2).$$

In general, if an equivalence relation is defined among the subsets

$$I_v = (i_1, \ldots, i_v), \quad 1 \leqq i_1 < i_2 < \ldots < i_v \leqq N,$$

with $I_{k_1, \ldots, k_r}$ denoting an equivalence class of subsets I_v for which there exist k_m integers i, $1 \leqq i \leqq M$, such that $i + nM$ belongs to I_v for exactly m values of n, $0 \leqq n \leqq r-1$, $m = 1, 2, \ldots, r$, $\sum m k_m = v$, then the number of subsets $(i_1, \ldots, i_v)$ contained in the class $I_{k_1, \ldots, k_r}$ is $\prod_{m=1}^{r} \binom{r}{m}^{k_m}$. The $(v-1)$-order interaction component of genetic variance may therefore be written

$$\sum_{I_v C I_N} \mathscr{E}(\alpha^2_{(X_i \mid i \varepsilon I_v)}) = \sum_{k_1, \ldots, k_r \mid \sum m k_m = v} \prod_{m=1}^{r} \binom{r}{m}^{k_m} \sum_{I_{k_1, \ldots, k_r}} \mathscr{E}(\alpha^2_{(X_i \mid i \varepsilon I_{k_1, \ldots, k_r})})$$

where the genetic variance component

$$\sigma^2_{k_1, \ldots, k_r} \underset{\text{def.}}{\equiv} \prod_{m=1}^{r} \binom{r}{m}^{k_m} \sum_{I_{k_1, \ldots, k_r}} \mathscr{E}(\alpha^2_{(X_i \mid i \varepsilon I_{k_1, \ldots, k_r})})$$

represents the sum of all $(\sum m k_m - 1)$-order interactions between additive effects at k_1 loci, dominance effects at k_2 loci, etc. The total genetic variance then becomes

$$\sigma^2_G = \sum_{k_1, \ldots, k_r \left| \begin{array}{l} 0 \leqq k_1, \ldots, k_r \leqq M \\ 1 \leqq \sum m k_m \leqq rM \end{array} \right.} \sigma^2_{k_1, \ldots, k_r}$$

A FIXED-EFFECTS MODEL FOR RESTRICTED RANDOM MATING SYSTEMS INVOLVING TWO PARENTS

Mating systems which place some restrictions on the selection of a mate generally, though not always, result in a generation to generation change in the expected genotypic frequency distribution. The utility of variance component analysis as a method of studying quantitative inheritance is considerably reduced when applied to a changing population; however, situations arise, as in many studies of naturally self-fertilized plants, where the cross-breeding necessary to maintain an unchanging population is not practicable, and the variance component method is applied in spite of its drawbacks. An alternative method of analysis particularly suited to these situations does exist, but requires realistically large sample sizes and has been widely shunned.

The linear models which have been constructed to accommodate diploid inbreeding systems such as selfing and backcrossing series have been confined almost exclusively to the case where each genetic factor is represented by exactly two alleles, as in systems arising from an initial cross between two inbred, homozygous lines. One such diploid model described by Ander on and Kempthorne (1954) uses the device, commonly employed in the analysis of variance, of defining fixed effects in the same manner as random effects would be defined if the levels of each factor were equally likely. This is equivalent to using as fixed effects the definitions given by the random-effects model applied to a diploid F_2 population where gene frequencies are all equal to 1/2. This same device applied to a haploid F_1 population generated by the cross of two parents gives a reasonable and natural definition of effects for the haploid two-allele case.

For a single factor difference the F_1 population is comprised of two equally frequent genotypes or genotypic values, say A and a, and the effects are then defined by

$$\mu = \tfrac{1}{2}A + \tfrac{1}{2}a$$

$$\alpha_A = A - \mu$$

$$= \frac{A-a}{2}$$

$$\alpha_a = a - \mu$$

$$= \frac{a-A}{2}$$

$$= -\alpha_A$$

so that

$$A = \mu + \alpha_A$$

$$a = \mu - \alpha_A$$

Similarly, for two independently segregating factors, say A-a and B-b, the F_1 population is comprised of the four equally frequent genotypes AB, Ab, aB and ab, and the random-effects model yields the following definitions of gene effects which will be adopted as the fixed effects:

$$\mu = \frac{AB + Ab + aB + ab}{4}$$

$$\alpha_A = \frac{AB + Ab - aB - ab}{4} = -\alpha_a$$

$$\alpha_B = \frac{AB - Ab + aB - ab}{4} = -\alpha_b$$

$$\alpha_{AB} = \frac{AB - Ab - aB + ab}{4} = -\alpha_{Ab} = -\alpha_{aB} = \alpha_{ab}$$

In this case, then,

$$AB = \mu + \alpha_A + \alpha_B + \alpha_{AB}$$

$$Ab = \mu + \alpha_A - \alpha_B - \alpha_{AB}$$

$$aB = \mu - \alpha_A + \alpha_B - \alpha_{AB}$$

$$ab = \mu - \alpha_A - \alpha_B + \alpha_{AB}.$$

The device used in genetics of expressing genotype as the symbolic product of the individual genes may be exploited here to obtain a simple rule for obtaining the above two-factor fixed effects. To emphasize the fact that a genotype such as AB denotes a symbolic product, a symbolic multiplication sign ' o ' will be inserted,

$$AB = A \circ B.$$

The two-factor array of genotypes (AB, Ab, aB, ab) may then be obtained as the *Kronecker product* of the two one-factor arrays; thus if ' * ' denotes Kronecker multiplication, then

$$\begin{aligned}(A, a) * (B, b) &= (A \circ B, A \circ b, a \circ B, a \circ b)\\ &= (AB, Ab, aB, ab).\end{aligned}$$

Similarly, the transformation of these four genotypes into the four effects, $\mu, \alpha_A, \alpha_B, \alpha_{AB}$ may be obtained as the Kronecker product of the two transformations

$$(\mu, \alpha_A) = \frac{1}{2}(A, a)\begin{pmatrix}1 & 1\\ 1 & -1\end{pmatrix} \quad \text{and} \quad (\mu, \alpha_B) = \frac{1}{2}(B, b)\begin{pmatrix}1 & 1\\ 1 & -1\end{pmatrix}.$$

Thus,

$$(\mu, \alpha_A) * (\mu, \alpha_B) = \frac{1}{2}(A, a)\begin{pmatrix}1 & 1\\ 1 & -1\end{pmatrix} * \frac{1}{2}(B, b)\begin{pmatrix}1 & 1\\ 1 & -1\end{pmatrix}$$

or

$$\begin{aligned}(\mu \circ \mu, \mu \circ \alpha_B, \alpha_A \circ \mu, \alpha_A \circ \alpha_B) &= \frac{1}{4}\left\{(A, a) * (B, b)\right\}\left\{\begin{pmatrix}1 & 1\\ 1 & -1\end{pmatrix} * \begin{pmatrix}1 & 1\\ 1 & -1\end{pmatrix}\right\}\\ &= \frac{1}{4}(AB, Ab, aB, ab)\begin{pmatrix}1 & 1 & 1 & 1\\ 1 & -1 & 1 & -1\\ 1 & 1 & -1 & -1\\ 1 & -1 & -1 & 1\end{pmatrix}\end{aligned}$$

By previous convention, μ serves as the unit element under the induced ' o ' multiplication of effects, and the product $\alpha_A \circ \alpha_B$ is written α_{AB}. These relations result in a simple rule for constructing effects, illustrated for the three-factor case by

$$\begin{aligned}\alpha_{ABC} &= \alpha_A \circ \alpha_B \circ \alpha_C\\ &= \frac{A-a}{2} \circ \frac{B-b}{2} \circ \frac{C-c}{2}\\ &= \frac{1}{8}(ABC - AbC - aBC + abC - ABc + Abc + aBc - abc)\end{aligned}$$

$$\alpha_{AC} = \alpha_A \circ \mu_B \circ \alpha_C$$

$$= \frac{A-a}{2} \circ \frac{B+b}{2} \circ \frac{C-c}{2}$$

$$= \frac{1}{8}(ABC + AbC - aBC - abC - ABc - Abc + aBc + abc)$$

and, similarly,

$$\begin{aligned}
ABC &= A \circ B \circ C \\
&= (\mu+\alpha_A) \circ (\mu+\alpha_B) \circ (\mu+\alpha_C) \\
&= \mu \circ \mu \circ \mu + \alpha_A \circ \mu \circ \mu + \mu \circ \alpha_B \circ \mu + \mu \circ \mu \circ \alpha_C + \\
&\qquad + \alpha_A \circ \alpha_B \circ \mu + \alpha_A \circ \mu \circ \alpha_C + \mu \circ \alpha_B \circ \alpha_C + \alpha_A \circ \alpha_B \circ \alpha_C \\
&= \mu + \alpha_A + \alpha_B + \alpha_C + \alpha_{AB} + \alpha_{AC} + \alpha_{BC} + \alpha_{ABC} \\
AbC &= (\mu+\alpha_A) \circ (\mu-\alpha_B) \circ (\mu+\alpha_C) \\
&= \mu + \alpha_A - \alpha_B + \alpha_C - \alpha_{AB} + \alpha_{AC} - \alpha_{BC} - \alpha_{ABC}
\end{aligned}$$

and so on.

APPLICATION OF THE FIXED-EFFECTS MODEL TO A FULL-SIB MATING SYSTEM DERIVED FROM TWO HAPLOID PARENTS

Full-sib mating starting from a cross of two haploid parents is an experimental breeding procedure particularly suited for the application of variance component analysis. In the absence of linkage and other complicating factors, the expected genotypic frequency distribution assigns equal probability to all of the 2^N different genotypes in this system, and remains constant from generation to generation. This stability of the population stems from the stability of the individual families; random mating among the full sibs within a family of this system reproduces the genotypic distribution of that family. As a consequence, the expected total genetic variance remains constant from generation to generation and a nested family structure is built up in which the family means of one generation are perfectly correlated with the family progeny means of the next generation. This structure is illustrated below for the case of a single-factor difference between the two original parents:

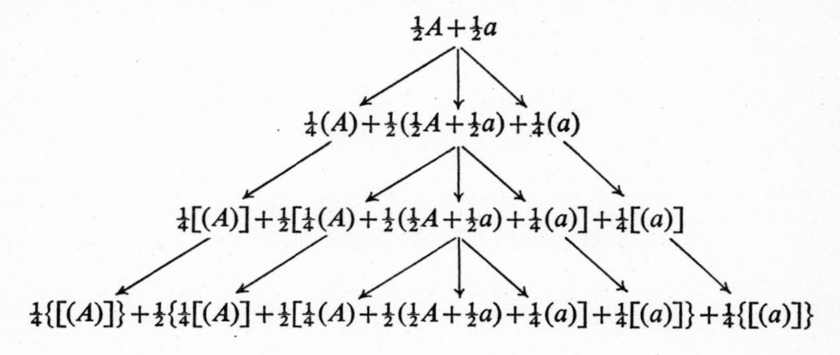

When random mating is practised in the first generation, each cross produces a family in the second generation which will be referred to as a (*1*; *2*)-family; a (*1*; *2*)-family is a collection of all individuals in generation 2 having common parents in generation 1. If random mating occurs among full sibs only in the second generation then each (*1*; *2*)-family produces a collection of (*2*; *3*)-families which collectively form a (*1*; *3*)-family; i.e., a (*2*; *3*)-family is a collection of all individuals in generation 3 having common parents in generation 2, and a (*1*; *3*)-family is a collection of all individuals in generation 3 having common grandparents in generation 1. In general, under successive random mating of full sibs, the individuals of the kth generation may be grouped into (*1*; k)-families, each (*1*; k)-family may be further subdivided into (*2*; k)-families, and so on to the final subdivision into ($k-1$; k)-families. For consistency, the entire population of generation k would be referred to as the (*0*; k)-family, and an individual in generation k would be called a (k; k)-family.

Since each generation of this system satisfies the assumption (1) underlying the random effects model, the expected total genetic variance in each generation may be expressed as

$$\sigma_G^2 = \sum_{k=1}^{N} \sigma_k^2$$

furthermore, in the present system, these variance components may be interpreted in terms of fixed effects as

$$\sigma_1^2 = \alpha_A^2 + \alpha_B^2 + \alpha_C^2 + \dots$$

$$\sigma_2^2 = \alpha_{AB}^2 + \alpha_{AC}^2 + \alpha_{BC}^2 + \dots$$

$$\sigma_3^2 = \alpha_{ABC}^2 + \alpha_{ABD}^2 + \alpha_{ACD}^2 + \dots$$

and so on. The expected genetic variance among (k; n)-family means is (see Appendix I)

$$\mathrm{V}(k\ ;\ n) = \sum_{\upsilon=1}^{N} \left(1 - \frac{1}{2^k}\right)^{\upsilon} \sigma_{\upsilon}^2$$

Consequently, in generation n, the variance among ($k+1$; n)-family means within (k; n)-families is

$$\mathrm{V}(k, k+1\colon\ n) = \mathrm{V}(k+1\ ;\ n) - \mathrm{V}(k\ ;\ n)$$

$$= \sum_{\upsilon=1}^{N} \left[\left(1 - \frac{1}{2^{k+1}}\right)^{\upsilon} - \left(1 - \frac{1}{2^k}\right)^{\upsilon}\right] \sigma_{\upsilon}^2$$

and the average variance $\overline{\mathrm{V}}$ (k; n) among individuals within (k; n)-families is

$$\overline{\mathrm{V}}\ (k\ ;\ n) = \sigma_G^2 - \mathrm{V}(k\ ;\ n)$$

$$= \sum_{\upsilon=1}^{N} \left[1 - \left(1 - \frac{1}{2^k}\right)^{\upsilon}\right] \sigma_{\upsilon}^2$$

The fact that each family is at equilibrium under random mating is reflected in the above calculations in that $V(k; n)$ is constant for all $n>k$. A further consequence of this within family equilibrium is that the covariance $\text{Cov}(k; m, n)$ between the $(k; m)$-family means in generation m and the $(k; n)$-family means in generation n is independent of m and n. In fact,

$$\text{Cov}(k; m, n) = V(k; n) = V(k; m) = V(k; k+1).$$

The covariance $\text{Cov}(k, k+1; m, n)$ of $(k+1; m)$ and $(k+1; n)$-family means within $(k; \text{—})$-families is, likewise, equal to $V(k, k+1; k+2)$.

An experimental population where these results might be applied could be constructed in various ways. One scheme is illustrated below, where P_1 and P_2 denote the two original parents, $S_1 = P_1 \times P_2$, $S_{0,1;2}$ is a $(1; 2)$-family, $S_{1,2;3}$ is a $(2; 3)$-family within a $(1; 3)$-family, and so on:

$P_1 \times P_2 \rightarrow n_{0,1;1}$ randomly chosen spores are set aside for the experiment
$\downarrow$

$(S_1 \times S_1)^{n_{0,1;2}} \rightarrow n_{1,2;2}$ randomly chosen spores from each of the $n_{0,1;2}$ crosses are set aside
$\downarrow$

$[(S_{0,1;2} \times S_{0,1;2})^{n_{1,2;3}}]^{n_{0,1;3}} \rightarrow n_{2,3;3}$ spores from each of the $n_{0,1;3}$ $n_{1,2;3}$ crosses are set aside
$\downarrow$

$\{[(S_{1,2;3} \times S_{1,2;3})^{n_{2,3;4}}]^{n_{1,2;4}}\}^{n_{0,1;4}} \rightarrow n_{3,4;4}$ spores from each cross are set aside.
$\downarrow$

The experiment then consists of growing out these $n_{0,1;1} + n_{0,1;2}n_{1,2;2} + \ldots$ spores in a completely randomized design and measuring the phenotype, Y, of each individual.

The phenotype Y of an individual in this experiment is determined in part by the genotype of the individual and in part by the particular environmental niche to which it was randomly assigned. If the genotypic value of a given genotype is defined to be the conceptual average phenotype of that genotype, where the average is taken over all stages of randomization in the experimental procedure, then the environmental effects

$$e = \text{phenotype} - \text{genotypic value}$$

are independent chance variables with mean zero. The total variance of Y is then expressible as

$$V(Y) = \sigma_G^2 + \bar{\sigma}_E^2$$

where $\bar{\sigma}_E^2$ is the average of the 2^N environmental variances associated with the 2^N different genotypes of the system. A different set of environmental conditions may be expected to produce a different set of values for these parameters.

The observed mean squares (MS) from an analysis of variance of the nested classification within each generation are related to the genetic variances $V(k, k+1; n)$ in the manner indicated in Table 1; because $V(k, k+1; n)$ is constant for all $n > k+1$, the n is dropped in the notation of Table 1, and $V(k, k+1; k+1)$ is written $\overline{V}(k, k+1)$.

Thus,

$$\overline{V}(0, 1) = \sum_{k=1}^{N} \sigma_k^2$$

$$\overline{V}(1, 2) = \sum_{k=1}^{N} \left[1 - \left(\frac{1}{2}\right)^k\right] \sigma_k^2$$

$$V(0, 1) = \sum_{k=1}^{N} \frac{1}{2^k} \sigma_k^2$$

$$\overline{V}(2, 3) = \sum_{k=1}^{N} \left[1 - \left(\frac{3}{4}\right)^k\right] \sigma_k^2$$

$$V(1, 2) = \sum_{k=1}^{N} \left[\left(\frac{3}{4}\right)^k - \left(\frac{1}{2}\right)^k\right] \sigma_k^2$$

$$\overline{V}(3, 4) = \sum_{k=1}^{N} \left[1 - \left(\frac{7}{8}\right)^k\right] \sigma_k^2$$

$$V(2, 3) = \sum_{k=1}^{N} \left[\left(\frac{7}{8}\right)^k - \left(\frac{3}{4}\right)^k\right] \sigma_k^2$$

Additional information concerning the variances $V(k, k+1)$ is contained in the observed covariances between family means in the successive generations. When the procedure outlined earlier is used to construct the experimental populations, the mean cross product $MCP(k, k+1; m, n)$ is an unbiased estimate of $V(k, k+1)$; thus, $V(0, 1)$ may be estimated by

$$\frac{1}{n_{0,1;3}-1}\left[\sum_{1}^{n_{0,1;3}} \bar{y}_{n_{1,2;2}} \bar{y}_{n_{1,2;3}n_{2,3;3}} - \bar{y}_{n_{0,1;3}n_{1,2;3}n_{2,3;3}} \sum_{1}^{n_{0,1;3}} \bar{y}_{n_{1,2;2}}\right]$$

where $\bar{y}_{n_{1,2;2}}$ is an observed $(1; 2)$-family mean, based on $n_{1,2;2}$ individuals, $\bar{y}_{n_{1,2;3}n_{2,3;3}}$ is the observed mean of the corresponding $(1;3)$-family in the third generation and is based on $n_{1,2;3}n_{2,3;3}$ individuals, and $\bar{y}_{n_{0,1;3}n_{1,2;3}n_{2,3;3}} = \bar{y}_3$ is the mean of the entire third generation, consisting of $n_{0,1;3}n_{1,2;3}n_{2,3;3}$ individuals. The sum in this expression is taken over the $n_{0,1;3}$ families common to both generations $(n_{0,1;3} \leqq n_{0,1;2})$. Other

TABLE 1

Generation	Source of variation	d.f.	M.S.	Mean square expectation
1	Among $(1;1)$ w/in $(0;1)$	$n_{0,1;1}-1$	$\mathrm{MS}(0,1;1)$	$\bar{\sigma}_E^2+\overline{\mathrm{V}}(0,1)$
2	Among $(1;2)$ w/in $(0;2)$	$n_{0,1;2}-1$	$\mathrm{MS}(0,1;2)$	$\bar{\sigma}_E^2+\overline{\mathrm{V}}(1,2)+n_{1,2;2}\mathrm{V}(0,1)$
	Among $(2;2)$ w/in $(1;2)$	$n_{0,1;2}(n_{1,2;2}-1)$	$\mathrm{MS}(1,2;2)$	$\bar{\sigma}_E^2+\overline{\mathrm{V}}(1,2)$
3	Among $(1;3)$ w/in $(0;3)$	$n_{0,1;3}-1$	$\mathrm{MS}(0,1;3)$	$\bar{\sigma}_E^2+\overline{\mathrm{V}}(2,3)+n_{2,3;3}\mathrm{V}(1,2)+n_{1,2;3}n_{2,3;3}\mathrm{V}(0,1)$
	Among $(2;3)$ w/in $(1;3)$	$n_{0,1;3}(n_{1,2;3}-1)$	$\mathrm{MS}(1,2;3)$	$\bar{\sigma}_E^2+\overline{\mathrm{V}}(2,3)+n_{2,3;3}\mathrm{V}(1,2)$
	Among $(3;3)$ w/in $(2;3)$	$n_{0,1;3}n_{1,2;3}(n_{2,3;3}-1)$	$\mathrm{MS}(2,3;3)$	$\bar{\sigma}_E^2+\overline{\mathrm{V}}(2,3)$
4	Among $(1;4)$ w/in $(0;4)$	$n_{0,1;4}-1$	$\mathrm{MS}(0,1;4)$	$\bar{\sigma}_E^2+\overline{\mathrm{V}}(3,4)+n_{3,4;4}\mathrm{V}(2,3)+n_{2,3;4}n_{3,4;4}\mathrm{V}(1,2)$ $+n_{1,2;4}n_{2,3;4}n_{3,4;4}\mathrm{V}(0,1)$
	Among $(2;4)$ w/in $(1;4)$	$n_{0,1;4}(n_{1,2;4}-1)$	$\mathrm{MS}(1,2;4)$	$\bar{\sigma}_E^2+\overline{\mathrm{V}}(3,4)+n_{3,4;4}\mathrm{V}(2,3)+n_{2,3;4}n_{3,4;4}\mathrm{V}(1,2)$
	Among $(3;4)$ w/in $(2;4)$	$n_{0,1;4}n_{1,2;4}(n_{2,3,4}-1)$	$\mathrm{MS}(2,3;4)$	$\bar{\sigma}_E^2+\overline{\mathrm{V}}(3,4)+n_{3,4;4}\mathrm{V}(2,3)$
	Among $(4;4)$ w/in $(3;4)$	$n_{0,1;4}n_{1,2;4}n_{2,3;4}(n_{3,4;4}-1)$	$\mathrm{MS}(3,4;4)$	$\bar{\sigma}_E^2+\overline{\mathrm{V}}(3,4)$

estimates of V(0, 1) are available in MCP(0, 1 ; 2, 4) and MCP(0, 1 ; 3, 4). Similarly, an unbiased estimate of V(1, 2) is

$$\text{MCP}\,(1, 2;\, 3,\, 4) = \frac{1}{n_{0,\,1\,;\,4}(n_{1,\,2\,;\,4}-1)}$$

$$\times \sum_{1}^{n_{0,\,1\,;\,4}} \left[\sum_{1}^{n_{1\ 2\,;\,4}} \bar{y}_{n_{2,\,3\,;\,3}} \bar{y}_{n_{2,\,3\,;\,4} n_{3,\,4\,;\,4}} - \bar{y}_{n_{1,\,2\,;\,4} n_{2,\,3\,;\,4} n_{3,\,4\,;\,4}} \sum_{1}^{n_{1,\,2\,;\,4}} \bar{y}_{n_{2,\,3\,;\,3}} \right].$$

Estimation of the genetic variance components σ_1^2, σ_2^2, etc., would ordinarily proceed from the above results by the method of least squares. Since the various mean squares and cross products are correlated and heteroskedastic a weighted least squares procedure should be used, with the weights determined from the inverse of the estimated variance-covariance matrix of these mean squares and mean cross products. The method for computing unbiased estimates of this dispersion matrix has been described by Robson (1958).

APPLICATION OF THE FIXED-EFFECTS MODEL TO A RECURRENT BACKCROSSING SYSTEM DERIVED FROM TWO HAPLOID PARENTS

Recurrent backcrossing is taken as an example of a breeding system poorly suited to the variance component method of quantitative genetic analysis. Such a procedure is a form of inbreeding, and in the limit the genotypic frequency distribution in each of the two backcrossed populations assigns probability 1 to the genotype of the recurring parent. Estimation of the genetic variance components

$$\sigma_1^2 = \alpha_A^2+\alpha_B^2+\alpha_C^2+\ldots$$

$$\sigma_2^2 = \alpha_{AB}^2+\alpha_{AC}^2+\alpha_{BC}^2+\ldots$$

$$\vdots$$

presents a very awkward problem in this case; a redeeming feature of inbreeding systems, however, is that they render the corresponding first degree parameters estimable. The parameters

$$A_1 = \alpha_A+\alpha_B+\alpha_C+\ldots$$

$$A_2 = \alpha_{AB}+\alpha_{AC}+\alpha_{BC}+\ldots$$

$$\vdots$$

which cannot be estimated from a system in which expected genotypic frequencies remain constant through successive generations, become estimable in systems with a changing distribution. The two types of systems, therefore, complement one another in providing information in a quantitative inheritance study.

If the genotypes of the two parents P_1 and P_2 are denoted by

$$P_1 = abcd...$$
$$P_2 = ABCD...$$

then in the absence of linkage and other complicating factors the mean of the nth recurrent backcross population to P_1 is expressible as (see Appendix II)

$$\bar{B}_n^1 = \mu + \sum_{k=1}^{N} (-1)^k \left(1 - \frac{1}{2^n}\right)^k A_k$$

and

$$\bar{B}_n^2 = \mu + \sum_{k=1}^{N} \left(1 - \frac{1}{2^n}\right) A_k.$$

Thus, the backcross series yield the equations

$$\bar{P}_1 = \mu - A_1 + A_2 - A_3 + \ldots \qquad \bar{P}_2 = \mu + A_1 + A_2 + A_3 + \ldots$$

$$\bar{F}_1 = \mu$$

$$\bar{B}_1^1 = \mu - \frac{1}{2}A_1 + \frac{1}{4}A_2 - \frac{1}{8}A_3 + \ldots \qquad \bar{B}_1^2 = \mu + \frac{1}{2}A_1 + \frac{1}{4}A_2 + \frac{1}{8}A_3 + \ldots$$

$$\bar{B}_2^1 = \mu - \frac{3}{4}A_1 + \frac{9}{16}A_2 - \frac{27}{64}A_3 + \ldots \qquad \bar{B}_2^2 = \mu + \frac{3}{4}A_1 + \frac{9}{16}A_2 + \frac{27}{64}A_3 + \ldots$$

$$\bar{B}_3^1 = \mu - \frac{7}{8}A_1 + \frac{49}{64}A_2 - \frac{343}{512}A_3 + \ldots \qquad \bar{B}_3^2 = \mu + \frac{7}{8}A_1 + \frac{49}{64}A_2 + \frac{343}{512}A_3 + \ldots$$

$$\vdots$$

An experimental population can easily be constructed in such a manner that the corresponding array of sample means are mutually statistically independent, so the least squares estimation problem is relatively simple.

The expected total genetic variance in the B_n^1 population may be written (see Appendix II)

$$V_1(n) = \sum_{\upsilon=1}^{N} \left(1 - \frac{1}{2^n}\right)^{\upsilon} \left[1 - \left(1 - \frac{1}{2^n}\right)^{\upsilon}\right] \sigma_{\upsilon}^2 - $$
$$- \sum_{j=0}^{N} \sum_{k=0}^{N} (-1)^{j+k} \left(1 - \frac{1}{2^n}\right)^{j+k} \sum_{\substack{I_j, I_k C I_N \\ I_j \neq I_k}} \alpha_{I_j} \alpha_{I_k}$$

The corresponding expression $V_2(n)$ is obtained by deleting the factor $(-1)^{j+k}$ under the second sum. The presence of cross product terms makes these expressions unmanageable in any practical sense, showing the futility of the variance component approach in this case. An additional complication arises in practice because the environmental component of variance changes from generation to generation along with the change in gene frequencies, and would need to be estimated separately for each generation by asexual replication.

This restricted applicability of the variance component method holds also for diploid and higher polyploid systems, and in no case can a breeding system be found which will yield estimates of both the first and second degree genetic parameters. In diploids, as in haploids, however, pairs of breeding systems stemming from two parents may be easily devised to accomplish this. An example of such complementary systems in the diploid case is the selfing series, derived from two homozygous parents, paired with recurrent back-crossing to the F_1 genotype. Anderson and Kempthorne (1954) discuss the estimation of first degree parameters from a selfing series, and van der Veen (1957) briefly describes the variance component analysis of the backcross to the F_1. This latter system exhibits a $(k; n)$-family structure analogous to that of the full sib mating system described here, and the total genetic variance in each of the recurrent backcross generations,

$$\sigma_G^2 = \sum_{\upsilon=0}^{N} \sum_{\substack{0 \leqq k_1, k_2 \leqq N \\ k_1 + 2k_2 = \upsilon}} \sigma_{k_1, k_2}^2,$$

may easily be partitioned into its hierarchal components by means of the following formula for the covariance of $(k; m)$- and $(k; n)$-family means,

$$\text{Cov}\,(k\,;\,m, n) = \sum_{\upsilon=1}^{N} \left(\frac{1}{2^{m+n-2k}}\right)^{\upsilon} \sigma_{\upsilon, 0}^2.$$

Other pairs of systems exist for this diploid case, of course; a random mating derived from the F_2 population, for example, may substitute for the backcross to the F_1, and virtually any inbreeding system will serve instead of the selfing series. The experimental use of pairs of breeding systems in a quantitative inheritance study has not been practised extensively with diploids, and it is to be hoped that Neurospora geneticists, with their more nearly ideal genetic material, will be able to exploit this concept.

REFERENCES

ANDERSON, V. L. & KEMPTHORNE, O. (1954) A model for the study of quantitative inheritance, *Genetics* **39**, 883–898.

KEMPTHORNE, O. (1955) The theoretical values of correlations between relatives in random mating populations, *Genetics* **40**, 153–167.

KEMPTHORNE, O. (1955) The correlations between relatives in random mating populations, *Cold Spring Harbor Symposia Quant. Biol.* **20**, 60–75.

ROBSON, D. S. (1957) Some biometrical formulae for the analysis of quantitative inheritance systems involving two haploid or inbred diploid parents, *Genetics* **42**, 487–498.

ROBSON, D. S. (1958) Applications of multivariate polykays to genetic covariance component analysis, *Biometrics* **14**, 142–143.

VAN DER VEEN, J. H. (1957) The heritable variance of $F_1 \times F_2$ progeny means, *Biometrics* **13**, 111–112.

APPENDIX I

Random Mating Among Full Sibs Derived From Two Haploid Parents

We may represent the $(k;m)$-family structure by means of moment generating functions, and at the same time show that gene frequencies remain constant from generation to generation under this breeding plan. Since there are but two alleles, $x_i = 1, 2$, at the ith locus then with respect to a single locus there are but three genetically distinct matings possible; namely, 1×1, 1×2, and 2×2. For $N = 1$, then, there are but three genetically different $(k; k+1)$-families. If we let $\phi_{ij}(t)$ denote the generating function within the family produced by the cross $i\times j$ then

$$\phi_{11}(t) = t, \quad \phi_{12}(t) = 1/2t+1/2t^2, \quad \phi_{22}(t) = t^2.$$

Under random mating within families, each of these three families reproduces its own generating function in the next generation. The family with $\phi_{11}(t) = t$, called the ϕ_{11} family, consists entirely of individuals carrying allele 1; hence, random mating within this family produces only individuals carrying allele 1. Likewise, the ϕ_{22} family consists entirely of individuals carrying allele 2 and hence reproduces itself under random mating. The ϕ_{12} family consists of individuals carrying allele 1 and those carrying allele 2, in equal frequency. Under random mating the crosses 1×1, 1×2, 2×2 therefore occur with frequencies 1/4, 1/2, 1/4, respectively; the generating function for the progeny of this family is then

$$1/4\phi_{11}(t)+1/2\phi_{12}(t)+1/4\phi_{22}(t) = 1/2t+1/2t^2 = \phi_{12}(t).$$

If we let $P_k(\phi_{ij})$ denote the frequency of the family ϕ_{ij} in generation k then we may write the generating function $\Phi_{k+1}(t)$ for generation $k+1$ as

$$\Phi_{k+1}(t) = \phi_{11}(t)[P_k(\phi_{11})+1/4P_k(\phi_{12})]+\phi_{12}(t)[1/2P_k(\phi_{12})]+ \\ +\phi_{22}(t)[P_k(\phi_{22})+1/4P_k(\phi_{12})]$$

Since $P_1(\phi_{12}) = 1$, this recursion has the solution

$$\begin{aligned}\Phi_{k+1}(t) &= 1/2(1-2^{-k})\,\phi_{11}(t)+2^{-k}\phi_{12}(t)+1/2(1-2^{-k})\,\phi_{22}(t)\\ &= 1/2(1-2^{-k})[t]+2^{-k}[1/2t+1/2t^2]+1/2(1-2^{-k})[t^2]\\ &= 1/2t+1/2t^2\end{aligned}$$

Thus, in generation $k+1$ the frequency of each allele is still 1/2; furthermore, since the generating functions $\phi_{ij}(t)$ reproduce themselves under full sib random mating we have, for $m \geqq k+1$, $\Phi_m(t) = \Phi_{k+1}(t)$. With respect to a single locus, then, the three genetically distinct $(k;m)$-families are ϕ_{11}, ϕ_{12}, ϕ_{22} with frequencies $1/2(1-2^{-k})$, 2^{-k}, $1/2(1-2^{-k})$, respectively.

The corresponding generating function $\Phi_m(t_1, \ldots, t_N)$ for the N independent chance variables $X_1, \ldots, X_N$ is then, letting $\theta_n = 2^{-n}$,

$$\Phi_m(t_1, \ldots, t_N) = \prod_{i=1}^{N} \Phi_m(t_i)$$

$$= \prod_{i=1}^{N} \left\{ 1/2(1-\theta_k)[t_i] + \theta_k[1/2t_i + 1/2t_i^2] + 1/2(1-\theta_k)[t_i^2] \right\}$$

$$= \sum_{v=0}^{N} \sum_{\beta=0}^{v} \theta_k^{v-\beta}(1/2[1-\theta_k])^{N-v+\beta}$$

$$\times \sum_{I_v \subset I_N} \sum_{I_\beta \subset I_v} \left[\prod_{i \varepsilon I_\beta} t_i \prod_{i \varepsilon I_v - I_\beta} (1/2t_i + 1/2t_i^2) \prod_{i \varepsilon I_N - I_v} t_i^2 \right]$$

Thus, each pair of subsets I_v, I_β, $I_\beta \subset I_v \subset I_N$, determines a $(k; m)$-family consisting of $2^{v-\beta}$ equally frequent genotypes which show genetic variation at the $v-\beta$ loci indexed by the set $I_v - I_\beta$.

The average genotypic value for the $(k; m)$-family given by the subsets I_v, I_β is most conveniently computed through the use of symbolic o-multiplication. We may write the population mean, μ, for generation m as

$$\bar{g} = \prod_{i=1}^{N}{}_{\mathrm{o}} \left\{ 1/2(1-\theta_k)[\bar{g}(x_i = 1)] + \theta_k[1/2\bar{g}(x_i = 1) + 1/2\bar{g}(x_i = 2)] \right.$$

$$\left. + 1/2(1-\theta_k)[\bar{g}(x_i = 2)] \right\}$$

$$= \prod_{i=1}^{N}{}_{\mathrm{o}} \left\{ 1/2(1-\theta_k)[\mu - \alpha_i] + \theta_k[\mu] + 1/2(1-\theta_k)[\mu + \alpha_i] \right\}$$

$$= \sum_{v=0}^{N} \sum_{\beta=0}^{v} \theta_k^{v-\beta}(1/2[1-\theta_k])^{N-v+\beta} \sum_{I_v \subset I_N} \sum_{I_\beta \subset I_v} \left[\prod_{i \varepsilon I_\beta}{}_{\mathrm{o}} (\mu - \alpha_i) \right.$$

$$\left. \times \prod_{i \varepsilon I_v - I_\beta}{}_{\mathrm{o}} \mu \prod_{i \varepsilon I_N - I_v}{}_{\mathrm{o}} (\mu + \alpha_i) \right]$$

so the mean of the $(k; m)$-family determined by I_v, I_β is

$$\prod_{i \varepsilon I_\beta}{}_{\mathrm{o}} (\mu - \alpha_i) \prod_{i \varepsilon I_v - I_\beta}{}_{\mathrm{o}} \mu \prod_{i \varepsilon I_N - I_v}{}_{\mathrm{o}} (\mu + \alpha_i) = \sum_{\delta=0}^{\beta} (-1)^\delta \sum_{\gamma=0}^{N-v} \sum_{I_\delta \subset I_\beta} \sum_{I_\gamma \subset I_N - I_v} \alpha_{I_\delta + I_\gamma}$$

The genetic variance $\mathrm{V}(k; m)$ among $(k; m)$-family means,

$$\mathrm{V}(k; m) = \sum_{v=0}^{N} \sum_{\beta=0}^{v} \theta_k^{v-\beta}(1/2[1-\theta_k])^{N-v+\beta}$$

$$\times \sum_{I_v I \subset_N} \sum_{I_\beta \subset I_v} \left[\sum_{\delta=0}^{\alpha} (-1)^\delta \sum_{\gamma=0}^{N-v} \sum_{I_\delta \subset I_\beta} \sum_{I_\gamma \subset I_N - I_v} \alpha_{I_\delta + I_\gamma} \right]^2 - \mu^2, \quad (1)$$

may be shown to reduce to

$$V(k\,;m) = \sum_{v=1}^{N} (1-\theta_k)^v \sigma_v^2. \tag{2}$$

To obtain this result we compute the coefficient of $\alpha_{I_p} \cdot \alpha_{I_q}$ in (1). Letting $I_r = I_p \cap I_q$ we get, by straightforward counting, the coefficient

$$\sum_{a,b,c} \sum_{v=a+b-c}^{N-p-q+r} \sum_{\beta=a+b-c}^{v-a-b+c} \theta_k^{v-\beta}(1/2[1-\theta_k])^{N-v+\beta} \binom{v-a-b+c}{\beta-a-b+c}\binom{N-p-q+r}{v-a-b+c}$$
$$\times \binom{p-r}{a-c}\binom{q-r}{b-c}\binom{r}{c}(-1)^{a+b}$$

omitting the factor 2 which appears when $I_p \neq I_q$. This reduces to

$$\sum_{a,b,c} (1/2[1-\theta_k])^{p+q-r}\binom{p-r}{a-c}\binom{q-r}{b-c}\binom{r}{c}(-1)^{a+b} = \begin{cases} (1-\theta_k)^p & \text{when } p=q=r \\ 0 & \text{otherwise} \end{cases}$$

except for the case $p = q = r = 0$; the coefficient of μ^2 in (1) is $(1-\theta_k)^0 - 1 = 0$. Thus,

$$V(k\,;m) = \sum_{v=1}^{N} (1-\theta_k)^v \sum_{I_v \subset I_N} \alpha_{I_v}^2$$

and (2) is established.

APPENDIX II

Recurrent Backcrossing Series Derived From Two Haploid Parents

Again, we may exhibit the $(k\,;m)$-family structure by means of moment generating functions. With respect to a single locus, the generating functions in generation B_{k+1}^1 and B_{k+1}^2 may be written respectively, as

$$\Phi_k^1(t) = \phi_{11}(t)[P_{k-1}^1(\phi_{11})+1/2P_{k-1}^1(\phi_{12})]+\phi_{12}(t)[1/2P_{k-1}^1(\phi_{12})]$$
$$\Phi_k^2(t) = \phi_{22}(t)[P_{k-1}^2(\phi_{22})+1/2P_{k-1}^2(\phi_{12})]+\phi_{12}(t)[1/2P_{k-1}^2(\phi_{12})].$$

Since

$$P_1^1(\phi_{11}) = P_1^1(\phi_{12}) = 1/2$$
$$P_1^2(\phi_{22}) = P_1^2(\phi_{12}) = 1/2$$

then

$$\Phi_k^1(t) = \left(1-\frac{1}{2^k}\right)\phi_{11}(t)+\frac{1}{2^k}\phi_{12}(t)$$

$$\Phi_k^2(t) = \left(1-\frac{1}{2^k}\right)\phi_{22}(t)+\frac{1}{2^k}\phi_{12}(t).$$

With respect to a single locus, then, the $(k; m)$-family structure is exhibited by writing

$$\Phi_m^1(t) = \left(1-\frac{1}{2^k}\right)[\phi_{22}(t)] + \frac{1}{2^k}\left[\left(1-\frac{1}{2^{m-k}}\right)\phi_{11}(t) + \frac{1}{2^{m-k}}\phi_{12}(t)\right]$$

$$\Phi_m^2(t) = \left(1-\frac{1}{2^k}\right)[\phi_{22}(t)] + \frac{1}{2^k}\left[\left(1-\frac{1}{2^{m-k}}\right)\phi_{22}(t) + \frac{1}{2^{m-k}}\phi_{12}(t)\right]$$

This gives, for an arbitrary number N of independently segregating loci,

$$\begin{aligned}\Phi_m^1(t_1, \ldots, t_N) &= \prod_{i=1}^{N}\left\{(1-\theta_k)[t_i] + \theta_k[(1-\theta_{m-k+1})t_i + \theta_{m-k+1}t_i^2]\right\} \\ &= \sum_{v=0}^{N}\theta_k^v(1-\theta_k)^{N-v}\sum_{I_v \subset I_N}\Bigg[\prod_{i\varepsilon I_v}[(1-\theta_{m-k+1})t_i + \theta_{m-k+1}t_i] \\ &\qquad \times \prod_{i\varepsilon I_N - I_v}(t_i)\Bigg].\end{aligned}$$

and a similar expression for $\Phi_m^2(t_1, \ldots, t_N)$.

The mean value $\bar{B}_m^1$ of generation B_m^1 is obtained by o-multiplication as

$$\bar{B}_m^1 = \prod_{i=1}^{N}{}_0[\mu-(1-\theta_m)\alpha_i] = \sum_{v=0}^{N}(-1)^v(1-\theta_m)^v\sum_{I_v \subset I_N}\alpha_{I_v}$$

or, to exhibit the $(k; m)$-family means, as

$$\begin{aligned}\bar{B}_m^1 &= \prod_{i=0}^{N}{}_0\left\{(1-\theta_k)[\mu-\alpha_i] + \theta_k[\mu-(1-\theta_{m-k})\alpha_i]\right\} \\ &= \sum_{v=0}^{N}\theta_k^v(1-\theta_k)^{N-v}\sum_{I_v \subset I_N}\left[\sum_{a=0}^{v}\sum_{b=0}^{N-v}(-1)^{a+b}(1-\theta_{m-k})^a\sum_{I_a \subset I_v}\sum_{I_b \subset I_N - I_v}\alpha_{I_a+I_b}\right]\end{aligned}$$

The corresponding expression for $\bar{B}_m^2$ is obtained by deleting the factor $(-1)^{a+b}$ from the coefficient of $\alpha_{I_a+I_b}$ in $\bar{B}_m^1$.

The covariance of $(k; m)$- and $(k; n)$-family means for the $[B_j^1]$ series is then

$$\begin{aligned}&\mathrm{Cov}_1(k; m, n) \\ &= \sum_{v=0}^{N}\theta_k^v(1-\theta_k)^{N-v}\sum_{I_v \subset I_N}\left[\sum_{a=0}^{v}\sum_{b=0}^{N-v}(-1)^{a+b}(1-\theta_{m-k})^a\sum_{I_a \subset I_v}\sum_{I_b \subset I_N - I_v}\alpha_{I_a+I_b}\right] \\ &\qquad \times\left[\sum_{a'=0}^{v}\sum_{b'=0}^{N-v}(-1)^{a'+b'}(1-\theta_{n-k})^{a'}\sum_{I_{a'} \subset I_v}\sum_{I_{b'} \subset I_N - I_v}\alpha_{I_{a'}+I_{b_1}}\right] \\ &\qquad -\left[\sum_{v=0}^{N}(-1)^v(1-\theta_k)^v\sum_{I_v \subset I_N}\alpha_{I_v}\right]\cdot\left[\sum_{v'=0}^{N}(-1)^{v'}(1-\theta_k)^{v'}\sum_{I_{v'} \subset I_N}\alpha_{I_{v'}}\right].\end{aligned}$$

By direct counting we obtain the coefficient of $\alpha_{I_v}^2$ in $\mathrm{Cov}_1\,(k\,;\,m,\,n)$ as

$$(1-\theta_m-\theta_n+\theta_{m+n-k})^v-(1-\theta_m)^v(1-\theta_n)^v$$

and the coefficient of $\alpha_{I_a}\,.\,\alpha_{I_b}$, $I_a \cap I_b = I_\delta \neq \phi$, as

$$(-1)^{a+b}[(1-\theta_m)^{a-\delta}(1-\theta_n)^{b-\delta}-(1-\theta_m)^{b-\delta}(1-\theta_n)^{a-\delta}]$$
$$\times[(1-\theta_m-\theta_n+\theta_{m+n-k})^\delta-(1-\theta_m)^\delta(1-\theta_n)^\delta]$$

Again, the factor $(-1)^{a+b}$ gets deleted to give the corresponding term in $\mathrm{Cov}_2\,(k\,;\,n,\,m)$.

THE PROBLEMS OF MULTIFACTORIAL GENETIC IN MAN

By F. Keiter
University of Würzburg, Hamburg, Germany

This paper tries to survey the possibilities of applying biometric principles to the study of inheritance in so difficult but important a subject as man. The paper contains no new mathematical considerations.

In Jean Sutter's article on the Copenhagen congress (1956) in *Eugen. Quart.*, vol. 2, we find the following statement: 'In general little pioneering was observed in acute problems such as . . . polygenic heredity, biometric and statistic analysis and others . . . Polygenic heredity was the subject of only one paper . . .' Such a relative lag in the acceptance of modern problems in anthropological genetics is to be regretted, the more because classical Mendelian hypotheses were of little success in this field. The criteria for monogeny as stated by Penrose and Keiter (e.g. bimodal distribution) are fulfilled in anthropological traits only in some very rare exceptions, as for example in some particulars of finger prints, which still have to be studied and explained much more carefully. It is true that some months ago F. Lenz published the hypothesis that the more extreme morphological differences might be the outcome of major genes with incomplete dominance. Without doubt, it is worth while to consider the possibility that with very different major genes running through different family strains but causing the same forms of the nose, lips, ears, etc., in other words with a high degree of heterogenism, statistical superposition of many families could produce the normal distributions and correlations usually found in multifactorial heredity. But major genes with supernormal efficiency in the midst of minor polygenes responsible for the more medium expression of the traits would necessarily cause too many extreme phenotypes. Such an excess against the rules of normal distribution and normal correlation is never found in our anthropological traits. That is reason enough to reject the new hypothesis of F. Lenz, which really never was more than a personal assumption without empiric and systematic proof.

For the dermatoglyphs of the feet and their patterning Wichmann has proved very exactly, by statistical means, that no monogenic hypothesis is able to suit the facts.

The prevalence of clearly symmetric normal distributions in our anthropological traits means of course, that dominance and interactions cannot be supposed to be of great importance in our data. Certain deviations from normality, however, have been shown already by Fisher and Gray and repeatedly further on, but only by sophisticated methods and hardly ever big enough to reach the level of clear significance.

Whereas some important problems of multifactorial and biometric genetic cannot well be studied in man, two contributions of anthropology have a specific value for that research. We know more on the variations in man than in any other species, Drosophila included. Twin research in man also outruns widely all twin research in animals. The questions of genotype/environment-interactions of course can be handled by twins much more clearly than by other means. But still ' environment ' in anthropological twin research is too much taken as a fixed unity, not as a variable in itself. The distinction between twins reared in the same family and twins reared apart is of course much too rough to be sufficient.

The anthropology of morphological variations was furthered to a maximum in Central Europe firstly by Rudolf Martin, then by the Vienna school of estimating non-metrical traits (' Morphognostik ') founded by R. Pöch and J. Weninger, of which school I am a pupil myself. The amount of specific knowledge accumulated in that field was one of the reasons why morphological paternity testing also was developed mainly in Central Europe. We have about fifty experts now for that task in applied anthropology. In my own Hamburg laboratory we have up to now more than half a million data on anthropological traits in parents and children, all written in a numerical code and waiting to a great part still for the workers—and the funds—to exploit them.

In non-metric characters, biometrical genetics must be grounded on auxiliary scales. So far as possible with that technique the impression prevails that the phenomena are the same as in the more exact work with metrical data: unimodal distribution, normal mathematical correlations, very low frequency of extreme values. The differences in the heritabilities of these more than hundred physiognomic or habitus-traits investigated by us are great, as already reported in Copenhagen.

It is an old myth still current, that there is some kind of ' family type ' reproducing the same face, the same nose, the same body form again and again within the sibship. I must declare, with some emphasis, that there is no statistical proof for such popular current opinions. If we estimate the different degrees of similarity in related and unrelated people, then we see quite clearly that every degree of resemblance regarding either the face as a whole or single physiognomic traits and complexes of such traits can be found here and there. There is only a higher chance for similarity in related persons. Really high degrees of similarity are exceptional even in the most nearly related persons, in sibs or in parent and child. The theory of multifactorial combinations as the basis for these findings holds very well.

Now I should like to say something on the problem of different manifestation of the same genes in different areas providing unequal conditions for their manifestation. This kind of phenomenon comes under the general heading of 'epistasy-hypostasy', or better perhaps under the heading of 'interactions between the phenogenetic milieu with the factors causing the trait'. I must, unfortunately, omit further considerations on conceptual frames and terminology. An extreme case of what I refer to here is the impossibility for manifestation of hypospadia in females without a penis. In the earlier days of Mendelism too many differences between the sexes were regarded as the direct outcome of a gene mechanism, mostly of sex linkage. By now, we know that the male body as a phenogenetic milieu shows some differences from the female body in nearly every trait. The traits are not directly sex-linked, only indirectly sex-influenced or sex-controlled.

But there is no reason why sex should be the only factor with a general controlling power on gene manifestation. For example, we know very well that we can compare successfully the anthropological traits already in three years old children with their parents if we use very simple transformations. The most general rule is that the manifestation of an hereditary trait in different ages and different sexes is constant if we use the position within the appropriate distribution curve as scale. The principle that we have to make *transformations* if we wish to get the best information on the genotype by observing the phenotype seems to me important enough to name some newer examples for it.

If we investigate hair-colors using the Fischer-Saller 'Haarfarbentafel' as a scale running from A to X, we find an inverse skewness in the distribution of this trait in children and in grown-ups. Of course, growing-up does not alter the genes, and it is probably nonsense to consider changing dominance relations or other far-fetched direct gene mechanisms. First we have to consider that fair hair is differentiated by visual observation on a finer scale than dark hair. As most children have fair hair and most adults dark hair, the skewness caused by this fact is inverted during the time of growth. Symmetrical normal distributions can be an indicator of 'free' manifestation. Percentages, which by definition are restricted between 0 and 100, easily cause an artificial skewness, particularly if the amounts average too near the 0 or the 100% level. Skewness is to be expected in any case where further variation in one direction is less easy going, more hindered than in the opposite direction. That hindrance may be a mathematical one, as in the case of percentages (or in a case of the impossibility of negative terms as in the number of children and so on). The fact that our traits in anthropology prove always symmetrically distributed if judged on proper scales means that the variational possibilities in both directions are usually free enough. Also in correlation tables between sibs or between parents and children, we find thoroughly symmetrical distributions.

But if we calculate in the same metrical trait the variance of the children of tall and short parents, then we find that tallness of the parents means also more variable children. I suspect that some findings of dominance in biometric traits are biased by too quickly taking such differentials in manifestation for indicators of special gene mechanisms. It is possible perhaps to change over to some sort of relative variability scale for getting free of this sort of 'interaction' between the children's variance and absolute size of the traits.

Another until now unexplained empiric regularity in my opinion also pertains to the same problem. In fifty anthropometric traits we have found a strong and clear connexion between the absolute size of the trait and its variation-coefficient. The smaller the trait, the bigger the variation compared to the corresponding mean. The thickness of the lips as a small trait is much more variable than the face height, the face height more variable than the body size. It is unthinkable that a direct connexion between this phenomenon and the number or kind of genes involved could be a useful explanation thereof. Perhaps we must think in terms of the organism as a whole allowing its smallest peculiarities as e.g. the thickness of the lips much freer and wider manifestation than the general structure has. That cannot be more than a hint, or the beginning of a hypothesis. The connexion between absolute size and variability of traits certainly deserves further consideration.

In my intention shortly to review some of the problems and results of biometric genetics in man, the next topic is a question of race mixture. As Trevor and others have shown, race mixture in man does not increase the variance in the offspring. That is a somewhat unexpected basic fact, which takes away much of the speculation on the biological dysharmonies of 'bastards' running through the millenia. In 54 metrical traits, we calculate from the work of Sieg in Negro-German crossed children after the last war a general mean standard deviation, which is the same as in purebred German children: 3.74 against 3.81. Another question is: what happens within a population with the children of parents which are far distant or rather similar in metrical traits? In that case also the distance between the parents does not influence the sigma of the offspring so long as that distance between parents is not extreme. With extremely distant parents there is in fact a slightly higher variability in the children.

The driving out of the eastern half of the German population to the western parts of Germany did not produce heterosis in body size. Coupling eastern with western German parents gives no taller children than are born in couples of common origin.

In the anthropology of behavioral traits we have reliable genetic data mostly from twin research. But by inference we must deem human behaviour an appropriate field for multifactorial genetics, for in animals the good fit of multifactorial hypotheses to the data on behaviour differences in different breeds and their crosses (e.g., in dogs) had already been established by the work of Fuller and others. Still another question is, to what extent medical genetics has to add more multifactorial thinking to its theoretical inventory.

Kallmann has expressed such a view in the Turin symposium 1957 for tuberculosis. I myself on the same occasion faced the more general implications of that question.

We by no means intend to make all human genetics multifactorial and biometric. But it seems as if classical Mendelism was a special and rather rare case in the broad area of gene interactions and gene efficiency: the special case of multifactorial genetics with only one pair of genes involved in the causing of a trait. If that is so then of course it is no longer justified to look on multifactorial heredity as a rare and rather inconvenient speciality, getting in textbooks and congresses of human geneticists only a minimum breathing room in a far off corner of their theoretical thinking.

REFERENCES

BAUERMEISTER, W. (1955) Vererbung einiger metrischer Merkmale des Kopfes, *Homo* **6,** 31–36.

FISHER, R. A. & GRAY, H. (1937) Inheritance in man: Boas data studied by the method of analysis of variance, *Ann. Eugen.* **8,** 74–93.

GRAB, B. (1956) Etude de la transmission héréditaire de certaines caractères anthropométriques à l'aide des méthodes statistiques, *J. Gen. Humaine*, **5,** 120–166, Geneva.

HOLT, S. (1954) Genetics of dermal ridges, *Ann. Eugen.* **18,** 211–231; (1955) *Ann. Eug.* **20,** 159–170; (1956) *Ann. Eug.* **20,** 270–281; (1958) *Ann. Eug.* 323–339.

KALLMANN, F. J. & JARVIK, L. (1957) Twin data on genetic variations in resistance to tuberculosis, *Symp. Medical genet. Torino*, 15–32.

KAUFMANN, H. (1956) Anthropométrie et génétique, *Arch. Suisse Anthr.* **2,** 152–157.

KEITER, F. (1954); Gesetzmäßigkeiten polygener Erbmerkmale beim Menschen. *Z. Morph. Anthrop.* **46,** 170–183; (1957) The range of applicability of multifact. genetics to man, Copenhagen-Congress, *Human Genetics*, 59–64; (1956) Vom klassischen Mendelismus zur kollektiven Genstatistik, *Z. Aerztl. Forsch.* **10,** 569–577; (1957) Vaterschaftsdiagnostik mittels " Trennlogarithmus ", *Z. Aertzl. Forsch.* **11,** 537–551, (extensive references on papers relating to biometrical paternity testing); (1957) Kollektive Genstatistik auch in der medizinischen Genetik? *Symp. Medical genet. Torino*, 145–155, Additivität und Interaktion bei anthropolpgischen Erbmerkmalen (in press).

KNEIPHOFF, H. (1959) Zur multifaktoriellen Genetik des Körperwuchses *Verh. Dtsch. Anthropol. Ges.* Kiel.

LENZ, F. (1958) Über vermeintliche " Wahrscheinlichkeit " von Vaterschaften *Anthropol. Anz.* **22,** 45–65.

MEYER-CORDING (1955) Die palmaren Hautleisten und ihre Vererbung *Z. Morph. Anthrop.* **47,** 147–186.

PONS, J. (1958) El numero de triradios digitales, *Genet. Iber.* **10,** 87–98; (1957) Correl. between different dermatoglyphical traits, *Congress on Human Genetics*, Copenhagen, 476–481.

SALLER, K. (1930) *Die Fehmaraner*, Jena.

SIEG, R. (1955) Mischlingkinder in Westdeutschland, *Beitr. Anthrop.* **4,** Mainz.

TANNER. (1954) Lack of sex linkage and of dominance in genes controlling human stature, *Genetical Congress Bellagio, Firenze*; (1957) Prediction of adult body measurements, *Congress on Human Genetics*, Copenhagen, 493.

TREVOR, J. C. (1953) *Race Crossing in Man*, London.

WICHMANN, D. (1956) Zur Genetik des Hautleistensystems der Fußsohle, *Z. Morph. Anthropol.* **47,** 331–381.

SIMULATION OF GENETIC SYSTEMS BY AUTOMATIC DIGITAL COMPUTERS. 5-LINKAGE, DOMINANCE AND EPISTASIS

By A. S. FRASER

CSIRO, Animal Genetics Section, Zoology Department, University of Sydney

INTRODUCTION

IN RECENT years a new field of mathematics has become of importance in many branches of experimental science. This is the *Monte Carlo* method, so called because it is based on the simulation of stochastic processes. Although there are many different types of Monte Carlo (M.C.) analyses they all have, as a common feature, the use of sets of random or pseudo-random numbers. Few of these M.C. analyses were practicable before the advent of high speed electronic computers since several hundreds of thousands of separate arithmetic steps are necessary for each analysis, and even the high speeds of such computers are useless unless the analyses are predominantly repetitive cycles of computation. Since the solution of the majority of genetic problems requires the resolution of repetitive sequences, it is easy and practical to apply M.C. methods to them (see Fraser 1957*a* and *b*). In this paper the problems involved in such analyses are discussed with particular reference to the SILLIAC electronic computer.

METHODS

Segregation

All genetic problems are based on segregation, and simulation of segregation must arrange that the two types of gamete are formed with equal probability. This can be done by generating a set of random numbers such that,

$$0 \leqq r_i \leqq 1$$

If these are tested against 0.5, then, in a set of unbiased random numbers, the occurrence of tests which exceed 0.5 will have the same probability as those which are less than 0.5 (dependent on the lack of bias in the set of random numbers) so that by making lower numbers represent one type of gamete and higher numbers the other, gametes can be chosen at random with equal probability.

Alternatively, where computers use a binary scale individual digits of a random number are 0 or 1 with equal probability, and segregation can be simulated by using the individual digits of a random number sequence to indicate the nature of the gametes.

The method most applicable depends to a large extent on the type of computer which is being used, since these differ both in their arithmetic speeds and in the size of their memories.

Identification of Genetic Structure

Given a means of simulating segregation the next requirement is for methods of identifying the genetic constitution of any particular genotype. In models based on two alternative alleles per locus, these can be represented by 0 and 1, and a specific genotype can be represented by a number written in the binary scale. In the SILLIAC a single register has forty binary digits and in this machine it is most efficient to use the individual digit method of representing genotypes for problems where the number of loci is forty or less. Further, it will be seen below that there are particular advantages in the ' digital ' method, but in machines where the speed of access to the memory is fast and the size of this memory is not limiting, it can be more efficient to use whole registers to represent single genes. Here only the sign of the number is used, i.e. + for one allele, − for the other.

Logical Operations

The representation of genetic structure by individual digits of a number allows use to be made of the ' logical ' operations which are available in most ' parallel arithmetic ' machines. Three types of logical operations are of particular interest to geneticists. These are the ' logical product ', ' equivalent ' and ' not-sum '. They are illustrated below for two three-digit binary numbers

001 and 011

which can be regarded as a single diploid genotype of three loci,

$$\frac{001}{011}$$

in which the first locus is homozygous for the 0 allele, the second locus is heterozygous, and the third locus is homozygous for the 1 allele.

The *logical product* of the two haploid components of this genotype is

001,

which identifies the loci homozygous for the 1 alleles.

The *logical equivalent* is

010,

which identifies the heterozygous loci.

The *logical not-sum* is

100,

which identifies the loci homozygous for the 0 alleles.

These logical operations allow the identification of the genetic constitution of a genotype of many loci when this is represented digitally.

The identification of a genotype can be combined with the simulation of segregation to simulate a wide range of breeding systems including many loci. The only important restriction is the time necessary for the solution of a problem; considering the many unexamined problems of quantitative genetics, this restriction is unlikely to be important for several years, since the more complex problems, requiring long periods of machine time, cannot be approached until the simpler problems have been examined to supply the necessary background of information.

Formation of Gametes

The simulation of formation of q gametes by a diploid organism characterized at n loci involves (a) identification of its genetic constitution. This is accomplished by forming the three logical combinations of the two haploid genotypes (A and B signify these two genotypes), and (b) by forming a matrix of order nq in which the rows represent individual gametes and the columns represent individual loci. The matrix is formed by placing a column of 1^s wherever the LP contains a 1, a row of 0^s wherever the LNS contains a 1, and a row of 0^s and 1^s at random wherever the LE contains a 1.

Determination of Phenotype

The simplest relation of genotype to phenotype is that of complete linearity, i.e. a completely additive system. Computation of the phenotypic value of a specific genotype then consists of adding all the digits and multiplying the result by the required constant (a). The relationship of the genotype to its phenotype on this basis is shown in Table 1. A common deviation from linearity is due to dominance. If we express the degree of dominance by a term d, then the genotype/phenotype relationship where there is dominance is also shown in Table 1.

TABLE 1. RELATIONSHIP OF GENOTYPE TO PHENOTYPE

Genotype	*Additive*	*Dominance*
1/1	$2a$	$2a$
1/0	a	ad
0/0	0	0

In the general case loci may differ in both their additive and their dominance components, and consequently the terms a and d must be replaced by vectors $\{a_i\}$ and $\{d_i\}$. If these be regarded as diagonal matrices then the phenotype of an individual genotype is given by,

$$\text{diag}\,[\text{A\&B}]\,.\,\text{diag}\,[a_i]+\text{diag}\,[\text{A}\equiv\text{B}]\,.\,\text{diag}\,[a_i]\,.\,\text{diag}\,[d_i] = \text{diag}\,[p_i]$$

and $$\sum p_i = P_{AB}.$$

Another cause of deviations from linearity are non-allelic interactions, i.e. epistasis. This can be considered in terms of a non-linear transformation of the ' additive + dominance phenotype '. In a M.C. analysis of the importance of epistasis which is discussed below, such a method of expressing epistasis has been used. It is, however, more generally valid to base any analysis of epistasis on the interactions of individual genes. The difficulty in such an approach lies in the size of the matrix necessary to define the interactions. Where n is the number of loci, the size of the complete interaction matrix is 2^{2n}, and, consequently, in problems where n is large, it is necessary to compromise by specifying (1) a set of m partial interaction matrices of size $2^{2n'}$. where n' is small, and (2) a matrix of order $n\,.\,(n'+1)$ where the elements of each row specify (i) the interacting loci, and (ii) the specific partial interaction matrix which is operative. This method allows complex locus × locus interactions to be investigated for systems of large numbers of loci.

Environmental Effects

The majority of unsolved problems of mathematical genetics occur in systems with environmental modification of the phenotype. This can be simulated by specifying a function, $r=f(x)$ such that if r is a random number in the range 0–1, then x is a random normal deviate in the range -1 to $+1$. Hastings (1955) has devised several functions which, using linear combinations of r, produce values closely corresponding to random normal deviates. It is possible by specifying different forms of the $r=f(x)$ function to simulate any degree or type of environmental modification of the ' potential ' or ' genetic ' phenotype. It is also possible to simulate genetic control of environmental stability and genotype–environment interactions. Such variations do not present any arithmetic difficulty; in these more complex problems the main difficulties lie in devising methods which lead to general answers rather than specific solutions.

Recombination

A wide variety of procedures will simulate linkage, but digital representation of genotypes considerably reduces both the required memory space and the time needed to simulate the formation of gametes.

The first step is to list the vector of frequencies of recombinant and non-recombinant classes. Below is the vector for the gametes produced by an individual heterozygous at three loci, where r_1 is the recombination between the 1st and 2nd loci, and r_2 is the recombination between the 2nd and 3rd loci.

		Types of gametes		
		000		$\frac{1}{2}(1-r_1)(1-r_2)=f_{000}$
		001		$\frac{1}{2}(1-r_1)r_2 = f_{001}$
		010		$\frac{1}{2}r_1r_2 = f_{010}$
$\frac{111}{000}$	produces	011	at frequencies.	$\frac{1}{2}r_1(1-r_2) = f_{011}$
		100		$\frac{1}{2}r_1(1-r_2) = f_{100}$
		101		$\frac{1}{2}r_1r_2 = f_{101}$
		110		$\frac{1}{2}(1-r_1)r_2 = f_{110}$
		111		$\frac{1}{2}(1-r_1)(1-r_2)=f_{111}$

This illustration is of a triple heterozygote in coupling, but the vector of frequencies of recombination f_i is the same no matter how the 0s and 1s are arranged; the vector of types of gametes depends on the nature of the parent chromosome. This is illustrated below for two genotypes.

		101			110
		100			111
		111			100
		110			101
101	produces	001	110	produces	110
010		000	100		111
		011			100
		010			101

For machine operation the vector of recombinant frequencies (f_i), is initially transformed to give,

$$(f_{000}\,;\ f_{000}+f_{001}\,;\ f_{000}+f_{001}+f_{010}\,;\ \dots \textstyle\sum f)$$

It is convenient to set this vector such that $\sum f = 1$. This vector is termed $\{F_i\}$.

A random number, r, is then generated in the range 0–1.

This number is then tested across (F_i) until,

$$F_i \leqq r \leqq F_{i+1}$$

Then the ith term in the vector of types of gametes is taken as the gamete produced. Repetition of this sequence will produce a sample of gametes in which the various types occur with probabilities corresponding to the frequencies of recombinants and non-recombinants.

Since the size of the $\{F\}$ vector is 2^n it is not possible to simulate recombination by this method for values of n greater than 6–7; at least in computers with memories of the order of one to two thousand registers. Where linkage of greater numbers of loci is followed it is necessary to use ‘ random walk ’ methods. The formation of each gamete is simulated by choosing one or other of the pair of homologous chromosomes as a starting point at random, then setting a random walk down the length of the chromosome, and deciding which way to go between each locus by testing a random number against two choices, i.e. continuing the walk along the same chromosome, or crossing over to the other chromosome. This method requires the generation of $n-1$ random numbers per gamete but less testing and less storage space. Again the most efficient method of simulating recombination must depend on the type of machine being used.

Selection

Simulation of selection requires identification of the frequency distribution of phenotypes. Given this distribution it is possible to set limit values against which the individual phenotypes can be tested. The simplest way is to re-order the individual phenotypes in ascending or descending sequence; limit values can then be set, taking a constant proportion of the total. This method has two marked disadvantages. Re-ordering in arithmetic sequence is a very long process, and the number of registers required is set by the number of progeny per generation, not by the number of parents.

Random numbers are usually generated within the machine by some cycle of orders which takes an initial constant, transforms this and then replaces the initial constant by its transform, e.g. the initial number is replaced by the central digits of its square. This means that a particular sequence of random numbers is fully determined given (i) the particular set of orders, i.e. the random number generator, and (ii) the 1st random number. Consequently a particular series of computations will be reproduced exactly, if the random number is re-set to the value which occurred at the beginning of the calculation. This can be used to simulate selection. At the beginning of a cycle of generation of progeny, and calculating their phenotypes, the value of the random number is stored. The various operations then proceed, but none of the individual genotypes or phenotypes are stored. Instead the phenotypes are used to calculate the constants of the frequency distribution of phenotype, i.e. the mean and variance. These constants are then used to calculate limit values for the selection of progeny, e.g. in selection against extremes the constant are used to calculate the maximum and minimum phenotypes of the progeny which are acceptable as parents in the subsequent generation. Then, by re-setting the random number to the value it had at the beginning of the cycle, it is possible to repeat the whole series of computations exactly except that on this run the individual genotypes which have phenotypes within the specified limits are retained as parents.

Constant versus Variable Parameters

A particular genetic problem can be examined by the M.C. method in two markedly different ways. The first can be termed the ' fixed ' parameter method since it depends on each run of the machine being based on fixed parameters (i.e. linkage, degree of dominance) which do not vary during the run. Different values of these genetic parameters are compared between different runs. The second method is termed the 'variable' parameter method because the values of the parameters are not fixed for a particular run, but can vary within prescribed limits. Each method has its particular applications and they are illustrated below for analyses of (i) the role of linkage in determining the patterns of response to selection (fixed parameters), and (ii) the effects of selection against extremes on dominance and epistasis (variable parameters).

Effects of Linkage

A Monte Carlo analysis of the effects of linkage on rates of advance under selection which was made by Fraser (1957*b*) provides a good example of the fixed parameter type of model.

In this analysis the programme simulated the effects of selection in a population of cross-breeding organisms in which there was no overlap of generations. A genotype of six loci was specified with two alternative alleles at each locus (1 and 0 respectively). The 1 type alleles were set as completely dominant to the 0 type alleles. These constants were not varied for any of the runs of the model.

The intensity of selection, size of population and degree of recombination could be varied for different runs, but were maintained at their specified values throughout each run, i.e. these parameters, although fixed for a specific run, could be varied between runs. Runs made for different values of these parameters therefore provide 'data' on the effects of size of population, intensity of selection and degree of recombination.

Since Cockerham and Martin (1958) have recently completed a Monte Carlo analysis of the effects of linkage which is similar to but far more comprehensive than that of Fraser (1957*b*), only a few of the results will be presented and discussed below.

Mather (1941, 1943), in his initial construction of the 'polygene' concept, deduced that the separate loci of a quantitative genetic system were linked in groups from the extent to which selection caused a characteristic to transgress the limits of variability of the initial population, and from the occurrence of sudden responses to selection following periods of little if any response to selection. There has been considerable discussion whether the second type of data could be said to demonstrate the occurrence of linkage. Further, no estimate could be placed on the tightness of linkage necessary to cause such phenomena, and therefore the primary aims of Fraser's Monte Carlo analysis were to determine whether similar sudden responses to selection would occur in simulated populations, and if so, at what values of recombination.

The first sets of runs are shown in Figs. 1 and 2. A population size of 100, from which 50 parents were selected, was set for all the runs and the six loci were specified as being in two linkage groups; each of three loci. Ten runs were made, two at each of five values of recombination, ranging from 0.5 (no linkage) to 0.005 (tight linkage). Although there is a clear relation between tightness of linkage and the rate of response to selection, none of these runs showed any periods of slow response followed by periods of sudden response. This would seem to throw doubt on Mather's conclusions. However, a second set of runs were made in which the size of the population and intensity of selection were set to approximate the same values which occurred in Mather's experiments. These runs are shown in Figs. 3 and 4. It is clear that in smaller populations with more intense selection the response to selection is more variable, particularly at the tighter intensities of linkage. This is very evident for one run at a recombination of 0.005 which closely resembles the results shown by Mather (1943).

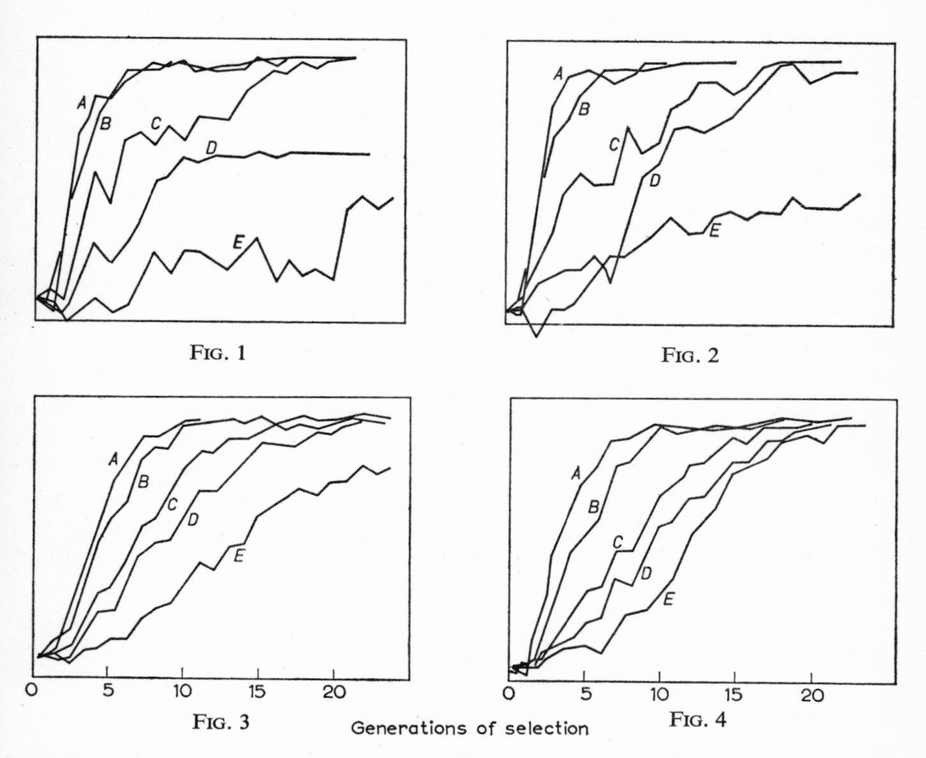

FIGS. 1–4. Advance under selection in populations where recombination varies from 50% (A), 25% (B), 5% (C), 2.5% (D) to 0.5% (E). Figs. 1–2 are for populations of 40 individuals with 4 selected as parents; Figs. 3–4 are for populations of 100 individuals with 50 selected as parents.

Although this finding cannot be regarded as conclusive, nevertheless the resemblance between the effect of tight linkage and the actual experimental data adds weight to Mather's conclusions. It is interesting that the types of selection response found by Mather, and regarded by him as proof of the importance of linkage in quantitative inheritance, would not have been found except at a narrow range of population size. This illustrates a major function of Monte Carlo analyses, namely, to determine the conditions in which an experiment has the maximum probability of producing definite results.

Dominance and Epistasis

The results of the ' linkage ' analysis, although they strongly support Mather's hypothesis, do not provide any information on the evolution of such systems. It is basic to this concept that the individual genes of polygenic units occur in balanced combinations. It seems unlikely that such combinations will be favoured by selection to any marked extent unless some epistasis occurs. A second Monte Carlo programme was therefore written which was designed to investigate the roles of dominance and epistasis in the evolution of polygenic systems. Although incomplete the results obtained with this programme are of sufficient interest to justify their being used to illustrate the ' variable ' parameter method.

The programme was constructed in such a way that the degrees of dominance and epistasis, and the tightness of linkage were under genetic control. Consequently if selection against phenotypic extremes was simulated then response to such selection could be measured by the reduction of phenotypic variability that occurred. This reduction could then be analysed into components due to homozygosity, dominance, epistasis, and linkage.

In this programme (i) the intensity of selection, (ii) the size of the population, and (iii) the *ranges* within which dominance, epistasis and linkage can vary are fixed for each run. With the first two parameters maintained constant, each run of the programme produces a genetic solution to the problem of reducing phenotypic variability insofar as this can be arrived at by choosing a value for dominance, epistasis and linkage. It is necessary to make a number of runs to determine whether more than one solution is probable, and if so, what the relative probabilities are of such solutions.

The initial runs of this programme were made in the absence of linkage. The number of loci per individual was 20. This value was selected for convenience (a SILLIAC register contains 40 binary digits and therefore each diploid genotype could be stored in a single register). The twenty loci were divided into four sub-genotypes, each of five loci. These are termed the *A*, *D*, *E* and *F* genotypes respectively. The *A* genotype is the basic genotype, which in the absence of the other genotypes, determines a purely additive phenotype. The dominance of the *A* loci is decided by the genetic structure of the D genotype; their epistasis is determined by the E and F genotypes respectively (the E genotype determines the first order deviations from linearity, and the F genotype determines the second order deviations). The determination of the phenotype of an individual therefore follows the sequence shown below.

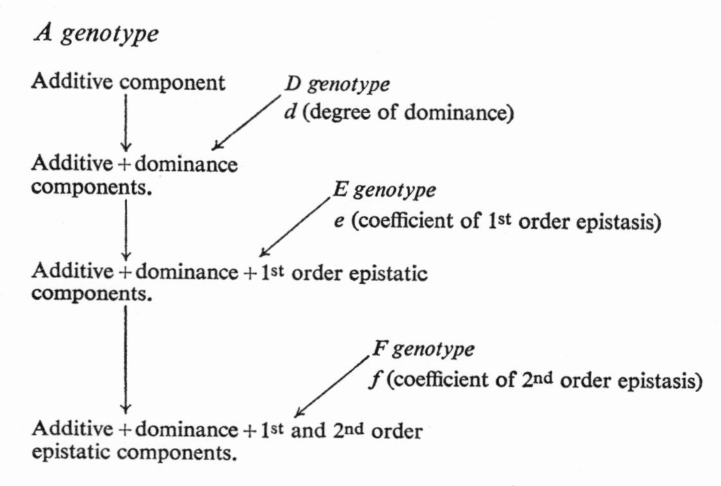

The relation of the D, E and F genotypes to the d, e and f coefficients of dominance and epistasis is determined on the basis of an additive action of the constituent loci. Consequently there are eleven possible values for d, e and f. These values are specified at the beginning of a run, i.e. they are 'fixed' parameters. However, the specific values appropriate to an individual are determined by that individual's genotype, which is not fixed.

Computing the phenotype appropriate to a specific genotype is accomplished by,

(1) determining the genetic structure of the A sub-genotype, i.e. determining the number of loci which are homozygous for the 1 type allele, and the number which are heterozygous. These numbers are termed x and y respectively. The additive component of the phenotype is then,

$$2x+y\ ;$$

(2) determining the number of 1 alleles in the D sub-genotype. This ranges from 0–10 and is used to derive the appropriate value of d. The additive+dominance components of the phenotype are then,

$$2x+dy = X\ ;$$

(3) similarly determining the appropriate coefficients of 1st and 2nd order components of epistasis: e and f. The total phenotype is then

$$X+e\,.\,X^2+f\,.\,X^3 = P$$

Although there are disadvantages inherent in this method of computing the phenotype, it has the marked advantages of being easy to programme and fast to compute.

The first runs of the programme were made at small population sizes (50 progeny and 10 parents). Each generation all of the progeny were ordered in arithmetic sequence of their phenotypes and the specified fractions of extremes were then discarded. Selection being against extremes, the phenotype limits varied from generation to generation. In these runs selection was restricted by a high degree of genetic fixation. However, it appeared that selection against extremes in this model caused (i) a shift of the *D* sub-genotype towards the *d* coefficient having a value of 1.0, i.e. towards no dominance, and (ii) shifts of the *E* and *F* sub-genotypes towards the *e* coefficient having a large positive and the *f* coefficient having a small negative value.

A second set of runs was made at a larger size of population and a lower intensity of selection (see Fig. 5). The number of progeny was 250, and of

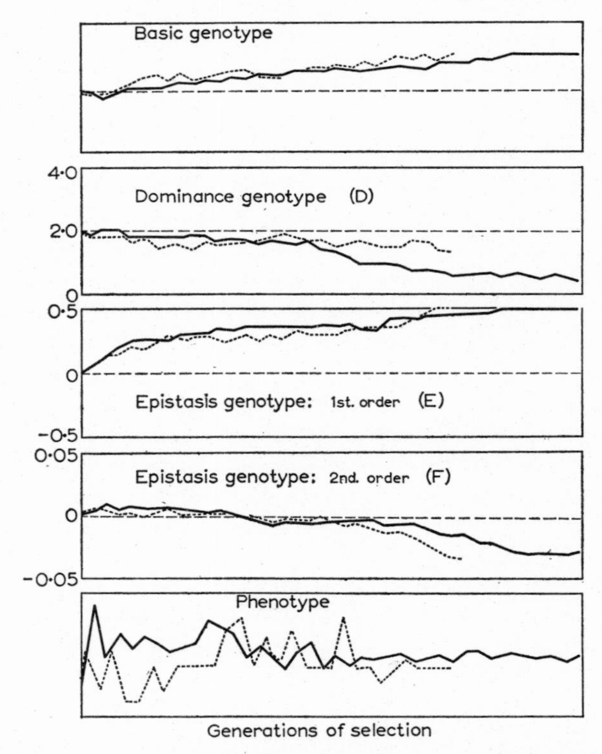

FIG. 5. Effects of selection in populations of size 250, with selection intensity set at 0.2 (50 parents selected per generation). The four sub-genotypes are plotted separately to show their relationships. Two runs were made.

parents 50. In these runs the amount of genetic fixation was much lower, only becoming important if the gene frequency of a specific sub-genotype exceeded 0.9–0.95. A very marked feature of the runs was the shift of the *D* sub-genotype such that the *d* coefficient approximated to a value of 1.0, i.e. selection against phenotypic extremes acted primarily against dominance. This effect took very few generations.

The effects of selection on the *E* and *F* sub-genotypes can be summarised by stating that there was a rapid initial increase of the *e* coefficient. This was followed by a slower increase until a final value of $+0.3 \leftrightarrow 0.4$ was reached. No change occurred in the *F* sub-genotype until the *e* coefficient had exceeded $+0.25 \leftrightarrow 0.35$. There was then a slow change in the *F* sub-genotype concomitant with the slow change occurring in the *E* sub-genotype. This resulted in the *f* coefficient becoming negative. The result at the end of the runs was a sigmoid relationship of genotype to phenotype.

As a check on the above results, a set of runs were made in which the ranges of the *d* and *e* coefficients were fixed at $2.0 \leftrightarrow 0.0$ and $+0.9 \leftrightarrow -0.1$. These ranges were selected because their mid points correspond to the values of *d* and *e* produced by selection in the previous runs. Consequently, these runs start at the point reached after 20–40 generations of selection in the other runs. If the results of these runs are generally valid then we would expect that in the final set of runs no consistent changes should occur in the *D* and *E* sub-genotypes. As can be seen from Fig. 6 this is what did happen. The only consistent change was of the *F* sub-genotype which changed such that the final value corresponded to that found in the previous runs.

It would be presumptuous to claim that the above results are a comprehensive study of dominance and epistasis. However, they do demonstrate the power of the 'variable' parameter method. Although many more runs are necessary, it appears from the available data that selection for decreased variability will strongly favour epistasis if this can be varied to a form that relates genotype/phenotype by a sigmoid function. (The existence of such functions is the basis of Waddington's concept of developmental canalisation, and Dun and Fraser (1958), have data which strongly indicate the genetic control of such functions.)

Conclusions

Although the M.C. method has only just begun to be applied to biometrical genetic problems, it is clearly an important tool, but should be regarded as no more than that. A major deficiency of 'mathematical genetics' has been the schism between the theoretician working with extremely simple genetic models, and the experimentalist working with actual genetic systems of high orders of complexity. The reason for this schism lies firstly in the high order of mathematical ability required for solution of problems based on even the simplest genetic models, and secondly, the inadequacy of classical methods

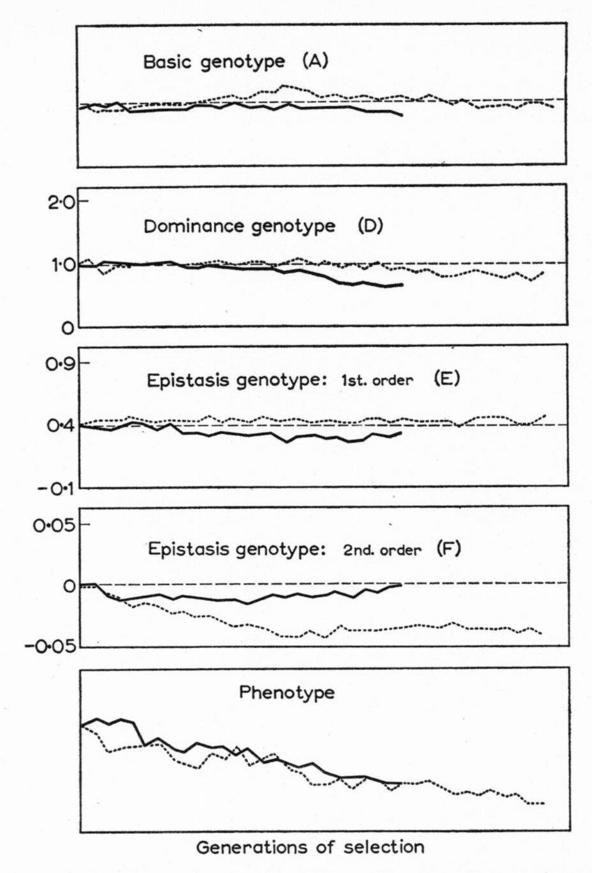

FIG. 6. As for Fig. 5, with ranges of D and C as discussed in the text.

for solution of the problems involved in actual genetic systems. The M.C. method solves both these difficulties, since a high degree of mathematical ability is *not* required to construct the necessary programmes, and the degree of complexity which can be simulated is limited only by the time necessary for the long sequences of computation, and if the problems are sufficiently important, then this is not an important limitation. It is, therefore, possible for any experimenter to parallel his experiments with theoretical analyses aimed at either elaboration of the concepts which he has evolved from consideration of the ' real ' data, or examination of the parameters to define the values which will give an optimum chance of success.

So far we have only considered the application of M.C. analyses to problems of selection. This is not their only or even their most efficient field of application. Two problems, not involving selection, are suitable for M.C.

analyses. These are (1) the validity of Mather's ' di-allele ' analyses of the components of hereditary variations, and (2) Waddington's concept of canalisation of development. The application of M.C. analyses to these problems does not contain any inherent difficulties, and will be certain to allow definition of the range of their applicability. One could go on listing fruitful fields for applying M.C. methods to biological problems. This would be redundant since the strength of this method lies in its basic simplicity and extreme applicability.

REFERENCES

COCKERHAM & MARTIN (1958) Unpublished.
DUN, R. B., & FRASER, A. S. (1958) *Nature* **181,** 1018–1019.
FRASER, A. S. (1957*a*) *Australian J. Biol. Sci.* **10,** 484–491.
FRASER, A. S. (1957*b*) *Australian J. Biol. Sci.* **10,** 492–499.
HASTINGS, C. (1955) *Approximations for Digital Computers,* Princeton University Press.
MATHER, K. (1941) *J. Genetics* **41,** 159–174.
MATHER, K. (1943) *Biol. Rev.* **18,** 32–64.

A MODEL OF A HOST-PATHOGEN SYSTEM WITH PARTICULAR REFERENCE TO THE RUSTS OF CEREALS

By CHARLES J. MODE
Department of Mathematics, Montana State College

INTRODUCTION

THE RUST fungi are living plants which live and reproduce on the stems and leaves of their hosts, the higher plants. Many kinds of rust exist in nature, but in this paper we will be concerned with the rusts of cereals. Moreover, we shall further restrict our considerations to the summer or red stage of the rusts. The rusts are a major hazard in the production of cereals, one of man's most important sources of food, and are particularly damaging to wheat and oats. Some species of rust which cause the greatest amount of damage to the cereals are stem rust of wheat, *Puccinia graminis tritici*, leaf rust of wheat, *Puccinia rubigo-vera tritici*, and crown rust of oats, *Puccinia cornata*. In seasons favorable for the development of the rusts, the number of pustules on the stems and leaves become excessive and cause considerable damage to the host by depriving it of water and nutrients necessary for the production of high yields and grain of good quality. Although the rust fungi are co-existent with the cereals throughout the world, they are most damaging in moderately moist and semi-arid regions. In the United States the losses from the rusts are the greatest in the great plains and middle western states.

All species of rust which have been studied have been found to consist of numerous, highly specialized races which differ in their ability to live and reproduce on a series of host varieties or strains called differentials. The ability of a particular race of rust to grow on a certain differential variety is usually classified in one of five ways—0, 1, 2, 3, or 4. If the reaction of a differential to a certain race of rust is in the 0, 1, or 2 class, the variety is said to be resistant; while if it is in the 3 or 4 class the variety is said to be susceptible.

A particular race of rust is distinguished from another by its reaction or its ability to grow on a set of differentials. As an illustration suppose three differential varieties are being used. The reaction of race of rust on the set of three differentials may be 0 on the first variety, 1 on the second, and 2 on the third; whereas the reaction of another race of rust on the same set of differentials may be 3 on the first variety, 1 on the second, and 0 on the third. A third race of rust would differ further in its reaction on the set of three differentials.

Now if a set of n differential varieties is genetically distinct, i.e. possesses different genes for rust reaction, each variety may react to a particular race of rust in one of five ways. Hence, if n differential varieties are used, it should be possible theoretically to distinguish 5^n races of rust relative to the set of n differentials. In practice 8–10 differentials are frequently used, but only 200 to 300 races of rust are actually found which is far short of the 390,625 to 9,965,625 races theoretically possible. The fact that the number of races actually found in nature is far short of the number theoretically possible suggests that the rust organism displays only a fraction of its potential variability, the differential varieties are not genetically distinct, or a combination of both.

In passing it should be mentioned that the class of reaction of a variety to a particular race of rust is under genetic control and is usually inherited in a simple Mendelian fashion. The degree of resistance or susceptibility, however, as measured by reproductive rate, may vary considerably within each class.

The rusts are most effectively controlled by the development of resistant varieties through plant breeding. The usual procedure is to find varieties which are resistant to the prevalent races of rust and then introduce this resistance into commercial strains by any one of a number of plant breeding techniques. After their development, the rust resistant varieties are released for production. All too frequently, however, these newly developed varieties succumb to the rust shortly after their release due to the emergence of new races or to changes in the prevalence of the old races. The efforts of the plant breeder to maintain resistance to the rust is repeatedly frustrated by these changes in the pathogen population, for he is unable to predict just what races will become prevalent and therefore is in no position to transfer the necessary resistance into the commercial strains until after the shifts in the pathogen population have occurred. As a result, the grower of cereals has little or no protection from the rusts during the time the new commercial strains are being developed.

To meet the challenge presented by these shifts in the pathogen population, it has been suggested that commercial varieties should consist of a mixture or a composite of strains differing in their capacity to resist different races of rust instead of the pure lines now in common usage. It is hoped that such a host population will have a stabilizing effect on the rust population, thus making it easier to maintain resistance to the rusts and lessen the damage sustained by the host during seasons of severe epiphytotics. The purpose of this paper is to construct a mathematical model of a host-pathogen system consisting of a mixture of host varieties and races of the pathogen. To simplify the mathematical arguments it will be assumed that both the host and the pathogen reproduce continuously in time, although the generations of the hosts in question are in fact discrete. Providing selection is slow, i.e.

the changes produced by selection in any given generation are small, we may approximate the situation by assuming continuous generation time.

The way in which the term variety is used also needs a word of explanation. Throughout the remainder of this paper variety will be taken to mean a particular strain or genotype which may be produced by a plant breeder. Since neither the host nor the pathogen reproduce by outbreeding, there will be no shuffling of genetic material as there is in an outbreeding system. Our units in the host-pathogen system we are about to consider are, therefore, not genes but varieties of the host and races of the pathogen.

A MODEL OF A HOST-PATHOGEN SYSTEM

We shall consider a host-pathogen system in which at time t there exists H members of the host population and P members of the pathogen population. Let h_i members of the host population be of the ith variety and p_j members of the pathogen population be of the jth race so that

$$H = \sum_{i=1}^{k} h_i \quad \text{and} \quad P = \sum_{j=1}^{k} p_j.$$

Such a system would contain k host varieties and k races of the pathogen relative to the set of k host varieties. Then at time t, $x_i = h_i \mid H$ is the proportion of the ith variety in the host population and $y_j = p_j \mid P$ is the proportion of the jth race in the pathogen population. Clearly

$$\sum_{i=1}^{k} x_i = \sum_{j=1}^{k} y_i = 1.$$

It is further assumed that the ith variety and the jth race occur at random in the sense that the probability of finding the ith variety and the jth race in combination is $x_i y_j$. This assumption seems reasonable since the spores of the pathogen are distributed over the host population by air currents.

In such a host-pathogen system two types of selection pressure should be considered. Firstly, the selection pressure exerted on the host by the pathogen, and secondly the selection pressure exerted on the pathogen by the host. Both these types of selection pressure will be measured by sets of constants designated by Fisher (1930) as the Malthusian parameters. These constants are measures of fitness or the ability of an organism to reproduce.

The Malthusian parameters are defined in such a way that the rate of increase or decrease in population number at some time t is proportional to the number existing at that time. In the system under consideration this rate of increase or decrease in number of a host variety or race of pathogen will depend on the particular combination of the host and pathogen. Consequently, two parameters must be specified for each combination; one representing the host population, the other the pathogen population.

Then under the assumptions

$$\frac{dh_i}{dt} = \lambda_{ij} h_i$$

becomes the rate of change in h_i in the presence of the jth race of the pathogen, and

$$\frac{dp_j}{dt} = \mu_{ij} p_j$$

becomes the rate of change in p_j in the presence of the ith variety of the host.

Here λ_{ij} and μ_{ij} are the Malthusian parameters which are measures of the fitness of the host and parasite in the ij^{th} combination. From biological considerations it is known that the μ's and λ's are inversely related. For when the ith host variety is resistant to the jth race, λ_{ij} will be positive and μ_{ij} will be negative. Conversely, if the ith variety is susceptible to the jth race, λ_{ij} will be negative and μ_{ij} will be positive.

To obtain the total change in the jth racial frequency, dy_j/dt, that is the change over the whole population, it will be assumed dy_j/dt is the sum of k components, namely a component due to the first host variety, a component due to the second host variety and so on, each component being appropriately weighted by the corresponding host frequency. Then if dy_{ij}/dt represents the rate of change of y_j in the presence of the ith host variety, the total change in y_j becomes

$$\frac{dy_j}{dt} = \sum_{i=1}^{k} x_i \frac{dy_{ij}}{dt} \quad (j = 1, 2, \ldots, k).$$

Proceeding in the same way for the host population, the total change in x_i, the frequency of the ith variety in the host population, is found to be

$$\frac{dx_i}{dt} = \sum_{j=1}^{k} y_j \frac{dx_{ij}}{dt} \quad (i = 1, 2, \ldots, k).$$

Under the assumptions we find the rate of change in x_i in the presence of the jth race of the pathogen becomes

$$\frac{dx_{ij}}{dt} = \frac{1}{H}\frac{dh_i}{dt} - \frac{h_i}{H} \cdot \frac{1}{H}\frac{dH}{dt}.$$

By assumption

$$\frac{dh_i}{dt} = \lambda_{ij} h_i$$

so that

$$\frac{1}{H}\frac{dh_i}{d} = x_i \lambda_{ij}.$$

The total change in H effected by the jth race may then be written

$$\frac{1}{H}\frac{\mathrm{d}H}{\mathrm{d}t} = \frac{1}{H}\sum_{i=1}^{k}\frac{\mathrm{d}h_i}{\mathrm{d}t}$$

$$= \sum_{i=1}^{k} x_i\lambda_{ij} = \lambda_{\cdot j} \quad \text{say.}$$

Hence,

$$\frac{\mathrm{d}x_{ij}}{\mathrm{d}t} = x_i(\lambda_{ij} - \lambda_{\cdot j})$$

The total change in x_i then becomes

$$\frac{\mathrm{d}x_i}{\mathrm{d}t} = x_i \sum_{j=1}^{k} y_j(\lambda_{ij} - \lambda_{\cdot j}).$$

To simplify the notation set

$$\lambda_{i\cdot} = \sum_{j=1}^{k} y_j\lambda_{ij} \quad \text{and} \quad \lambda_{\cdot\cdot} = \sum_{j=1}^{k} y_j\lambda_{\cdot j}.$$

The total change in x_i may then be expressed more simply as

$$\frac{\mathrm{d}x_i}{\mathrm{d}t} = x_i(\lambda_{i\cdot} - \lambda_{\cdot\cdot}) \quad (i = 1, 2, \ldots, k).$$

Proceeding in the same way for the pathogen population, we find the total change in y_j, the frequency of the jth race of the pathogen, becomes

$$\frac{\mathrm{d}y_j}{\mathrm{d}t} = y_j(\mu_{\cdot j} - \mu_{\cdot\cdot}) \quad (j = 1, 2, \ldots, k)$$

where $\mu_{\cdot j} = \sum_{i=1}^{k} x_i\mu_{ij}$, $\mu_{i\cdot} = \sum_{j=1}^{k} y_j\mu_{ij}$, and $\mu_{\cdot\cdot} = \sum_{i=1}^{k} x_i\mu_{i\cdot}$.

We are thus led to a set of differential equations describing rate of change in varietal and racial frequencies with respect to time.

At this point it is instructive to find the rate of change in mean fitness with respect to time in both the host and pathogen populations. Toward this end we shall partition the variation and covariation in fitness at any time t. To accomplish this partition three distinct cases must be considered, (1) the variation in fitness from the standpoint of the host population, (2) the variation in fitness from the standpoint of the pathogen population, and (3) the covariation in fitness when the host and pathogen populations are considered jointly. In what follows it will be shown that the total variance or covariance may be partitioned into components attributable to the host varieties, the races pathogen, and the interaction of the varieties and races.

Now the total variance in fitness from the standpoint of the host population may be partitioned as shown below:

$$\sum_{i=1}^{k}\sum_{j=1}^{k} x_i y_j(\lambda_{ij}-\lambda_{..})^2 = \sum_{i=1}^{k} x_i(\lambda_{i.}-\lambda_{..})^2+\sum_{j=1}^{k} y_j(\lambda_{.j}-\lambda_{..})^2+$$

$$\sum_{i=1}^{k}\sum_{j=1}^{k} x_i y_j(\lambda_{ij}-\lambda_{i.}-\lambda_{.j}+\lambda_{..})^2$$

To simplify notation set

$$\text{Var}(H) = \sum_{i=1}^{k}\sum_{j=1}^{k} x_i y_j(\lambda_{ij}-\lambda_{..})^2,\ \text{Var}(H; V) = \sum_{i=1}^{k} x_i(\lambda_{i.}-\lambda_{..})^2,$$

$$\text{Var}(H; R) = \sum_{j=1}^{k} y_j(\lambda_{.j}-\lambda_{..})^2,$$

and $$\text{Var}(H; RV) = \sum_{i=1}^{k}\sum_{j=1}^{k} x_i y_j(\lambda_{ij}-\lambda_{i.}-\lambda_{.j}+\lambda_{..})^2.$$

The above expression may be written more simply as

$$\text{Var}(H) = \text{Var}(H; V)+\text{Var}(H; R)+\text{Var}(H; VR)$$

where Var (H) is the total variance in fitness in the host population while Var $(H; V)$, Var $(H; R)$, and Var $(H; VR)$ stand for the variance in fitness attributable to the host varieties, the races of the pathogen, and the interaction of the varieties and races respectively.

The total variance in fitness from the standpoint of the pathogen population as well as the covariance in fitness may be partitioned in the same way. Continuing as before, the total variance in fitness in the pathogen population may be expressed as

$$\text{Var}(P) = \text{Var}(P; V)+\text{Var}(P; R)+\text{Var}(P; VR)$$

where

$$\text{Var}(P) = \sum_{i=1}^{k}\sum_{j=1}^{k} x_i y_j(\mu_{ij}-\mu_{..})^2,\ \text{Var}(P; V) = \sum_{i=1}^{k} x_i(\mu_{i.}-\mu_{..})^2,$$

$$\text{Var}(P; R) = \sum_{j=1}^{k} y_j(\mu_{.j}-\mu_{..})^2,$$

and $$\text{Var}(P; VR) = \sum_{i=1}^{k}\sum_{j=1}^{k} x_i y_j(\mu_{ij}-\mu_{i.}-\mu_{.j}+\mu_{..})^2$$

and are designated as the total variance in fitness in the pathogen population and the variance in fitness attributable to the host varieties, the races of the pathogen, and the interaction of the varieties and races respectively.

Following the same procedure, the total covariance in fitness of the host and pathogen population may be partitioned as follows:

$$\text{Cov}(H, P) = \text{Cov}(H, P; V) + \text{Cov}(H, P; R) + \text{Cov}(H, P; VR)$$

where

$$\text{Cov}(H, P) = \sum_{i=1}^{k} \sum_{j=1}^{k} x_i y_j (\lambda_{ij} - \lambda_{\cdot\cdot})(\mu_{ij} - \mu_{\cdot\cdot}),$$

$$\text{Cov}(H, P; V) = \sum_{i=1}^{k} x_i (\lambda_{i\cdot} - \lambda_{\cdot\cdot})(\mu_{i\cdot} - \mu_{\cdot\cdot}),$$

$$\text{Cov}(H, P; R) = \sum_{j=1}^{k} y_j (\lambda_{\cdot j} - \lambda_{\cdot\cdot})(\mu_{\cdot j} - \mu_{\cdot\cdot}),$$

and

$$\text{Cov}(H, P; VR) = \sum_{i=1}^{k} \sum_{j=1}^{k} x_i y_j (\lambda_{ij} - \lambda_{i\cdot} - \lambda_{\cdot j} + \lambda_{\cdot\cdot})(\mu_{ij} - \mu_{i\cdot} - \mu_{\cdot j} + \mu_{\cdot\cdot}).$$

Just as in the host and pathogen populations we shall call Cov (H, P) the total covariation in fitness and Cov $(H, P; V)$, Cov $(H, P; R)$, and Cov $(H, P; VR)$ the covariation in fitness attributable to the varieties, the races, and the interaction of the races and varieties respectively.

Returning to the immediate problem, from the calculus we find the rate of change in mean fitness with respect to time in the host population is

$$\frac{d\lambda_{\cdot\cdot}}{dt} = \sum_{i=1}^{k} \frac{\partial\lambda_{\cdot\cdot}}{\partial x_i} \frac{dx_i}{dt} + \sum_{j=1}^{k} \frac{\partial\lambda_{\cdot\cdot}}{\partial y_j} \frac{dy_j}{dt},$$

and the time rate of change in mean fitness in the pathogen population is

$$\frac{d\mu_{\cdot\cdot}}{dt} = \sum_{i=1}^{k} \frac{\partial\mu_{\cdot\cdot}}{\partial x_i} \frac{dx_i}{dt} + \sum_{j=1}^{k} \frac{\partial\mu_{\cdot\cdot}}{\partial y_j} \frac{dy_j}{dt}.$$

But

$$\lambda_{\cdot\cdot} = \sum_{i=1}^{k} \sum_{j=1}^{k} x_i y_j \lambda_{ij};$$

therefore,

$$\frac{\partial\lambda_{\cdot\cdot}}{\partial x_i} = \sum_{j=1}^{k} y_j \lambda_{ij} = \lambda_{i\cdot},$$

and

$$\frac{\partial\lambda_{\cdot\cdot}}{\partial y_j} = \sum_{i=1}^{k} x_i \lambda_{ij} = \lambda_{\cdot j}.$$

Similarly,

$$\frac{\partial\mu_{\cdot\cdot}}{\partial x_i} = \sum_{i=1}^{k} y_j \mu_{ij} = \mu_{i\cdot},$$

and

$$\frac{\partial\mu_{\cdot\cdot}}{\partial y_j} = \mu_{\cdot j}.$$

Substituting $\frac{dy_i}{dt}$ and $\frac{dx_i}{dt}$ into the above expressions, the rate of change in mean fitness with respect to time in the host and pathogen populations respectively becomes

$$\frac{d\lambda_{..}}{dt} = \text{Var}\,(H; V) + \text{Cov}\,(H, P; R),$$

and

$$\frac{d\mu_{..}}{dt} = \text{Var}\,(P; R) + \text{Cov}\,(H, P; V).$$

We are thus led to a result analogous to Fisher's fundamental theorem of natural selection. Fisher's fundamental theorem, which is applicable to random mating diploid populations, states that the rate of change in mean fitness at any time is proportional to the additive genetic variance present. In the host-pathogen system under consideration, we see the time rate of change in mean fitness in the host population is proportional to the variance in the host population attributable to host varieties plus the covariance attributable to the races of the pathogen. The rate of change in mean fitness in the pathogen population, on the other hand, is proportional to the variance in pathogen population attributable to the races plus the covariance in fitness attributable to the host varieties. Unlike a random mating diploid population in which the mean fitness always increases with time, in the present host-pathogen system the mean fitness in both the host and pathogen populations may either increase or decrease with time depending on the sign and magnitude of the covariance components.

AN EQUILIBRIUM POPULATION

At equilibrium the frequencies of the host varieties and races of the pathogen cease to change and $dx_i/dt = dy_j/dt = 0$ $(i, j = 1, 2, ..., k)$, or equivalently $\lambda_{i.} = \lambda_{..}$ and $\mu_{.j} = \mu_{..}$ which implies $\lambda_{i.} = \lambda_{i'.}$ $(i \neq i')$ and $\mu_{.j} = \mu_{.j'}$ $(j \neq j')$. Setting $i' = j' = k$, we obtain two sets of $k-1$ equations each which, when subjected to the conditions,

$$\sum_{i=1}^{k} x_i = \sum_{j=1}^{k} y_j = 1,$$

can be solved to obtain the frequencies of the host varieties and races of the pathogen at equilibrium. After a little manipulation we get the equilibrium equations in the form

$$\sum_{j=1}^{k-1} a_{ij} y_j = c_i \quad (i = 1, 2, ..., k-1)$$

$$\sum_{i=1}^{k-1} b_{ij} x_i = d_j \quad (j = 1, 2, ..., k-$$

where $a_{ij} = (\lambda_{ij} - \lambda_{kj} - \lambda_{ik} + \lambda_{kk})$, $c_i = \lambda_{kk} - \lambda_{ik}$, $b_{ij} = \mu_{ij} - \mu_{ik} - \mu_{kj} + \mu_{kk}$ and $d_j = \mu_{kk} - \mu_{kj}$.

A solution of the equilibrum equations are, by Cramér's rule,

$$\hat{y}_j = \frac{C_j}{A}$$

$$(i, j = 1, 2, \dots, k-1)$$

$$\hat{x}_i = \frac{D_i}{B}$$

where A and B are the determinants of the coefficients of the x's and y's and C_j and D_i are the determinants obtained by substituting the terms on the right for the unknown in question. It should be noted that these solutions exist if and only if the determinants A and B do not vanish. We further require that $x_i \geqq 0$ and $y_j \geqq 0$.

From the solution of the equilibrium equations it will be noted that the frequencies of the races of the pathogen of equilibrium is a function of the fitness of the host. Likewise, the equilibrium frequencies of the host varieties is a function of the fitness of the pathogen. This result clearly expresses the interlocking nature of the host-pathogen system at equilibrium.

The next question that arises is that of stability of this equilibrium. Accordingly we shall find the necessary and sufficient conditions for stability. To find these conditions it is convenient to introduce vector-matrix notation. Let Z be a column vector whose components are the x's and y's so that $Z' = (x_1 \dots x_k, \quad y_1 \dots y_k)$. Then

$$\frac{dZ}{dt} = \begin{pmatrix} \frac{dx_1}{dt} \\ \vdots \\ \frac{dx_k}{dt} \\ \frac{dy_1}{dt} \\ \vdots \\ \frac{dy_k}{dt} \end{pmatrix} = \begin{pmatrix} x_1(\lambda_{1\cdot} - \lambda_{\cdot\cdot}) \\ \vdots \\ x_k(\lambda_{k\cdot} - \lambda_{\cdot\cdot}) \\ y_1(\mu_{\cdot 1} - \mu_{\cdot\cdot}) \\ \vdots \\ y_k(\mu_{\cdot k} - \mu_{\cdot\cdot}) \end{pmatrix} = F(Z) \quad \text{say.}$$

Now let $Z_0' = (\hat{x}_1 \ldots \hat{x}_k, \hat{y}_1 \ldots \hat{y}_k)$ be a point which satisfies the equations $F(Z_0) = 0$ and let $\delta Z' = (\delta x_1 \ldots \delta x_k, \delta y_1 \ldots \delta y_k)$ be the variations from the point of equilibrium. The variational equations may then be written as

$$\frac{\mathrm{d}(\delta Z)}{\mathrm{d}t} = A\,\delta Z + f(\delta Z)$$

when A is the Jacobian matrix evaluated at equilibrium, i.e. $A = (a_{ij}) = (\partial F/\partial Z_i \mid z_0)$, and $f(\delta Z)$ represents terms whose degree is greater than one.

Providing the variations are conservative in the sense that the terms represented by $f(\delta Z)$ are negligible, the necessary and sufficient conditions that Z_0 be a point of stable equilibrium are that all solutions of the variational equations tend to zero as $t \to \infty$. These conditions are met if all the characteristic roots of the A matrix are negative and real. Lastly the characteristic roots of A will have the desired properties if A is real and if a matrix B is negative definite where B is obtained from A by defining $b_{ii} = a_{ii}$ and $b_{ij} = b_{ji} = \frac{1}{2}(a_{ij} + a_{ji})$ $(i, j = 1, 2, \ldots, k)$.

For the present system, the variational equations for the x's can be shown to be

$$\frac{\mathrm{d}(\delta x_i)}{\mathrm{d}t} = [\lambda_{i\,.} - \lambda_{\,..} - x_i \lambda_{i\,.}]\, \delta x_i - x_i \sum_{i \neq i'} \lambda_{i'\,.}\, \delta x_{i'} + \sum_{j=1}^{k} x_i(\lambda_{ij} - \lambda_{.\,j})\, \delta y_j$$

$$(i = 1, 2, \ldots, k).$$

But

$$\sum_{i=1}^{k} \delta x_i = 0, \quad \text{so that} \quad \delta x_k = -\sum_{i=1}^{k-1} \delta x_i$$

and similarly

$$\delta y_k = -\sum_{j=1}^{k-1} \delta y_j$$

Hence

$$\frac{\mathrm{d}(\delta x_i)}{\mathrm{d}t} = [\lambda_{i\,.} - \lambda_{\,..} + x_i(\lambda_{k\,.} - \lambda_{i\,.})]\, \delta x_i + x_i \sum_{i' \neq i} (\lambda_{k\,.} - \lambda_{i'\,.})\, \delta x_{i'} +$$

$$x_i \sum_{j=1}^{k-1} (\lambda_{ij} - \lambda_{.\,j} - \lambda_{ik} + \lambda_{.\,k})\, \delta y_j$$

But from the conditions for equilibrium $\lambda_{i\,.} - \lambda_{i'\,.} = 0 = \lambda_{i\,.} - \lambda_{\,..}$. Therefore the variational equations become

$$\frac{\mathrm{d}(\delta x_i)}{\mathrm{d}t} = x_i \sum_{j=1}^{k-1} (\lambda_{ij} - \lambda_{.\,j} - \lambda_{ik} + \lambda_{.\,k})\, \delta y_j \quad (i = 1, 2, \ldots, k-1)$$

Proceeding as above, the variational equations for the y's can be shown to be

$$\frac{\mathrm{d}(\delta y_j)}{\mathrm{d}t} = y_j \sum_{i=1}^{k-1} (\mu_{ij} - \mu_{i\,.} - \mu_{kj} + \mu_{k\,.})\, \delta y_j \quad (j = 1, 2, \ldots, k-1).$$

Letting $\delta Z'^* = (\delta x_1 \ldots \delta x_{k-1}, \delta y_1 \ldots \delta y_{k-1})$, the variational equation may be written as $\mathrm{d}(\delta Z^*)/\mathrm{d}t = A^* \delta Z^*$ where

$$A^* = \begin{pmatrix} 0 & M \\ N & 0 \end{pmatrix},$$

and

$$M = (m_{ij}) = \hat{x}_i(\lambda_{ij} - \hat{\lambda}_{.\,j} - \lambda_{ik} + \hat{\lambda}_{.\,k}), \qquad N = (n_{ij}) = \hat{y}_j(\mu_{ij} - \hat{\mu}_{i\,.} - \mu_{kj} + \hat{\mu}_{k\,.})$$

$(i, j = 1, 2, \ldots, k-1)$, and 0 is the zero matrix and $\wedge$ means evaluated at equilibrium. Now all the characteristic roots of A^* cannot be negative and real since the matrix B^* where $b^*_{ii} = a^*_{ii}$ and $b_{ij} = b_{ji} = \frac{1}{2}(a^*_{ij} + a^*_{ji})$ $(i, j = 1, 2, \ldots, k-1)$ cannot be negative definite. We are then led to the conclusion that the equilibrium is unstable so that any variations will cause the system to drift away from the point of equilibrium.

It is interesting to note that at equilibrium

$$\mathrm{Var}\,(H) = 2\ \mathrm{Var}\,(H;\, R)$$

$$\mathrm{Var}\,(P) = 2\ \mathrm{Var}\,(P;\, V)$$

$$\mathrm{Cov}\,(H, P) = \mathrm{Cov}\,(H, P;\, VR).$$

In words, the total variance in the host population is equal to twice the variance attributable to races, the total variance in the pathogen population is equal to twice the variance attributable to the varieties, and the total covariance is equal to the covariance attributable to the interaction of the varieties and races.

THE PROPERTIES OF AN EQUILIBRIUM POPULATION

An equilibrium population may have certain desirable properties from the standpoint of the plant breeder. In the first place if the equilibrium were stable, the races of the pathogen relative to a set of host varieties would tend to remain in constant proportions; consequently the plant breeder would no longer have to cope with rapid shifts in the racial frequencies of the pathogen population as he does in a system consisting of a single host variety. In our model of a system consisting of a mixture of host varieties a stable equilibrium could not be realized. This does not mean, however, that a stable equilibrium could not exist in nature. A model is at best only an approximation and may not be a true representation of reality.

On the other hand, if the equilibrium were unstable but if the drift away from the point of equilibrium were very slow, the system may remain in equilibrium for sufficiently long periods of time to solve the problem of constantly shifting racial frequencies from the practical point of view. Providing the mixture of host varieties were to act in such a way as to slow down the changes in racial frequencies, the plant breeder may be in a position to check the drift toward ascendency of a new race by inserting a resistant variety into the system thus establishing a new equilibrium. By repeating this process indefinitely, it may be possible to keep the pathogen population in control. It should be emphasized, however, that a host population consisting of a mixture of varieties would be superior to a population consisting of a single variety only if the mixture tended to slow down the rise to ascendency of new races. Actually, the mixture may act in just this way, for it seems quite likely that some varieties in the system may be partially resistant to the new race and thus show its rise to ascendency, giving the plant breeder more time to cope with the situation.

In addition to the constant proportions property, an equilibrium population must have other properties in order to be of use to the plant breeder. For the host-pathogen system under consideration, the amount of damage sustained by the host in a given season or time interval is dependent upon two factors, firstly the initial numbers in the pathogen population, and secondly the rate at which these numbers increase. At equilibrium it may be shown that the rate of change in number in the pathogen population is given by $dP/dt = P\hat{\mu}_{..}$, where $\hat{\mu}_{..}$ is the mean fitness of the pathogen population at equilibrium. Solving the above differential equation, we find $P = P_0 e^{\hat{\mu}_{..} t}$, where P_0 is the initial number in the pathogen population or the number present at time $t = 0$. Upon inspection of the above two equations, the beginning statement becomes evident.

Further consideration of an equilibrium population leads to the conclusion that $\hat{\mu}_{..}$ should be close to zero if the system containing a mixture of host varieties is to be of use to the plant breeder. For under such circumstances, the number of individuals in the pathogen population would tend to remain constant or would slowly increase or decrease with time depending on the sign of $\hat{\mu}_{..}$. If $\hat{\mu}_{..}$ were negative, the number of individuals in the pathogen population would slowly decrease with time; if $\hat{\mu}_{..}$ were positive, the number would slowly increase. Since the damage sustained by the host is dependent at least in part upon the total number of individuals reached by the pathogen population in a given season, the damage to the host may not be great if this number could be kept sufficiently small, or were not given the opportunity to build up. It should be pointed out, however, that if the number of individuals in the pathogen population are very large at the time the system reaches equilibrium, the pathogen could still cause considerable damage to the host even if the races remained in constant proportion. In conclusion then, not only must the races remain in relatively constant proportion but the numbers in the pathogen population must be kept at such a level as to cause a small amount of damage to the host in order for a mixture of host varieties to be of use to the plant breeder.

DISCUSSION

It seems plausible that knowing the fitness of the races of the pathogen on a set of host varieties and the frequency of the races in the pathogen population, the plant breeder could construct a host-pathogen system such that an equilibrium was established and the mean fitness of the pathogen population was near zero. This could be accomplished by requiring that $\hat{\mu}_{\cdot j}$ and $\hat{\mu}_{i\cdot}$ $(i, j = 1, 2, \ldots, k)$ be approximately zero, since

$$\hat{\mu}_{\cdot\cdot} = \sum_{j=1}^{k} \hat{y}_j \hat{\mu}_{\cdot j} = \sum_{i=1}^{k} \hat{x}_i \hat{\mu}_{i\cdot}\,.$$

These conditions would also guarantee that the pathogen population would be in equilibrium, for if $\mu_{\cdot j}=0$, $dy/dt=0$ $(j = 1, 2, \ldots, k)$.

A question which naturally arises is whether or not the fitness of the pathogen or a set of host varieties could be measured. Aside from technical difficulties, the problem seems solvable at least theoretically. We know from the definition of fitness that $dp_j/dt = p_j\mu_{ij}$. Integrating we have $\log p_j = \mu_{ij}t + C$ where p_j is the number of the jth race, μ_{ij} is the Malthusian parameter for the ij^{th} combination of race and variety, t is time, and C is a constant. Hence, if a race were propagated on a variety and if the numbers in the pathogen population could be determined at time intervals, the μ_{ij} could be estimated by least squares. So far as the author knows no attempt has been made to measure the fitness of races of rust on cereal varieties. If reliable estimates of fitness could be obtained, the plant breeder may be in a position to take more decisive steps toward the solution of his problem. What is needed is some research to obtain estimates of fitness.

SUMMARY

In breeding for resistance to rusts in cereals, and indeed plant pathogens in general, the efforts of the plant breeder are frequently nullified by shifts in the racial frequencies of the pathogen population. It has been suggested that the plant breeder could cope with the situation more effectively if the commercial varieties consisted of a mixture or composite of strains rather than the single strains now in common usage. A model of a host-pathogen system consisting of a mixture of host varieties or strains and races of the pathogen was constructed and analyzed. Under the conditions of the model, an equilibrium in which the frequencies of the host varieties and races of the pathogen remained constant could be reached. This equilibrium was unstable, however. That is any variations in the varietal and racial frequencies would cause the system to drift away from the point of equilibrium.

It was suggested that even if the equilibrium were unstable, the system may remain at the point of equilibrium for sufficiently long periods of time to solve the problem of constantly shifting racial frequencies from the practical point of view. If a population in equilibrium is to be of use to the plant breeder, however, the number of individuals in the pathogen population at the time the equilibrium is established must be relatively small so that the host is not damaged excessively. Furthermore, the number must be kept small. It was further suggested that the number of individuals in pathogen population may be kept small if the plant breeder constructed a system in which $\hat{\mu}_{..}$, the mean fitness of the pathogen population at equilibrium, was zero.

REFERENCES

BELLMAN, R. (1953) *Stability Theory of Differential Equations*, McGraw-Hill, New York.
FISHER, R. A. (1930) *The Genetical Theory of Natural Selection*, Clarendon Press, Oxford.

DESIGN OF EXPERIMENTS

EXPERIMENTAL DESIGN ON THE MEASUREMENT OF HERITABILITIES AND GENETIC CORRELATIONS

By Alan Robertson

Institute of Animal Genetics, Edinburgh

INTRODUCTION

In this short summary of the paper given, I propose to discuss in general terms the conclusions reached in two papers now in the press on the estimation of heritabilities and genetic correlations by the analysis of variance method. The problem then centres around the group size at the point of minimum sampling variance of the estimates.

SINGLE CLASSIFICATION

This would be illustrated by the half-sib analysis in which no two half-sibs had the same dam. I will assume throughout that non-genetic contributions to half-sib similarities have been effectively excluded by an adequate experimental design. I shall also be concerned throughout solely with sampling variances and not with the sampling distributions. I shall use the following nomenclature

t	intra-class correlation
σ_p^2	total variance
N	number of groups
n	group size
$T(=Nn)$	total population size.

The analysis of variance then reads

	d.f.	*Exp. M.S.*
Between groups	$N-1$	$\sigma_p^2(1+(n-1)t)$
Within groups	$N(n-1)$	$\sigma_p^2(1-t)$

The two mean squares are then independent and, as t can be expressed as a function of them, its sampling variance can be easily worked out. The formula has been known for a long time and is

$$V(\hat{t}) = \frac{2(1-t)^2(1+(n-1)t)^2}{(N-1)n(n-1)}$$

If we then apply the condition that Nn is constant, we can find the optimum structure. Putting $Nn = K/t$, we find that at the minimum,

$$N = K+2$$

$$n = \frac{1}{t} \frac{K}{K+2}$$

Thus if the population size is large, the optimum group size is $1/t$. At population sizes in which there would be only a few groups at the optimum, the optimum size is reduced somewhat, the rule being to take 2 more groups than the simple formula would indicate, i.e., $N = Tt+2$.

Examination of the expression away from the optimum reveals that it is extremely inefficient to take small values of n. If t and n are small, it will be obvious that $V(t)$ is roughly proportional to $1/(n-1)$. Small values of n should be avoided at all costs.

If we are in a position to obtain optimum values of n (this will of course depend very much on the animal concerned), we have then roughly

$$V(\hat{t}) \approx \frac{8t}{T}$$

Substituting $$t = \tfrac{1}{4}h^2,$$

we have $$V(\hat{h}^2) \approx \frac{32h^2}{T}$$

In the case of estimates from parent-offspring correlations with n pairs of animals, we have

$$V(\hat{h}^2) = \frac{4}{n}$$

$$= \frac{8}{T}$$

It then follows that, if we can get group sizes close to the optimum for the character concerned, for the same total number of animals measured the half-sib method will be more accurate than the parent-offspring method if $h^2 < \frac{1}{4}$ and vice-versa.

DOUBLE CLASSIFICATION

We do in fact often have to deal with a double nested classification of sires and dams within sires. Writing t_1, t_2 for the sire and dam intra-class correlation coefficients, the analysis of variance reads—with S sires, d dams per sire, and n offspring per dam.

	d.f.	*Exp. M.S.*
Between sires	$S-1$	$1-t_1-t_2+nt_2+ndt_1$
Between dams Within sires	$S(d-1)$	$1-t_1-t_2+nt_2$
Within dams	$Sd(n-1)$	$1-t_1-t_2$.

We can then express t_1 and t_2 in terms of these mean squares and so obtain variance estimates. Without going into tedious algebra, the conclusions are as follows, if we assume that $t_1 = t_2$.

(1) the best estimate of t_1 is obtained when each dam has one offspring, i.e., all the sire progeny are half-sibs.

(2) in joint estimation of t_1 and t_2, the optimum structures are incompatible, i.e., for t_1 when $ndt \approx 1$ and for t_2 when $dt \approx 1$.

(3) if we then impose the condition that $V(\hat{t_1}) = V(\hat{t_2})$, which might apply if we wish to compare the two, we find that, irrespective of t, the optimum number of dams per sire should be between 4 and 10 (3 being perhaps acceptable but 2 most inefficient) and that n is given roughly by

$$\frac{1}{t}\frac{1}{(d+1)^{\frac{1}{2}}}.$$

We thus have to accept a dam family size below that optimum for the estimation of t_2 at the expense of a sire family size above that optimum for t_1.

If we accept *a priori* that $t_2 > t_1$, and therefore are in the main interested in the estimate of h^2 from t_1, the optimum value of n will be somewhat reduced and that of d increased.

THE ESTIMATION OF GENETIC CORRELATIONS

Before discussing design in the estimation of genetic correlations from the analysis of variance and covariance, we must first discuss the general formula for the sampling variance of genetic correlations. The discussion will be confined to a single classification. If we partition the variance and covariance in the two characters 1, 2 into terms like σ^2_{w1} and $\mathrm{Cov}\,(1, 2)_b$—w and b referring to within and between groups, the correlations can be expressed as

$$r_w = \frac{\mathrm{Cov}\,(1, 2)_w}{\sigma_{w_1}\,\sigma_{w_2}}$$

and

$$r_g = \frac{\mathrm{Cov}\,(1, 2)_b}{\sigma_{b_1}\,\sigma_{b_2}}$$

Assuming the design to have been efficient in removing non-genetic variation between groups, we can then call the between group correlation, r_g, the 'genetic correlation' between the two characters. No estimates of the sampling variance of this estimate have so far been obtained, except in the case of parent-offspring correlations.

In the case of two characters with the same heritability, an expression can be obtained by throwing the analysis into the form of a group by character interaction and making use of the fact that correlation between pairs of points with identical variance can be expressed as an analysis of variance within and between pairs. A proportion $1+r$ of the total variance then appears in the between pairs term and $1-r$ in the within pairs term. Expressing both characters in standard measure, the joint analysis of variance then reads

	d.f.	Exp. M.S.	
Between groups	$N-1$	$(1-t)(1+r_w)+nt(1+r_g)$	A
Group × characters	$N-1$	$(1-t)(1-r_w)+nt(1-r_g)$	B
Within groups			
Between individuals	$N(n-1)$	$(1-t)(1+r_w)$	C
Residual	$N(n-1)$	$(1-t)(1-r_w)$	D

and
$$\hat{r}_g = \frac{A-C-(B-D)}{A-C+B-D}$$

We have thus expressed r_g in terms of four independent mean squares and can thus obtain an expression for $V(\hat{r}_g)$.

The expression is fairly complex but when $r_g = r_w$, it simplifies to

$$V(\hat{r}_g) = \frac{(1-r_g^2)^2}{n^2t^2}\left(\frac{(1+(n-1)t)^2}{N-1}+\frac{(1-t)^2}{N(n-1)}\right)$$

$$\approx \frac{(1-r_g^2)^2}{N-1}\left[\frac{(1+(n-2)t)^2+(n-1)t^2}{n(n-1)t^2}\right]$$

This formula is extremely similar to that for the sampling variance of t on a single character from the same data

$$V(\hat{t}) = \frac{2(1-t)^2(1+(n-1)t)^2}{(N-1)n(n-1)}$$

except for the term in t^2 in the bottom line. In fact, it turns out that we can, in general, state that the standard error of r_g is given by

$$\text{s.e. }(\hat{r}_g) \approx \frac{1-r_g^2}{\sqrt{2}}\, C\,.\, V(\hat{h}^2)$$

if the two characters have the same heritability and if $r_g = r_w$ and the sampling variances refer to the same set of data. This applies to the analysis of variance method, irrespective of the degree of relationship, and also to the parent-offspring regression method. In this latter case, it agrees with the formulae derived by Reeve (1955). It follows further from the similarity of the formulae that the optimum structures for both heritability and genetic correlation are the same.

GENOTYPE–ENVIRONMENT INTERACTION

A genetic correlation may also be obtained by measuring the two characters on different set of relatives. In this, it exactly parallels an experiment on genotype–environment interaction. In fact, considerable light can be thrown on problems of genotype–environment interactions by expressing them in terms of the genetic correlation between the same character on the two environments, as Falconer (1952) has pointed out. No interaction then gives a genetic correlation of unity and, what is most important, the degree of departure of the correlation from unity measures the biological importance of the interaction.

The sampling variance of r_g in this case is given by

$$V'(\hat{r}_g) \approx \frac{(1+nt(1-r_g^2))^2 + r_g^2}{(N-1)n^2t^2}$$

where n is the group size in *each* environment. If $nt > 1$, then the sampling variance increases as r_g decreases. It follows that any errors we are likely to make in the simple detection of statistical interaction will be more frequently in the denial of interaction when one exists than in the reverse direction. We should therefore calculate our optimum structure for an intermediate value of r_g. I have for convenience taken $r_g^2 = 0.5$. Then the optimum group size in *each* environment is given by

$$nt = \frac{\sqrt{(1+r_g^2)}}{1-r_g^2}$$

which, for $r_g^2 = 0.5$, equals 2.4. Thus at the optimum, we require groups, in each environment, about twice as large as required for the determination of the heritability in that environment alone. If we take as an example, $t = 0.05$ and require a standard error of r_g of 0.2, we require 23 groups each with 48 animals in each environment.

The groups that we are using may be in fact different strains rather than groups of relatives, in which case t is the observed intra-class correlation which may be much higher than we would expect for groups of relatives within a population. If the strains in each environment are split into replicates, then n would refer to the number of replicates and t to the observed correlation between replicates.

REFERENCES

FALCONER, D. S. (1952) The problem of environment and selection, *Am. Naturalist* **86,** 293–298.

REEVE, E. C. R. (1955) The variance of the genetic correlation coefficient, *Biometrics* **11,** 357–374.

THE INTERPRETATION OF CALCULATED HERITABILITY COEFFICIENTS WITH REGARD TO GENE AND ENVIRONMENTAL EFFECTS AS WELL AS TO GENOTYPE–ENVIRONMENT INTERACTIONS

By Henri L. Le Roy

Animal Breeding Institute, Swiss Federal Institute of Technology, Zurich, Switzerland

The purpose of this paper is:

I. To give general solutions for analysis of variance and regression analysis applied to problems dealing with quantitative inheritance, where all components are random, except the general mean.

II. To show the effects of gene, environment, and in particular the role played by genotype–environment interactions with regard to the structure of heritability estimates.

I. GENERAL FORMULAE FOR INTERPRETING ANALYSES OF VARIANCE

Two-way-classification

This kind of analysis can be used, for example, for uncovering interactions between genotypes and environments and to construct heritability estimates.

Let us suppose that there are two factors A and B with a and b levels. Each of the $a \, . \, b$ combinations (subgroups) contains c observations. The statistical model is

$$X_{ijk} = \mu + a_i + b_j + (ab)_{ij} + d_{ijk}, \quad \begin{array}{l} i = 1, \ldots a \\ j = 1, \ldots b \\ k = 1, \ldots c \end{array}$$

$$E(X_{ijk}) = \mu, \; E(a_i \, . \, b_j) = \ldots = E[(ab)_{ij} \, . \, d_{ijk}] = 0,$$

and

$$\sigma^2(x_{ijk}) = \sigma^2_A + \sigma^2_B + \sigma^2_{AB} + \sigma^2_D$$

Therefore the analysis of variance is that displayed in Table 1:

Table 1

Source of variation	d.f. (i)	M.S. (i)	E[M.S. (i)]
A-groups	$a-1$	M.S. (A)	$[\sigma^2_X - (1)] + c[(1) - (2) - (3) + (4)] + bc[(2) - (4)]$
B-groups	$b-1$	M.S. (B)	$[\sigma^2_X - (1)] + c[(1) - (2) - (3) + (4)] + ac[(3) - (4)]$
$A \, . \, B$	$(a-1)(b-1)$	M.S. (AB)	$[\sigma^2_X - (1)] + c[(1) - (2) - (3) + (4)]$
Deviations	$ab(c-1)$	M.S. (D)	$[\sigma^2_X - (1)]$

where $\sigma_1^2 = [(2)-(4)]$,

$\sigma_2^2 = [(3)-(4)]$, (see Anderson and Bancroft 1952)

$\sigma_3^2 = [(1)-(2)-(3)+(4)]$,

and $\sigma_4^2 = [\sigma_X^2-(1)]$.

$(1) = \text{Cov}\,(x_{ijk} \,.\, x_{ijk'})_{k \neq k'}$ = Cov. between observations within the ij^{th} subgroup,

$(2) = \text{Cov}\,(x_{ijk} \,.\, x_{ij'k'})_{j \neq j'}$ = Cov. between obs. in the ith A-group but in different B-groups,

$(3) = \text{Cov}\,(x_{ijk} \,.\, x_{i'jk'})_{i \neq i'}$ = Cov. between obs. in the jth B-group but in different A-groups,

and $(4) = \text{Cov}\,(x_{ijk} \,.\, x_{i'j'k'})_{\substack{i \neq i' \\ j \neq j'}}$ = Cov. between obs. in different A- and B-groups.

Hierarchical Classification

Many practical calculations on heritability coefficients and intra-class correlations are based on this analysis. We are discussing the two-fold hierarchical classification, which can be expanded very easily to more-fold classifications. The model should be written

$$X_{ijk} = \mu + a_i + b_{ij} + d_{ijk}, \qquad \begin{array}{l} i = 1, \ldots a \\ j = 1, \ldots b \\ k = 1, \ldots c \end{array}$$

$$E(X_{ijk}) = \mu, \; E(a_i \,.\, b_{ij}) = \ldots = E(b_{ij} \,.\, d_{ijk}) = 0,$$

and

$$\sigma^2(x_{ijk}) = \sigma_A^2 + \sigma_B^2 + \sigma_D^2$$

Hence we can set up the analysis of variance displayed in Table 2:

TABLE 2

Source of variation	d.f. (i)	M.S. (i)	E[M.S. (i)]
A-groups	$a-1$	M.S. (A)	$[\sigma_X^2-(1)]+c[(1)-(2)]+bc[(2)-(3)]$
B-groups in A	$a(b-1)$	M.S. (B/A)	$[\sigma_X^2-(1)]+c[(1)-(2)]$
Deviations	$ab(c-1)$	M.S. (D)	$[\sigma_X^2-(1)]$

where $\sigma_1^2 = [(2)-(3)]$,

$\sigma_2^2 = [(1)-(2)]$,

and $\sigma_3^2 = [\sigma_X^2-(1)]$.

$(1) = \text{Cov}\,(x_{ijk} \,.\, x_{ijk'})_{k \neq k'}$ = Cov. between observations within the jth B-group in the ith A-group,

$(2) = \text{Cov}\,(x_{ijk} \,.\, x_{ij'k'})_{j \neq j'}$ = Cov. between obs. within the ith A-group, but not belonging to the same B-group,

and $(3) = \text{Cov}\,(x_{ijk} \,.\, x_{i'j'k'})_{i \neq i'}$ = Cov. between obs. not belonging to the same A-group.

Regression Analysis Combined with Analysis of Variance

The analysis is used for calculating heritability coefficients on the basis of half-sib-correlation and parent-offspring-regression (intra sire dam-daughter-regression).

If we assume that there are b paired observations, x and y in a groups, and that y depends partly on x, we obtain the following three analyses (the first two are identical and simplifications of the two-fold hierarchical classifications, mentioned in the section on Hierarchical classification.):

The assumptions are:

$$X_{ij} = \mu + a_i + d_{ij}, \qquad Y_{ij} = \mu + a'_i + d'_{ij},$$

$$E(X_{ij}) = E(Y_{ij}) = \mu$$

$$E(a_i \,.\, d_{ij}) = E(a'_i \,.\, d'_{ij}) = 0$$

$$\sigma^2(x_{ij}) = \sigma^2_A + \sigma^2_D \qquad \sigma^2(y_{ij}) = \sigma^2_{A'} + \sigma^2_{D'}$$

The analysis of variance for the x- and y-values is given in Table 3:

TABLE 3

Source of variation	d.f. (i)	M.S. (i)	E[M.S. (i)]
A-groups	$a-1$	$_x$M.S.(A)	$[\sigma^2_X - (1)] + b[(1) - (2)]$
		$_y$M.S.(A)	$[\sigma^2_Y - (1')] + b[(1') - (2')]$
Deviations (within A)	$a(b-1)$	$_x$M.S.(D)	$[\sigma^2_X - (1)]$
		$_y$M.S.(D)	$[\sigma^2_Y - (1')]$

where $\sigma^2_1 = [(1)-(2)]$, $\sigma^2_{1'} = [(1')-(2')]$,
$\sigma^2_2 = [\sigma^2_X-(1)]$, and $\sigma^2_{2'} = [\sigma^2_Y-(1')]$.

$(1) = \text{Cov}\,(x_{ij} \,.\, x_{ij'})_{j\neq j'}$ = Cov. between x-values within the ith A-group

$(1') = \text{Cov}\,(y_{ij} \,.\, y_{ij'})_{j\neq j'}$ = Cov. between y-values within the ith A-group

$(2) = \text{Cov}\,(x_{ij} \,.\, x_{i'j'})_{i\neq i'}$ = Cov. between x-values belonging to different A-groups

$(2') = \text{Cov}\,(y_{ij} \,.\, y_{i'j'})_{i\neq i'}$ = Cov. between y-values belonging to different A-groups

The analysis for the products $x.y$ is given in Table 4

TABLE 4

Source of variation	d.f. (i)	M.P. (i)	E[M.P. (i)]
A-groups	$\frac{1}{2}-1$	xy M.P.(A)	$[(1^*) - (2^*)] + b[(2^*) - (3^*)]$
Deviations	$a(b-1)$	xy M.P.(D)	$[(1^*) - (2^*)]$

where $\mathrm{Cov}_1 = [(2^*)-(3^*)]$ and $\mathrm{Cov}_2 = [(1^*)-(2^*)]$.

$(1^*) = \mathrm{Cov}\,(x_{ij} \,.\, y_{ij})$ = Cov. for the x- and y-values which belong together within the ith A-group,

$(2^*) = \mathrm{Cov}\,(x_{ij} \,.\, y_{ij'})_{j \neq j'}$ = Cov. for x- and y-values which do not belong together in the ith A-group,

and $(3^*) = \mathrm{Cov}\,(x_{ij} \,.\, y_{i'j'})_{i \neq i'}$ = Cov. for x- and y-values, when the x- and y-values are in different A-groups.

II. PRACTICAL APPLICATIONS OF GENERAL FORMULAE OF SECTION I

IIA. *Two-way-classification*

(*a*) Suppose that the A-groups represent different individual groups which are unrelated to each other, but with equally related individuals within the same groups, and that the B-groups correspond to different environments (levels of different climate, feeding, etc.).

Therefore the terms (1), (2), (3), and (4) are identical with [see IA]:

(1) = Cov (genet. related individuals within the same environment),

(2) = Cov (genet. related individuals in different environments),

(3) = Cov (genet. unrelated individuals within the same environment), and

(4) = Cov (genet. unrelated individuals in different environments).

A practical example of this kind of analysis is the experiment with identical twins.

Under the assumption that the observed phenotype (P_{ijk}) is the result of genotype (ge) and environmental ($ep+et$) actions, then the structure of the linear statistical model can be written as

$$P_{ijk} = \mu + ge_i + ep_j + (ge \,.\, ep)_{ij} + et_{ijk}$$

where

μ = general mean,

ge_i = effect of the ith genotype,

ep_j = effect of the jth environment,

$(ge \,.\, ep)_{ij}$ = effect of the interaction between ge_i and ep_j, and

et_{ijk} = environmental effects which acts at random.

$$E(P_{ijk}) = \mu, \quad E(ge_i) = E(ep_j) = E[(ge \,.\, ep)_{ij}] = E(et_{ijk}) = 0,$$

$$E(ge_i \,.\, ep_j) = \ldots = E[(ge \,.\, ep)_{ij} \,.\, et_{ijk}] = 0$$

$$\sigma^2(P_{ij}) = \sigma^2_{Ge} + \sigma^2_{Ep} + \sigma^2_{Ge\,.\,Ep} + \sigma^2_{Et}$$

$$\sigma^2(ge_i) = \sigma^2_A + \sigma^2_D + \sigma^2_{AA} + \sigma^2_{AD} + \sigma^2_{DD} + \ldots$$ (see Kempthorne 1954a)

and $$\sigma^2_E = \sigma^2_{Ep} + \sigma^2_{Et}.$$

Furthermore, if we distinguish (for completeness only) sex-linked and maternal effects (other than sex-linked), we can split up the phenotypic covariances between individuals into different parts which are

1. genetical part : ${}_{Ge}\mathrm{Cov}\,(P\,,P')$ (see Kempthorne 1954a)
2. environmental part: ${}_{Ep}\mathrm{Cov}\,(P\,,P')$ (see Le Roy 1959)
3. interactional part : ${}_{Ge\,.\,Ep}\mathrm{Cov}\,(P\,,P')$ (see Le Roy 1959)

[4. sex-linked and maternal effects: ${}_{S,\,M}\mathrm{Cov}\,(P\,,P')$, will not be explained further (see Kempthorne 1957, Le Roy 1959)].

Applied to the analysis on identical twins, the interpretations of the covariance terms are:

$E[{}_P\mathrm{Cov}(P,P')]$	$=$	$E[{}_{Ge}\mathrm{Cov}(P,P')]$	$+$	$E[{}_{Ep}\mathrm{Cov}(P,P')]$	$+$	$E[{}_{Ge\,.\,Ep}\mathrm{Cov}(P,P')]$
$E(1)$	$=$	σ^2_{Ge}	$+$	σ^2_{Ep}	$+$	$\sigma^2_{Ge\,.\,Ep}$
$E(2)$	$=$	σ^2_{Ge}	$+$	0	$+$	0
$E(3)$	$=$	0	$+$	σ^2_{Ep}	$+$	0
$E(4)$	$=$	0	$+$	0	$+$	0

Using identical twins, b is equal to 2 and c is equal to 1. Therefore, there is no M.S.(D) (see IA). The expectations of the mean squares M.S.(i) are:

$$E[\mathrm{M.S.}(AB)] = \sigma^2_4+\sigma^2_3,$$

where $\sigma^2_4 = \sigma^2_{Et}\ [=\sigma^2_P-E(1)]$

$$\sigma^2_3 = [\sigma^2_{Ge}+\sigma^2_{Ep}+\sigma^2_{Ge\,.\,Ep}]-[\sigma^2_{Ge}]-[\sigma^2_{Ep}]+[0] = \sigma^2_{Ge\,.\,Ep}\,.$$

$E[\mathrm{M.S.}(AB)]$ then is equal to $\sigma^2_{Et}+\sigma^2_{Ge\,.\,Ep}$

$E[\mathrm{M.S.}(B)] \ = \sigma^2_4+\sigma^2_3+a\,.\,\sigma^2_2,$ where $\sigma^2_2 = E(2) = \sigma^2_{Ge}$

$E[\mathrm{M.S.}(A)] \ = \sigma^2_4+\sigma^2_3+2\,.\,\sigma^2_1,$ where $\sigma^2_1 = E(3) = \sigma^2_{Ep}$.

From the above analysis, the heritability has to be constructed as follows:

$$ {}_{IT}h^2_{\text{constructed}} = \frac{\sigma^2_2}{\sigma^2_1+\sigma^2_2+\sigma^2_3+\sigma^2_4} = \frac{\sigma^2_{Ge}}{\sigma^2_{Ge}+\sigma^2_{Ep}+\sigma^2_{Ge\,.\,Ep}+\sigma^2_{Et}} = \frac{\sigma^2_{Ge}}{\sigma^2_P}$$

(b) In poultry it is possible to use full-sibs (or half-sibs), e.g. 4 or 6 or more full-sibs in 2 or more environments. Hence we obtain (e.g. for egg production):

$E[{}_P\mathrm{Cov}(P,P')]$	$=$	$E[{}_{Ge}\mathrm{Cov}(P,P')]$	$+$	$E[{}_{Ep}\mathrm{Cov}(P,P')]$	$+$	$E[{}_{Ge\,.\,Ep}\mathrm{Cov}(P,P')]$
$E(1)$	$=$	w	$+$	σ^2_{Ep}	$+$	$k_{FS}\,.\,\sigma^2_{Ge\,.\,Ep}$
$E(2)$	$=$	w	$+$	0	$+$	0
$E(3)$	$=$	0	$+$	σ^2_{Ep}	$+$	0
$E(4)$	$=$	0				

where $w = {}_{Ge}\mathrm{Cov}(FS) = \frac{1}{2}\sigma^2_A+\frac{1}{4}\sigma^2_D+\frac{1}{4}\sigma^2_{AA}+\frac{1}{8}\sigma^2_{AD}+\frac{1}{16}\sigma^2_{DD}$ (2-loci epistasy).

The factor k_{FS} allows for the part of $\sigma^2_{Ge\,.\,Ep}$ which acts as a correlation effect between related animals. For a schematic numerical example, Le Roy (1959) found the following structures of the phenotypic covariations for related individuals exposed to the same permanent environment (only additive gene actions were considered):

$$_P\text{Cov (identical twins)} = \sigma^2_A + \sigma^2_{Ep} + \sigma^2_{Ge\,.\,Ep}$$

$$_P\text{Cov (full-sibs)} = \frac{1}{2}\sigma^2_A + \sigma^2_{Ep} + \frac{20}{44}\sigma^2_{Ge\,.\,Ep}$$

$$_P\text{Cov (half-sibs)} = \frac{1}{4}\sigma^2_A + \sigma^2_{Ep} + \frac{9}{44}\sigma^2_{Ge\,.\,Ep}$$

$$_P\text{Cov (parent-offspring)} = \frac{1}{2}\sigma^2_A + \sigma^2_{Ep} + \frac{18}{44}\sigma^2_{Ge\,.\,Ep}.$$

Then we have

$$\sigma^2_1 = {}_{Ge}\text{Cov }(FS), \quad \sigma^2_2 = \sigma^2_{Ep}, \quad \sigma^2_3 = k_{FS}\,.\,\sigma^2_{Ge\,.\,Ep},$$

and $$\sigma^2_4 = \sigma^2_{Ge} - w + \sigma^2_{Et} + (1-k_{FS})\sigma^2_{Ge\,.\,Ep}.$$

The constructed heritability coefficient is given by

$$_{FS}h^2_{\text{constructed}} = \frac{2\,.\,\sigma^2_1}{\sigma^2_1+\sigma^2_2+\sigma^2_3+\sigma^2_4} = \frac{\sigma^2_A + \frac{1}{2}\sigma^2_D + \frac{1}{2}\sigma^2_{AA} + \frac{1}{4}\sigma^2_{AD} + \frac{1}{8}\sigma^2_{DD}}{\sigma^2_{Ge} + \sigma^2_{Ep} + \sigma^2_{Ge\,.\,Ep} + \sigma^2_{Et}}$$

(*c*) Using half-sibs, the $h^2_{\text{constructed}}$ can be found in analogy to the coefficients found in (*a*) and (*b*), and is equal to

$$_{HS}h^2_{\text{constructed}} = \frac{4\,.\,\sigma^2_1}{\sigma^2_1+\sigma^2_2+\sigma^2_3+\sigma^2_4} = \frac{\sigma^2_A + \frac{1}{4}\sigma^2_{AA}}{\sigma^2_{Ge} + \sigma^2_{Ep} + \sigma^2_{Ge\,.\,Ep} + \sigma^2_{Et}}$$

where $$\sigma^2_1 = {}_{Ge}\text{Cov }(HS), \quad \sigma^2_2 = \sigma^2_{Ep}, \quad \sigma^2_3 = k_{HS}\,.\,\sigma^2_{Ge\,.\,Ep},$$

and $$\sigma^2_4 = \sigma^2_{Ge} - {}_{Ge}\text{Cov }(HS) + \sigma^2_{Et} + (1-k_{HS})\sigma^2_{Ge\,.\,Ep}.$$

(*d*) Assuming that *a* sires are mated to *a* different sets of *d* dams in *a* seasons, and that during the experiment (polyallel crossing) every sire is once mated to each dam, with c offspring from each mating, we get the following results:

$$\sigma_1^2 = [(d-1)(3)+d(a-1)(4)-d(5)]/(b-1)$$

$$\sigma_2^2 = \left[(2)-\frac{d}{b-1}(5)\right]$$

$$\sigma_3^2 = \left[(1)-(2)-\frac{1}{b-1}\{(d-1)(3)+d(a-1)(4)-d(5)\}\right],$$

and $\quad \sigma_4^2 = \sigma_P^2-(1),$

where (1) = Cov (FS, all within the same season),
(2) = Cov (maternal HS in different seasons),
(3) = Cov (paternal HS in the same season),
(4) = Cov (paternal HS in different seasons), and
(5) = Cov (genet. unrelated individuals in the same season).

Furthermore the expectations for the covariances are:

$$\begin{aligned}
E(1) &= {}_{Ge}\text{Cov}\,(FS) \;\; +\sigma_{Ep}^2+k_{FS}\cdot\sigma_{Ge\,.\,Ep}^2\\
E(2) &= {}_{Ge}\text{Cov}\,(HS)_m+\;0\;+\quad 0\\
E(3) &= {}_{Ge}\text{Cov}\,(HS)_p+\sigma_{Ep}^2+k_{HS}\cdot\sigma_{Ge\,.\,Ep}^2\\
E(4) &= {}_{Ge}\text{Cov}\,(HS)_p+\;0\;+\quad 0\\
E(5) &= \quad 0 \quad +\sigma_{Ep}^2+\quad 0
\end{aligned}$$

If there are no seasonal effects, we may put (3) = (4), and (5) = 0, and the analysis becomes identical with that in section IA.

If real seasonal effects and genotype–environment interactions exist, then the covariance components σ_1^2, σ_2^2, σ_3^2, and σ_4^2 are expected to be (2 loci):

$$\sigma_1^2 = \frac{1}{4}\sigma_A^2+\frac{1}{16}\sigma_{AA}^2-\frac{1}{b-1}\sigma_{Ep}^2+\frac{d-1}{b-1}\cdot k_{HS}\cdot\sigma_{Ge\,.\,Ep}^2,$$

$$\sigma_2^2 = \frac{1}{4}\sigma_A^2+\frac{1}{16}\sigma_{AA}^2-\frac{d}{b-1}\sigma_{Ep}^2,$$

$$\sigma_3^2 = \frac{1}{4}\sigma_D^2+\frac{1}{8}\sigma_{AA}^2+\frac{1}{8}\sigma_{AD}^2+\frac{1}{16}\sigma_{DD}^2+\frac{b}{b-1}\sigma_{Ep}^2+\left(k_{FS}-k_{HS}\cdot\frac{d-1}{b-1}\right)\sigma_{Ge\,.\,Ep}^2,$$

$$\sigma_4^2 = \frac{1}{2}\sigma_A^2+\frac{3}{4}\sigma_D^2+\frac{3}{4}\sigma_{AA}^2+\frac{7}{8}\sigma_{AD}^2+\frac{15}{16}\sigma_{DD}^2+(1-k_{FS})\sigma_{Ge\,.\,Ep}^2+\sigma_{Et}^2,$$

and $\sigma_P^2 = \sigma_1^2+\sigma_2^2+\sigma_3^2+\sigma_4^2+\dfrac{d}{b-1}(5) = \sigma_{Ge}^2+\sigma_{Ep}^2+\sigma_{Ge\,.\,Ep}^2+\sigma_{Et}^2.$

Since $$4\left\{\sigma_1^2+\frac{1}{b-1}(5)-\frac{d-1}{b-1}[(3)-(4)-(5)]\right\}=\sigma_A^2+\frac{1}{4}\sigma_{AA}^2,$$

and $$4\left\{\sigma_2^2+\frac{d}{b-1}(5)\right\}=\sigma_A^2+\frac{1}{4}\sigma_{AA}^2,$$

there are two values for $h^2_{\text{constructed}}$ with the same structure but different errors, which are not easy to find.

$h^2_{\text{constructed}}=\dfrac{\sigma_A^2+\frac{1}{4}\sigma_{AA}^2}{\sigma_P^2}$	(based on σ_1^2 or σ_2^2)

IIB. *Hierarchical Classification*

Taking the M.S.(A) as M.S.(between ♂♂), and the M.S.(B/A) as M.S.(between ♀♀ within ♂♂), the M.S.(D) becomes identical with M.S.(between full-sibs).

We shall discuss two extreme cases:

1. The half-sibs are kept within a certain *region* (r), the full-sibs are managed within *subregions* (sr) within the region for half-sibs. We assume furthermore that between regions (r) and between subregions (sr) there exist environmental effects, symbolised by (Er) and (Esr).
2. All $a.b.c$ offsprings are randomly distributed over the whole environmental region in discussion.

For the case (1) we find

$$E(1)={}_{Ge}\text{Cov}\,(FS)+\sigma_{Er}^2+\sigma_{Esr}^2+k_{FS}\cdot\sigma^2_{Ge.Er}+k'_{FS}\cdot\sigma^2_{Ge.Esr},$$

$$E(2)={}_{Ge}\text{Cov}\,(HS)+\sigma_{Er}^2+k_{HS}\cdot\sigma^2_{Ge.Er},$$

and $$E(3)=0,$$

where $\sigma_{Er}^2+\sigma_{Esr}^2=\sigma_{Ep}^2,\quad \sigma^2_{Ge.Er}+\sigma^2_{Ge.Esr}=\sigma^2_{Ge.Ep}.$

Hence

$$\sigma_1^2=\frac{1}{4}\sigma_A^2+\frac{1}{16}\sigma_{AA}^2+\sigma_{Er}^2+k_{HS}\cdot\sigma^2_{Ge.Er}$$

$$\sigma_2^2=\frac{1}{4}\sigma_A^2+\frac{1}{4}\sigma_D^2+\frac{3}{16}\sigma_{AA}^2+\frac{2}{16}\sigma_{AD}^2+\frac{1}{16}\sigma_{DD}^2+\sigma_{Esr}^2+(k_{FS}-k_{HS})\sigma^2_{Ge.Er}+k'_{FS}\cdot\sigma^2_{Ge.Esr},$$

and $$\sigma_3^2=\frac{1}{2}\sigma_A^2+\frac{3}{4}\sigma_D^2+\frac{3}{4}\sigma_{AA}^2+\frac{7}{8}\sigma_{AD}^2+\frac{15}{16}\sigma_{DD}^2+\sigma^2_{Ge.Ep}-k_{FS}\cdot\sigma^2_{Ge.Er}-k'_{FS}\cdot\sigma^2_{Ge.Esr}+\sigma_{Et}^2.$$

Furthermore the phenotypic variation is equal to

$$\sigma_P^2 = \sigma_1^2 + \sigma_2^2 + \sigma_3^2.$$

The three constructed heritability values available are:

$$_{♂}h^2_{\text{constr.}} = \frac{4 \cdot \sigma_1^2}{\sigma_P^2} = \left[\sigma_A^2 + \frac{1}{4}\sigma_{AA}^2 + 4(\sigma_{Er}^2 + k_{HS} \cdot \sigma_{Ge\,.\,Er}^2)\right] \Big/ \sigma_P^2$$

$$_{♀}h^2_{\text{constr.}} = \frac{4 \cdot \sigma_2^2}{\sigma_P^2} = \left[\sigma_A^2 + \sigma_D^2 + \frac{3}{4}\sigma_{AA}^2 + \frac{1}{2}\sigma_{AD}^2 + \frac{1}{4}\sigma_{DD}^2 + 4(\sigma_{Esr}^2 + \{k_{FS} - k_{HS}\}\sigma_{Ge\,.\,Er}^2 + k'_{FS} \cdot \sigma_{Ge\,.\,Esr}^2)\right] \Big/ \sigma_P^2$$

$$_{♂+♀}h^2_{\text{constr.}} = \frac{2(\sigma_1^2 + \sigma_2^2)}{\sigma_P^2} = \left[\sigma_A^2 + \frac{1}{2}\sigma_D^2 + \frac{1}{2}\sigma_{AA}^2 + \frac{1}{4}\sigma_{AD}^2 + \frac{1}{8}\sigma_{DD}^2 + 2(\sigma_{Ep}^2 + k_{FS} \cdot \sigma_{Ge\,.\,Er}^2 + k'_{FS} \cdot \sigma_{Ge\,.\,Esr}^2)\right] \Big/ \sigma_P^2$$

For case (2), the following terms in the nominator of $h^2_{\text{constr.}}$ are omitted:

$$\sigma_{Er}^2, \quad \sigma_{Esr}^2, \quad \sigma_{Ge\,.\,Er}^2 \quad \text{and} \quad \sigma_{Ge\,.\,Esr}^2.$$

It must be mentioned that random distribution over all regions and subregions is not identical with $\sigma_{Er}^2 = \sigma_{Ers}^2 = 0$, owing to the assumptions that $Er \neq 0$, and $Esr \neq 0$. These two components are included in the phenotypic variance. The same is true for $\sigma_{Ge\,.\,Ep}^2$.

In case (1), the numerator of the heritability constructed contains certain parts of environmental and genotype–environment interaction terms. Corrections for environmental effects can be made, if there are genetically unrelated individuals in regions and subregions available for estimating σ_{Er}^2 and σ_{Esr}^2 by intraclass correlations. In the cases where the interactions are negligible and corrections are made for σ_{Er}^2 and σ_{Esr}^2, we arrive at the same h^2-value as in case (2). but the estimates in case (1) have larger errors (caused by corrections).

IIc. *Combined Regression Analysis and Analysis of Variance*

If the M.S.(A) for x and y are identical with the M.S.(between ♂♂), the M.S.(D) for x and y is equal to M.S.(within ♂♂). Under the assumption that b different dams (x) with one offspring (y) for each sire are included, we get the following results:

CASE 1: there are environmental effects between sire groups (*Er*) and between dam-offspring groups (*Esr*) within sire.

For x: $E(1) = \sigma^2_{Er}$, and $E(2) = 0$.

For y: $E(1') = {}_{Ge}\text{Cov}(HS) + \sigma^2_{Er} + k_{HS} \cdot \sigma^2_{Ge\,.\,Er}$, and $E(2') = 0$

$$\sigma^2_1 + \sigma^2_2 = \sigma^2_{1'} + \sigma^2_{2'} = \sigma^2_P = \sigma^2_{Ge} + \sigma^2_{Ep} + \sigma^2_{Ge\,.\,Ep} + \sigma^2_{Et}.$$

For $x\,.\,y$: $E(1^*) = {}_{Ge}\text{Cov}_{(\text{dam-offspring})} + \sigma^2_{Er} + \sigma^2_{Esr} + k_{P\,.\,0} \cdot \sigma^2_{Ge\,.\,Er} + k'_{P\,.\,0} \cdot \sigma^2_{Ge\,.\,Esr}$

$E(2^*) = \sigma^2_{Er}$, and $E(3^*) = 0$.

The constructed heritability values are:

(*a*) based on *HS*-correlation

$$_{HS}h^2_{\text{constr.}} = \frac{4\,.\,\sigma^2_{2'}}{\sigma^2_{1'} + \sigma^2_{2'}} = \left[\sigma^2_A + \frac{1}{4}\sigma^2_{AA} + 4(\sigma^2_{Er} + k_{HS} \cdot \sigma^2_{Ge\,.\,Er})\right] \Big/ \sigma^2_P$$

(*b*) based on dam-offspring regression (see page 110)

$$_{P\,.\,0}h^2_{\text{constr.}} = \frac{2\,.\,\text{Cov}_2}{\sigma^2_P}$$

$$= \left[\sigma^2_A + \frac{1}{2}\sigma^2_{AA} + 2(\sigma^2_{Esr} + k_{P\,.\,0} \cdot \sigma^2_{Ge\,.\,Er} + k'_{P\,.\,0} \cdot \sigma^2_{Ge\,.\,Esr})\right] \Big/ \sigma^2_P$$

CASE 2: The $a\,.\,b$ offsprings are randomly distributed over the whole discussed environmental region.

The results are obtained by omitting the terms σ^2_{Er}, σ^2_{Esr}, $\sigma^2_{Ge\,.\,Er}$, and $\sigma^2_{Ge\,.\,Esr}$ in the numerator of the constructed heritabilities for the case (1).

Corrections for σ^2_{Er} (in $_{HS}h^2_{\text{constr.}}$) are possible:

$$_{HS}h^2_{\text{constr. corrected}} = 4[\sigma^2_{2'} - (2^*)]/\sigma^2_P \quad \text{or} \quad 4[\sigma^2_{2'} - (1)]/\sigma^2_P.$$

Corrections for σ^2_{Esr} are only possible if there are genetically unrelated individuals in the same subregion available for estimating σ^2_{Esr}.

REFERENCES

ANDERSON, R. L. & BANCROFT, T. A., (1952) *Statistical Theory in Research*, McGraw-Hill, New York.

KEMPTHORNE, O. (1954a). The correlations between relatives in a random mating population. *Proc. Roy. Soc.* B **143,** 103–113.

KEMPTHORNE, O. (1954b) The theoretical values of correlations between relatives in random mating populations. *Genetics,* **40,** 168–174.

KEMPTHORNE, O. (1957) *An Introduction to Genetic Statistics*, Wiley, New York.

LE ROY, H. L. (1959) *Statistische Methoden der Populationsgenetik. Ein Grundriss für Genetiker, Agronomen und Biomathematiker*, Verlag Birkhäuser, Basel/Stuttgart (in print).

AN EXPERIMENTAL DESIGN FOR SEPARATING GENETIC AND ENVIRONMENTAL CHANGES IN ANIMAL POPULATIONS UNDER SELECTION

By Kenneth Goodwin, G. E. Dickerson, and W. F. Lamoreux
Kimber Farms, Inc., Niles, California

INTRODUCTION

During recent years, animal geneticists have become increasingly aware of the need for techniques which will accurately measure genetic response to selection in their experimental populations. Among the factors which have led to this heightened interest in controls for selection experiments, the following may be cited:

1. Breeders are now commonly confronted with the need for making genetic improvement in species (e.g., poultry) which have been subjected to many generations of selection, and in which multiple objectives must be considered. The response under these conditions is not expected to be so apparent as when improvement is sought for a single trait in a population previously unselected for that trait, and very precise methods are necessary to determine the extent to which selection alters performance.

2. New techniques, notably those designed to utilize heterosis (such as strain-crossing, recurrent selection, and inbreeding and hybridization), have been suggested as desirable replacements for long-established breeding practices. Thus faced with a choice of several programs, breeders will wish to determine as accurately and economically as possible which of these systems yields the greatest genetic gains.

3. In animal breeding, the greatest usefulness of quantitative genetic theory is its accuracy in predicting selection response, and the investigator's responsibility in this area has not been discharged until the adequacy of the theory has been measured by appropriate experiments. By way of example, the heritability of a trait, when defined as the proportion of the phenotypic variance due to the average effects of genes, is commonly combined with the selection differential to provide an estimate of the permanent genetic improvement to be expected among the progeny. This predictive function of the estimate of heritability is currently in need of evaluation, because its optimum application is limited by the extent to which it reveals the *real* or *effective* progress to be expected following selection. Obviously, a valid test of this must rest upon experiments which accurately separate the environmental from the genetic changes during several generations of selection.

The nature of the problem in poultry flocks is indicated in a recent analysis of a closed flock of White Leghorns (Dickerson, 1955). In comparing time trends with expected response for several traits, he concluded that the population was at a ' fluctuating plateau ', even though heritability estimates for individual traits remained high. To the apparent failure of expected genetic gains to be realized, the term ' genetic slippage ' was given. Similarly, the study by Lerner and Dempster (1951) of two populations of chickens led them to conclude that there was a cessation of genetic progress after several years of selection.

Kyle and Chapman (1953), working with rats, measured the response of ovarian weight to injections of gonadotrophic hormones and found that selection for high response agreed fairly well with predictions, but selection for low response was less than expected. Recent papers by Clayton, Morris and Robertson (1957) and Clayton and Robertson (1957) have shown that in their populations of *Drosophila*, selected for number of abdominal sternital bristles, selection ' upward ' gave fair agreement with expectation during early generations, but selection ' downward ' during this time responded less than expected. However, after 20 to 30 generations selection response had largely ceased in all lines, although genetic variation was still present.

The problem of devising adequate controls for selection experiments has not been ignored. In general, three similar methods have been used to measure the efficiency of selection by making comparisons among contemporary populations maintained under conditions that remove systematic environmental bias and minimize error from the uncontrolled random environmental influences.

(1) A procedure which has been used in some instances is to select in opposite directions for the same trait in two strains of common genetic origin, as was done by MacArthur (1949) in his studies of body size in mice. While this technique conclusively demonstrates the effectiveness of selection in creating changes in the two segments of the population, its usefulness in revealing the relative efficiencies of selection in the two directions is limited by the extent to which changes in the environment during the experiment remain unknown. The latter point is of paramount interest in breeding work with domestic animals, where the environment is commonly less subject to control than in laboratory experiments.

(2) Another commonly used procedure is to make parallel comparisons of results from several different systems of breeding, beginning with a common foundation stock (e.g. Bell, Moore and Warren, 1955). When the divergence created between alternative breeding systems is the only information desired, separation of environmental from genetic trends is unnecessary. However, the absolute response obtained from any one breeding system cannot be measured by contemporary comparison with another strain which is itself subject to genetic change.

(3) Maintenance by random selection or by ' relaxed selection ' of a control strain for comparison with one or more other strains under selection has been used in chickens (Skaller, 1956; Gowe, 1956, and King, 1958), and in other species as, for example, *Drosophila* (Robertson, 1955). Such a control strain is subject to limitations arising from (*a*) changes in gene frequency due to natural selection or chance fluctuations, (*b*) inbreeding effects, and (*c*) the wider range of gene recombinations permitted in the absence of selection which may increase the mean deviation from optimum genetic balance and thus depress performance, particularly in the early generations. The latter limitation would apply even though the breeding animals used to perpetuate the control strain were systematically selected to represent all strata of the population. The likelihood of change in performance resulting solely from altered recombinations of genes perhaps would be lessened if the control population were formed by crossing several strains, and if several generations of relaxed selection were allowed to elapse before using it as a control strain, but it would be desirable to avoid the necessity of such assumptions.

While the researcher must always make assumptions regarding the behavior of his control animals, it is desirable in genetic selection experiments to keep these assumptions as few as possible. It is the purpose of this paper to describe a critical experimental procedure for measuring genetic trends in animal populations subjected to selection during several generations, and to present examples of its application in a closed flock of White Leghorn chickens.

EXPERIMENTAL METHOD

The procedure to be described depends essentially upon the use of matings which are repeated identically during two successive breeding seasons. From this basic idea, a breeding scheme can be developed which: (*a*) measures environmental changes by means of inter-year comparisons of progeny groups of the same generation, (*b*) measures genetic changes by means of intra-year comparisons of progeny groups of two successive generations, and (*c*) measures changes in maternal effects associated with aging of the dam.

Description of Matings and Progeny

The mating scheme used for isolating the desired comparisons is illustrated in Fig. 1 and described in the following section. The terminology used is that appropriate to poultry breeding, but can be given general application if it be remembered that cockerels and pullets are young males and females in their first breeding season (i.e. approximately one year old), while yearlings are adult birds in their second breeding season (i.e., approximately two years old).

The *A* matings, set up in year 1, consist of cockerels mated with pullets. Selection of these cockerels and pullets takes place in the fall of the year in

YEAR		SELECTED MATINGS Cockerels × Pullets	REPEATED MATINGS Second-year sires Second-year dams + Full-sister pullets
1	Mating	A	
	Offspring	B_A	
		S_1	
2	Mating	B	A′
	Offspring	C_B	$B_{A'}$
		S_2	S_3
3	Mating	C	B′ + B″
	Offspring	D_C	$C_{B'}$ $C_{B''}$

FIG. 1. Diagram of the general mating scheme described in the text.

which they are hatched, and is based upon the part-year performance of the individual, the full-sibs and the half-sibs. In addition to the daughters obtained from these matings (offspring B_A), enough cockerel chicks are saved so that males from each full-sib family are available for selection as breeders during the following breeding season (year 2). Previous to housing the daughters for the measurement of egg production and egg quality, their parents may be re-evaluated on the basis of a longer period of performance including their own fertility and hatchability records. Any desired proportion of the families originally hatched may be discarded at this time, although such culling is based entirely upon the performance of the parents without any consideration of information (e.g., livability) available for the progeny themselves. Full performance records thus can be obtained for a sample of progeny tested in each full-sib family from the parents chosen in the final evaluation based solely on performance of the parental generation.

In year 2 the *B* matings are made, using cockerels and pullets selected from the progeny (B_A) of the *A* matings. The point at which selection is practised between years 1 and 2 is shown as S_1.

In addition, in year 2, the matings of the previous year are repeated so that identical matings (less those removed by death of either parent) are made in two successive years (matings *A* and *A*′). The progeny of the two series of matings made in year 2 are identified in Fig. 1 as C_B (from selected cockerel × pullet breeders) and $B_{A'}$ (from matings repeated a second year). This latter group of progeny ($B_{A'}$) is made up of full sisters of many of the birds used in the *B* matings. If one could assume that direct maternal influences are unimportant or that they do not change with age of dam, the comparison between progeny in $B_{A'}$ with their full sibs in B_A would provide an unbiased estimate of environmental change from year 1 to year 2, and a similar comparison of C_B with $B_{A'}$ would estimate genetic change from generation B to generation C. Since such an assumption is not warranted, further matings (B'') are necessary.

In year 3 the procedure for selecting cockerels and pullets for breeding from among progeny C_B is carried out as for years 1 and 2, to set up a new series of cockerel × pullet matings (C matings). Also the cockerel × pullet matings of the previous year (B matings) are repeated (B' matings). To these B' mating pens are added the females shown as the B'' matings. These B'' females are obtained from progeny $B_{A'}$ and are full sisters of the hens in mating B, in so far as available. In setting up mating $B'+B''$ in year 3, full sisters of the two ages are paired, each pair consisting of a yearling hen in B' and her pullet full sister in B'', both mated to the same male. When a B mating is broken up by the death of a female parent after the C_B progeny have been produced, a sister of the dead parent is added to the sire's pen in the repeated B' mating. This increases the data available for a comparison of $C_{B''}$ with C_B.

This general procedure, outlined in Fig. 1 for three generations, is continued in subsequent generations with a new set of cockerel × pullet matings selected each year and the matings of survivors repeated the following year, after which they are discarded. The breeding population for any one year consists then of cockerel × pullet matings (e.g. C), second-year male × second-year female matings repeated identically from the previous year (e.g. B') and second year male × pullet matings (e.g. B''). In the B'' matings and in similar subsequent matings the sires are those used for the repeated matings, and the pullets are full sisters of the pullet breeders mated with these sires in the preceding year.

The progeny groups D_C and $C_{B''}$ differ systematically only in that one generation of selection (S_2 in Fig. 1) has intervened between them. Selection of the dams to be used in the B'' matings (S_3) is identical to that used in setting up mating B the previous year (S_1) with respect to families used. Variation which may occur between years in the selection of individual birds within families introduces no systematic bias if (*a*) size of family is, on the average, comparable in the progeny groups B_A and $B_{A'}$, (*b*) a similar proportion of birds is selected from a given family in each case, (*c*) a similar weighting is assigned to each trait in the selection practised at S_1 and S_3, and (*d*) genetic environmental interactions are of small magnitude or vary randomly from year to year. Of course the experimental errors of these differences include random effects of environment and of genetic segregation. The fact that grand dams of D_C were full-sisters of, rather than the same, dams that produced the $C_{B''}$ progeny will increase error from genetic sampling somewhat.

Comparisons to be Made

From the groups of progeny available one may measure directly the environmental and genetic trends, and estimate the extent to which maternal effects change with aging of dams.

Since each of the pairs of repeated matings (A, A'; B, B', etc.), is identical except for natural selection due to mortality, any difference between the progeny from the initial matings and those from the repeated matings is due to: (*a*) environmental differences between years, (*b*) any change in maternal effects associated with aging, and (*c*) experimental error from random variation in the sample of parental genes and in environmental influences received by the progeny. On the other hand, differences between the progeny from selected cockerel × pullet matings and from the yearling repeated matings, all hatched in the same year, are of a genetic nature except for any age difference in maternal influence and random error. The addition of the third type of mating (B''), utilizing pullet breeders selected from among the progeny of a repeated mating, makes possible the isolation of the genetic and environmental trends without confusion with change in maternal effects resulting from differences in age of dams.

In the comparisons outlined below, the following assumptions are made:

(1) In determining the environmental trend ($C_{B''}-C_B$) and the effect of aging upon maternal effects ($C_{B''}-C_{B'}$) comparisons are limited to pairs of progenies produced by full sisters mated to the same males, eliminating from the comparison $C_{B''}$ birds without an aunt in the corresponding set of matings. This introduces no bias, because such eliminations are based on the survival of the parent rather than on performance of the progeny themselves.

(2) In determining the genetic trend ($D_C-C_{B''}$) groups of progeny are used in the comparison only if the grand dam in mating B has a full sister in mating B''.

(3) All groups to be compared within a year are hatched, reared and housed in such a manner that pen and individual environmental effects are randomly distributed among birds of the different groups.

Isolation of Environmental Trends ($C_{B''}-C_B$)

The procedure for isolating the environmental trend from year 2 to year 3 is described by the following relationships:

$$C_{B''} = \mu+g_C+y_3+m_1+mg_B+my_2$$
$$C_B = \mu+g_C+y_2+m_1+mg_B+my_1$$

$$C_{B''}-C_B = (y_3-y_2)+(my_2-my_1).$$

In this model, deviations of either record ($C_{B''}$ or C_B) from the general mean (μ) would depend upon several factors. First, the deviation in genotype peculiar to generation C is described as g_C. The expected means for genotypes of the two groups of progeny are the same, except for genetic sampling error, since they are from the same sires and from full-sister dams.

There is also a year effect, shown as y_3 and y_2. Here is the critical difference in the two records, since they were made by progeny raised in different years.

Three types of maternal influences are recognized. These are a general maternal effect of pullet breeders (m_1) as compared with older breeders, any genetic effect upon maternal influence peculiar to a given generation (mg_B), and any maternal influence resulting from an environmental effect on the dams reared in a given year (my_2 and my_1). Only the latter would be included in the difference, $C_{B''}-C_B$. This is properly included as an environmental effect upon the records of $C_{B''}$ and C_B so that the difference between the two records is a direct estimate of the environmental change from year 2 to year 3.

Isolation of Genetic Trends $D_C-C_{B''}$

The genetic trend may be estimated in a similar manner, the proper comparison being $D_C-C_{B''}$, where:

$$D_C = \mu+g_D+y_3+m_1+mg_C+my_2$$

$$C_{B''} = \mu+g_C+y_3+m_1+mg_B+my_2$$

$$D_C-C_{B''} = (g_D-g_C) + (mg_C-mg_B).$$

In this comparison, birds differing by one generation of selection (that used in setting up mating C) are compared. The average environmental effect upon D_C and $C_{B''}$ can be the same, since they are each hatched in year 3. Similarly, any non-maternal environmental effect upon the maternal influence of their dams is identical (my_2) since their dams were all hatched in year 2. Any maternal effect which changes with selection (i.e., an effect of the dam's genotype upon direct maternal influence) is properly included in the genetic trend (mg_C-mg_B). Thus $D_C-C_{B''}$ provides a direct estimate of the genetic trend from generation C to generation D.

Isolation of Maternal Effects ($C_{B''}-C_{B'}$)

The maternal effect associated with aging may be estimated in a like manner, by comparing $C_{B''}$ with $C_{B'}$:

$$C_{B''} = \mu+g_C+y_3+m_1+mg_B+my_2$$

$$C_{B'} = \mu+g_C+y_3+m_2+mg_B+my_1$$

$$C_{B''}-C_{B'} = (m_1-m_2)+(my_2-my_1).$$

Here the maternal effects associated with aging $(m_1 - m_2)$ are confounded with any effect upon maternal influence which the particular environment in which the parents were grown may have had $(my_2 - my_1)$.

Providing the samples of progeny raised are adequate, the sampling error of the progeny means arising from genetic segregation and random environmental effects can be minimized, so that the principal non-random sources of variation for each record would be as indicated in the models given above.

Within-Strain and Between-Strain Comparisons

The series of matings described can be used either for measuring environmental and genetic changes in a population which is itself subjected to selection procedures (within-strain comparisons), or as a control for other strains for which a measure of selection response is desired (between-strain comparisons). We have used it in both ways in our flocks.

For making within-strain comparisons the procedure followed has been exactly as described above.

For making between-strain comparisons, a slight variation in procedure is desirable in order to obtain samples of the basic strain which can be kept with the strain to be controlled (the ' unknown '). This has been done by mating an unselected group of daughters of the cockerel × pullet matings (e.g. C_B) with unselected sons of the same matings, and placing a sample of the chicks thus obtained with the ' unknown '. In the following year, unselected matings of daughters of the repeated matings (e.g. $C_{B'}$) with unselected sons of the same matings are made and a sample of chicks placed with the next generation of the ' unknown '. Comparison of the successive generations of the unknown with control strain progeny from the same generations of control strain parents (i.e., C_B and $C_{B'}$, respectively) estimates genetic change in the unknown. This procedure allows one generation of relaxed selection to intervene before the critical comparisons are made, and requires that two samples of chicks from the basic strain (e.g., the progeny of random matings in group D_C and in group $C_{B'}$) be placed with each generation of the ' unknown '. Any effect of relaxed selection is not expected to introduce bias providing the procedure is carried out in a similar fashion during successive years. Unselected samples of the basic strain, when placed with an ' unknown ' for making between-strain comparisons, also provide supplementary estimates of genetic and environmental changes in the control strain itself.

In our material, flock matings (in contrast to single male matings) are used to provide the samples of chicks for between-strain comparisons, and the only restriction imposed on setting up these matings (aside from the fact that they are made at random) is one designed to offset the effect of mortality among the breeders. It is evident that some progeny groups originally available for the unselected matings at C_B will not be represented again among the progeny groups at $C_{B'}$, because some matings will have been eliminated due to the death of one or the other parent. To circumvent this in so far as possible, it has been our practice, in setting up the unselected matings at C_B, to use only those progeny groups whose parents are still surviving and either have produced chicks, or very likely will produce chicks, in the repeated matings.

Paternal Effects and Second-year Maternal Effects

Since the progeny of two-year old males are compared with those of one-year old males in making the critical comparisons for genetic and environmental changes, an implicit assumption made in this procedure is that non-genetic effects of the male (paternal effects) do not change with aging. This would seem acceptable for most traits, although direct evidence for its support is not now available. It should be borne in mind that cockerels and yearling males are both relatively young in a male's potential reproductive life, and males of an advanced age are not used. An exception occurs in measuring fertility, for which trait a known reduction takes place in yearling males below their performance as cockerels, and the procedure is not useful for measuring this on a within-strain basis. This does not apply for between-strain comparisons, where all males used are cockerels.

Another assumption made is that any maternal effects carried over from a breeding female to her granddaughters (second-year maternal effects as, for example, a maternal effect upon A' breeders which might influence the records of progeny group $C_{B''}$) are of little consequence. This would again seem to be a reasonable assumption in chickens, although in applying the procedure to mammalian species where nursing effects on the young enter the picture, it would be desirable to have more information regarding their possible importance. Obtaining such information would necessitate further special tests, but it could be done by using both the $C_{B''}$ and $C_{B'}$ progeny groups as breeders and comparing performance among their progeny. The $C_{B''}$ female breeders would be pullets from pullet dams, whereas the $C_{B'}$ breeders would be pullets from two-year old dams.

Effect of Mortality and Size of Populations

Since it is evident that some matings cannot be repeated because one or the other, or both, of the parents have died after their use in the cockerel × pullet matings, it is necessary to consider the effect of this upon the procedure, and the extent to which such eliminations by death may be expected to occur.

When it has been impossible to repeat a mating because of the death of either parent, the progeny produced in the cockerel × pullet matings by the dead parent are removed from all later comparisons. This procedure has been stated in more detail above, under the section dealing with assumptions necessary in making the comparisons. No bias is introduced due to this, because full-sister families are eliminated only on the basis of the performance of the parent, and not on the basis of their own performance.

The only important effect of mortality of either parent is to reduce the numbers of birds available for the critical comparisons. This could be a serious objection to the procedure, especially if mortality among males were excessive. In our experience this has not been a problem, and in Table 1 is presented the size of the populations with which we have worked. In general 15 to 17 cockerels, mated to seven or eight dams each, are started each year, and an average of 61.0% of all matings has been repeated the following year.

One way to correct for unavoidable mortality would be to keep in reserve a suitable number of brothers of the cockerels to be tested, substituting a brother in the event of the death of a male in the experiment. Since the original selection of cockerels to be tested can be based only on the part-year performance of their sibs and half-sibs, or the performance of their parents and aunts, and not on information available concerning the young male himself (except his apparent state of health) the brother substituted should be no better or worse, *on the average*, than the original male used. Such substitutions would, of course, increase experimental error but should not introduce bias. Any increase of experimental error from this source may be more than offset by a corresponding reduction of experimental error from increasing the number of comparisons possible, especially if mortality among males is high.

Traits and Selection Procedures

In our flocks, multiple traits representing an array of economically important characteristics, are measured and considered in the selection of the young cockerels and pullets. They fall in four general categories:

(*a*) Fertility and hatchability, measured as a percentage.

(*b*) Viability, measured as a percentage.

(*c*) Egg production, including age at sexual maturity measured as age in weeks at the time the first egg is laid, and rate of lay measured as a percentage during a given period of time after the first egg is laid.

(*d*) Various egg quality traits such as egg weight, albumen quality, and other factors of interior and exterior quality.

Selection has been based primarily upon an index weighting which takes into account the heritability of the trait, its genetic correlation with other traits, and its economic importance, relative to other traits. In our poultry flock, selection of the cockerels and pullets is made during the fall of the year in which they are hatched, and is thus based upon a part-year record. The parents' records are re-evaluated at approximately 60 weeks of age, before their daughters are housed to obtain individual records of egg production and

TABLE 1. NUMBERS OF SIRES, DAMS, AND THEIR TRAPNESTED DAUGHTERS USED IN EACH TYPE OF MATING DURING A FIVE YEAR PERIOD

	Cockerel × Pullet matings			Repeated matings					% of original matings repeated
Year	Sires	Pullet Dams	Daughters†	Sires	Yearling Dams	Daughters†	Pullet Dams	Daughters†	
1954	18	120	922	—	—	—	—	—	—
1955	17	130	750	13	61	401	—	—	50.8
1956	15	110	711	15	93	658	45	318	71.5
1957	17	110	844	13	73	473	50	382	66.4
1958	17	110	901	13	61	446	41	353	55.4
Average	16.8	116.0	825.6	13.5	72.0	494.5	45.3	351.0	61.0

† Number of trapnested daughters for which individual records were kept. Additional daughters, not trapnested, were also kept for measuring mortality.

egg quality. Approximately 30% of the families originally hatched are normally discarded at this time. The choice of families to keep or discard is based solely on the lengthened record now available for the parents, including their fertility and hatchability as well as egg production, egg quality and livability. No culling is done on the basis of any information known about the progeny themselves.

Selection of the pullets to be added to the repeated matings (S_3 in Fig. 1) is done at the same time and on the same basis as selection at S_2, and, in so far as possible, is kept identical to the selection made the previous year at S_1.

SAMPLING ERRORS OF ESTIMATES

The experimental design described herein provides three methods for estimating the rate of genetic change in any population. These differ in application and in sampling variation as follows:

Repeated Intra-year Comparisons of Successive Generations

This estimate of genetic change is available only within the repeated mating control strain itself. The rate of genetic change (ΔG_1) over a period of k years is the mean of k independent intra-year differences between the means of the current ($\bar{X}$) and the repeated ($\bar{X}''$) preceding generation (e.g., $D_C - C_{B''}$ in Fig. 1).

The $\bar{X}$ and $\bar{X}''$ populations are from parents of two different generations. Each year provides an independent estimate of response to selection. Hence, the error variance appropriate for assessing reality of response is the one for variation in response between years. It contains contributions from intra-year variation among full-sibs (E), among dams (D), among sires (S), and from real fluctuations in response between years (GY), the standard error being

$$\sigma_{\overline{\Delta G_1}} = \sqrt{\frac{V_{\bar{X}} + V_{\bar{X}''}}{k}} = \sqrt{\frac{2}{k}\left(\frac{E}{nds} + \frac{D}{ds} + \frac{S}{s} + GY\right)} \qquad (1)$$

with $(k-1)$ degrees of freedom, where:

n = number of progeny in a full-sib family

d = number of dams in a sire-progeny

s = number of sires in a generation-year,

and assuming that n, d, and s are alike for $\bar{X}$ and $\bar{X}''$.

Supplementary estimates of $\overline{\Delta G_1}$ can be obtained from samples of $\bar{X}$ and $\bar{X}''$ produced from flock matings and housed with any ' unknown ' population in a series of hatch-location replications within each year.

Comparison of Gross and Environmental Change in the Same Population

Linear regression of generation means on time measures rate of *genetic plus environmental* change (i.e., b_{XY}, using means corresponding to B_A, C_B, and D_C in Fig. 1). All progeny of the current generation can be included in computing b_{XY}, whereas only progeny of repeated grandparents are usable in computing ΔG_1 from intra-year comparisons of generations.

Rate of environmental change ($\overline{\Delta E}$) is simply the mean of k differences between years for the paired samples of the same generation (e.g., $C_{B''} - C_B$ in Fig. 1).

Rate of genetic change is estimated by subtracting the environmental from the gross regression on time:

$$\overline{\Delta G_2} = b_{XY} - \overline{\Delta E}.$$

Its standard error is:

$$S_{\overline{\Delta G_2}} = \sqrt{V_{b_{XY}} + V_{\overline{\Delta E}} - 2\ \text{Cov}} = \sqrt{\frac{V_X}{\sum y^2} + \frac{2V_{X'}}{k} - 2r \,.\, \sigma_b \sigma_{\overline{\Delta E}}} \qquad (2)$$

where:

degrees of freedom are $(k-1)$,

$\sum y^2 = \dfrac{k^2 + (k-2)^2 + \ldots + (k+1-k)^2}{2}$ for the $(k+1)$ points of b_{XY},

$V_{X'} = \left(\dfrac{E}{nds} + \dfrac{D}{ds} + GY\right)$, because there is no sire variance in the measure of environmental change, $C_{B''} - C_B$.

$V_X = \left(\dfrac{E}{nds} + \dfrac{D}{ds} + \dfrac{S}{s} + GY\right)$, and may be estimated from the variance between years in the intra-year estimates of response ($\Delta G_1 = \overline{X} - \overline{X}''$) adjusting for differences in d and s;

$r < 0.5$ since between any two years error variation in $\overline{X}$ for the first year bears a correlation of -0.7 with error variation in both gross and the environmental estimates of change, and the sample included in the first year is not identical for computation of b_{XY} and ΔE.

Main effects of environmental changes between years influence b_{XY} and $\overline{\Delta E}$ alike (i.e., $r_E = 1$), and thus are not represented in sampling error of $\overline{\Delta G_2}$.

Comparison of Gross and Environmental Change of Independent Populations

When samples of the repeated mating control strain are maintained in the same series of environments with another ' unknown ' population for which estimation of genetic change is desired

$$\overline{\Delta G_3} = b_{X_U Y} - \overline{\Delta E}, \quad \text{where} \quad \overline{\Delta E} = \frac{\sum_k (\Delta E)_i}{k}$$

In this case, estimates of $b_{X_U Y}$ and $\overline{\Delta E}$ are independent. Hence, the standard error is:

$$S_{\overline{\Delta G_3}} = \sqrt{\frac{V_{X_U}}{\sum y^2} + \frac{2V_{X_C}}{k}} \tag{3}$$

recognizing that n, d, and s may be quite different for the samples of the control strain than for the ' unknown ' population sharing the same environments. Also, if the samples of current and repeated generations of the control housed with the ' unknown ' are produced from unselected ' flock ' matings, the variance of the estimated environmental change between years will include sampling variation in sire effects (S), so that

$$V_{X_C} = \left(\frac{E}{nds} + \frac{D}{ds} + \frac{S}{s} + GY\right)$$

Comparison of Gross Change in Two Independent Populations

For purposes of comparison, it is of interest to note that if genetic constancy of the control strain over k years could be assumed, the estimate of genetic rate of change would be:

$$\overline{\Delta G_4} = b_{(X_U - X_C)y}$$

and its standard error would be:

$$S_{\overline{\Delta G_4}} = \sqrt{\frac{V_{(X_U - X_C)}}{\sum y^2}} \tag{4}$$

with $(k-1)$ degrees of freedom.

If neither population is assumed to be genetically constant, $b_{(X_U - X_C)y}$ estimates the differential rate of genetic change $(\Delta G_U - \Delta G_C)$, but the standard error remains the same.

As before, expected composition of

$$V_{X_U - X_C} = 2\left(\frac{E}{nds} + \frac{D}{ds} + \frac{S}{s} + GY\right)$$

and the actual magnitude of $S_{\overline{\Delta G_4}}$ would be computed from the deviations of successive $(\overline{X}_U - \overline{X})$ values from linear regression on time.

Relative Precision of Alternative Estimates

Some idea of the standard errors to be expected for the several methods may be obtained by substituting appropriate constants in the formulas for $S_{\Delta G}$. Of course, no useful estimates of the magnitude of variance in response between years (GY) are available as yet. For purposes of comparison, if we assume that

$$n = 7 \qquad g^2 = 0.5 \text{ and } 0.2$$
$$d = 3 \qquad E = 1-0.5g^2$$
$$s = 16 \qquad D = 0.25g^2$$
$$k = 4 \text{ to } 25 \qquad S = 0.25g^2$$
$$GY = 0$$

the expected *standard errors* in *standard deviation units* each with $(k-1)$ degrees of freedom, are

g^2	k	G_1	G_2	G_3	G_4
0.50	4	0.080	0.044	0.087	0.050
	9	0.053	0.029	0.054	0.018
	16	0.040	0.022	0.040	0.008
	25	0.032	0.018	0.032	0.004
0.20	4	0.058	0.038	0.064	0.037
	9	0.039	0.025	0.040	0.013
	16	0.029	0.020	0.030	0.006
	25	0.023	0.016	0.024	0.003

$S_{\overline{\Delta G}}$ for other values of g^2 for all but ΔG_2 are proportional to

$$\sqrt{4+g^2[n(d+1)-2]}.$$

$S_{\overline{\Delta G}}$ for other numbers of sires (s) are proportional to $1/\sqrt{s}$. Contribution of GY to $S_{\overline{\Delta G}}$, although not included in the table above, will be approximately proportional to $\sqrt{[(GY)/k]}$ except for $\overline{\Delta G_4}$ where the proportion is $\sqrt{[(GY)/(\sum y^2)]}$.

These standard errors may be compared with yearly genetic responses expected from selection of any given intensity. For example, if truncation selection of the best 40% for some total performance score is practised, response expected on simplest assumptions is approximately

$$\Delta G = 0.5\sigma \text{ when heritability is } 0.5$$
$$\Delta G = 0.2\sigma \text{ when heritability is } 0.2.$$

In as short a period as 4 years of selection for $g^2 = 0.5$, $\overline{\Delta G_1} = 0.5\sigma \pm 0.08$ would have $P<0.01$. Of course a longer period would be required for highly significant results for lower heritability or for less intense selection (e.g., about six years for $g^2 = 0.2$).

The $\overline{\Delta G_2}$ estimates of response in the control strain itself appear to be more efficient than the $\overline{\Delta G_1}$ estimates for reasons explained earlier.

The $\overline{\Delta G_3}$ estimates for response in an independent population using the repeated mating control are nearly as efficient as those in the control strain itself.

The $\overline{\Delta G_4}$ estimates are much more efficient, but require the assumption of negligible genetic change in the control strain over an indefinite number of years, whereas the other three estimates of $\overline{\Delta G}$ do not.

EXAMPLES

Long-term trends, while most useful for genetic interpretations, are not yet available; however, a sample of results from three generations is presented as an illustration of the use of the technique. These are given in Figs. 2 and 3.

Three traits are summarized:

(1) Per cent rate of lay computed for individuals from the time the first egg was laid until October 31st of the pullet year.

(2) Per cent mortality in full-sib families from 11 weeks of age until October 31st of the pullet year.

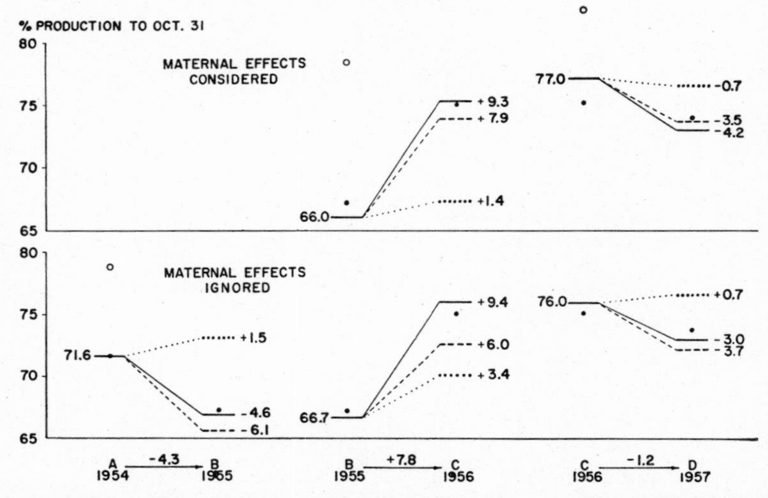

FIG. 2. Phenotypic (solid lines), genetic (dotted lines), and environmental (dashed lines) changes in rate of lay to October 31st of the pullet year for three pairs of generations or years when maternal changes ignored and for two pairs of generations or years when maternal changes considered. Solid dots show phenotypic changes in all progeny of selected matings; open circles indicate superiority of selected breeders over population average. In computing population means, equal weighting was given to full-sib averages.

(3) Egg weight (grams) obtained for individuals by averaging weights from a sample of approximately three eggs from each pullet at approximately 31 weeks of age.

In Fig. 2, phenotypic changes in per cent production (rate of lay) between generations and years are segregated into genetic and environmental components. Comparisons may be made ignoring the possible effects of changes in maternal effects by utilizing only the cockerel × pullet matings and the repeated matings (lower graph), or by taking changes in maternal effects into account (upper graph). Three pairs of comparisons are available for the former, and two for the latter. Phenotypic changes for all progeny of the young selected population are shown by the black dots in the chart, the actual changes being −4.3, +7.8, and −1.2% for the three pairs of years. Phenotypic changes for the 'restricted' population (i.e., when the number of families available for comparisons has been reduced by removing those in

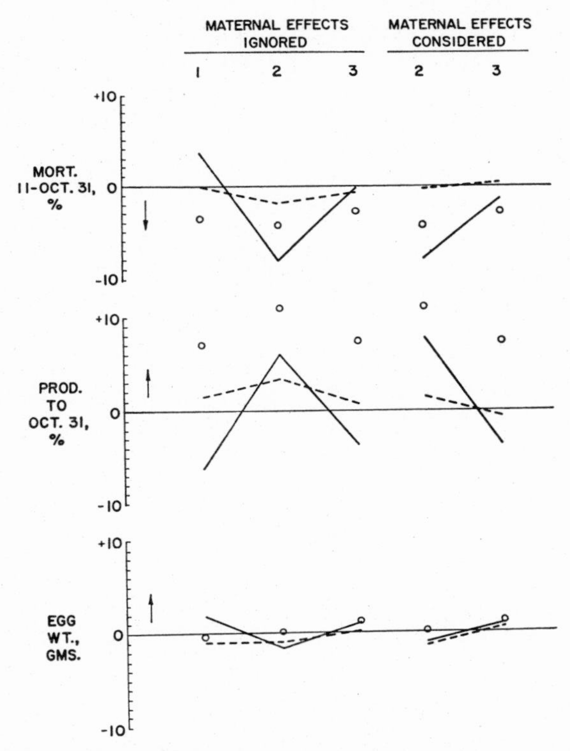

FIG. 3. Environmental and genetic changes for three traits. Comparisons 1, 2 and 3 correspond to the three pairs of years shown in Fig. 2. Environmental changes connected by solid line, genetic changes by dashed line. Intended direction of selection shown by arrows; actual superiority of selected breeders over population mean shown by open circles.

which the parents were not repeated) are shown by the solid lines and would be an unbiased estimate of changes in the entire young selected population. The environmental changes between years are shown by the dashed lines, and the genetic changes by the dotted lines. In four of the five comparisons, a genetic gain is indicated even though in two of the three years studied the environment worsened between years and the phenotypic level dropped.

In Fig. 3 are presented the environmental (solid lines) and genetic (dashed lines) changes observed thus far for the three traits sampled. Each change for a given pair of comparisons is expressed as a deviation from zero. Thus, if changes in maternal effects are ignored, and comparison 1 (the change from 1954 to 1955) is considered for per cent mortality, the environmental change showed an increase of 3.6%, while the genetic change was zero. In the next pair of years (comparison 2, 1955 to 1956), the environmental change was −8.1%, while the genetic change was −2.1%, and so on.

It may be seen that, for environmental changes, when the environment worsened (i.e., per cent mortality increased over the previous year), there was a corresponding decrease in rate of lay and an increase in egg size. When the environment improved (as in comparison 2, where a decrease in mortality occurred) rate of lay also improved, but egg size became smaller.

Some genetic improvement in rate of lay and in viability and a loss in egg size is suggested if age-change in maternal effects is ignored, but not when possible age-change in maternal effects is removed. These tentative results are in harmony with the expected negative relationship of rate of lay with weight of egg (Hutt, 1949; Schultz, 1953).

Results with two traits not shown in the graph are also worthy of mention. In one of these, adult body weight, the environmental changes for the three pairs of years were −0.09, +1.10, and −0.27 lb respectively, while the genetic changes for the three corresponding generations were −0.06, −0.19, and −0.11 lb. The large environmental change of +1.10 lb in comparison 2 is presumably due to a change in the age at which the birds were weighed, since this was done at 18 weeks of age in 1955 and at 31 weeks of age in 1956. Measurements of genetic changes were relatively unaffected, however, since estimates of genetic changes are all done on a within-year basis. This illustrates that with this procedure estimates of the genetic trend over a period of years are influenced only indirectly (through altered mean and variability) by changes between generations in the time or method of measurement, should these occur by accident or be deliberately introduced in the selection program for extraneous reasons.

The other trait, hatchability of fertile eggs, illustrates the manner in which large genetic and environmental differences found when changes in maternal effects are ignored, are largely removed by the comparisons taking aging effects into account. The differences between percentage figures for the comparisons available are:

	Maternal effects ignored		Maternal effects considered	
	Envir. change	Genetic change	Envir. change	Genetic change
Comparison 1	−5.0	+6.4	—	—
Comparison 2	−4.3	+6.1	−0.1	−0.1
Comparison 3	−2.6	+1.5	−2.4	+1.0

Even after accounting for changes due to aging of the dam, some discrepancies may remain in the measurement of hatchability, due to inconsistencies between years in classifying eggs as fertile or infertile by the 'candling' method.

DISCUSSION AND SUMMARY

More general application of techniques which will measure absolute genetic change in animal selection experiments is imperative, if investigators and breeders are to provide critical interpretations which will advance our knowledge in this area. While at first thought the cost of such measurements may seem prohibitive, a more careful appraisal suggests that selection experiments without such measurements, and thus not susceptible to critical analysis, may be even more costly.

The repeated mating technique as here described can be applied within any strain in which it may be desirable to maintain continuous selection and at the same time measure the effects of such selection. This may be an important consideration in commercial breeding programs, where it is desirable to keep the control strain competitive and thus minimize the costs of the measurements obtained.

In adapting this procedure for use solely as a control strain, it should be recognized that elimination of some objectives will permit a reduction in the size of the population and in the amount of facilities needed.

Where a measure of the environmental trend is the only objective, breeding facilities will be used most efficiently if the pullet and cockerel breeders are selected each year only from full-sib families whose parents are alive at the time the repeated matings are set up. Since the same males are to be used in the repeated matings, the loss of males between their first and second breeding season would, however, limit the proportion of C_B families usable for measuring the environmental trend.

A reduction in facilities needed could be realized by re-using each sire only if: (*a*) young breeders have been chosen from among his progeny, or (*b*) one or more pullet full sisters of a female to which he was mated the previous year are available for use with him in mating B''. Similarly, the dam should be used in the repeated matings only if young breeders have been chosen from among her first-year progeny. This would eliminate all B' matings without further usefulness, as well as any dams whose progeny would be useful only for comparing $C_{B'}$ with $C_{B''}$. While this would preclude a direct measure of the change in maternal effects with aging of the dam, it would not affect the two critical comparisons, $C_{B''} - C_B$ (environmental trend) and $D_C - C_{B''}$ (genetic trend).

Under such a scheme, the strain might or might not be maintained in numbers great enough to allow selection pressure to be applied in choosing the young breeders. In the latter case (i.e., no selection) it is only necessary to set up enough matings each year so that the offspring of those capable of being repeated (possibly one-half of the original matings) will provide a reasonably broad base for continuing the strain.

Use of a minimum-sized population would have the disadvantage that effective selection in the strain would cease, and the amount of inbreeding might increase. Where these limitations are more important than are the limitations in facilities available, maintenance of the strain on a larger base would permit some selection to be practiced even though the young breeders were chosen only from full-sib groups whose parents have survived between the first and second breeding seasons. This would place an important restriction upon the selection procedure used, but the environmental and genetic changes could be measured accurately.

If experiments demonstrate that the average change in maternal effects between the first and second breeding seasons is negligible and random, it will be unnecessary to include the matings of pullet full-sisters of dams used the previous year (B''). This would permit direct comparisons between progeny from new and repeated matings and would greatly simplify the problem. It must be emphasized, however, that if this alternative is adopted it is essential that a representative sample (usually all) of the pullet-cockerel matings, except those eliminated by natural mortality, be repeated. If any matings are eliminated selectively on the basis of progeny performance the comparisons provide biased (and therefore invalid) estimates of genetic and environmental trends.

It is in this respect that the technique described in this paper differs from the principle of continuing a few selected matings (e.g., chosen on the basis of first year progeny performance) for two or more generations, as has been carried out in the past by many chicken and turkey breeders, and possibly others.

Although the control-strain procedures outlined here apply specifically to the domestic fowl, the same principles can be adapted for measurement of genetic and environmental trends in selection experiments with other species. The procedures outlined for poultry could be adapted with little change to litter-bearing mammals. For example, in swine there is an important age-change in direct maternal influence and numbers are apt to be an important limiting factor. Hence, the critical comparisons (e.g., $C_{B''} - C_B$ and $D_C - C_{B''}$, Fig. 1) could be obtained with maximum efficiency by (1) selecting boar and gilt breeders only from gilt litters whose parents are available to produce a full-sib litter at 2 years of age and by (2) using for the litters at 2 years of age only those sows from whose gilt litters the boar or gilt breeders were chosen. These restrictions would insure that most of the matings of gilts (e.g., *B*, Fig. 1) in one year could be duplicated one year later with full-sister gilts mated to the same boar or to a full-brother.

In selection experiments with cattle and sheep, use of control strain matings of the type outlined would be difficult, if not entirely impractical. Perhaps those conducting selection experiments with these species must be content to compare alternative breeding methods rather than to measure absolute genetic and environmental trends. Also, more precise work with poultry, swine or laboratory animals may show that control strains maintained by ' relaxed ' selection remain sufficiently constant to make them useful in conjunction with selection experiments in large animals.

Comparison of contemporary progenies by *sires* of *two* different generations is an alternative technique for measuring response from selection that may be more feasible in experiments with large animals than replication of generations. Dams of each age and generation would need to be assigned equally to sires of the two groups. The selected young sires used in a given year (or their brothers, or their frozen semen) would simply be retained for use one, two, three or even four years later in comparison with the current selected young sires. This approach is being used in sheep breeding work in Australia*.

For maximum usefulness it is hoped that investigators will test the value of the procedure described here under a variety of conditions. Four important conditions which could vary from one experiment to another are: (*a*) the particular environmental circumstances encountered, such as diet, housing, and exposure to disease, (*b*) the level of improvement of the flock at the time the experiment is initiated, (*c*) the numbers and kinds of traits for which selection is practised, and (*d*) the method of selection used. To be of maximum usefulness in the interpretation of current poultry breeding problems, and to avoid a pitfall common to many selection experiments, it would be desirable to start with a highly improved strain and to practice simultaneous selection for all traits commonly considered important in poultry breeding operations (egg production, egg size, mortality, egg quality, etc.). This would avoid the criticism that genetic improvement in relatively unimproved stock may not be comparable with that to be expected in improved strains, or the suspicion that improvement in one trait was realized at the expense of another.

Note: Since the preparation of this manuscript, Dr. R. S. Gowe and his associate have published two papers in *Poultry Science* (March, 1959) discussing in detail their use of a random bred control stain in chickens, and the theoretical consequences of gene drift in such a population.

* Personal communication from Helen N. Turner, Research Officer, CSIRO, Sidney Australia.

REFERENCES

BELL, A. E., MOORE, C. H. & WARREN, D. C. (1955) The evaluation of new methods for the improvement of quantitative characteristics, *Cold Spring Harbor Symposia Quant. Biol.* **20,** 197–212.

CLAYTON, G. A., MORRIS, J. A. & ROBERTSON, A. (1957) An experimental check on quantitative genetical theory. I. Short-term responses to selection, *J. Genet.* **55,** 131–151.

CLAYTON, G. A. & ROBERTSON, A. (1957) An experimental check on quantitative genetical theory. II. The long-term effects of selection. *J. Genet.* **55,** 152–170.

DICKERSON, G. E. (1955) Genetic slippage in response to selection for multiple objectives, *Cold Spring Harbor Symposia Quant. Biol.* **20,** 213–224.

GOWE, R. S. (1956) The performance of a control strain of S. C. White Leghorn stock over four generations on test at several locations, *Poultry Sci.* **35,** 1146.

HUTT, F. B. (1949) *Genetics of the Fowl,* 1st ed., 590 pp., McGraw-Hill, New York. (Page 356).

KING, S. C. (1958) Personal communication.

KYLE, W. H. & CHAPMAN, A. B. (1953) Experimental check of the effectiveness of selection for a quantitative character, *Genetics* **38,** 421–443.

LERNER, I. M. & DEMPSTER, E. R. (1951) Attenuation of genetic progress under continued selection in poultry, *Heredity* **5,** 75–94.

MACARTHUR, J. W. (1949) Selection for small and large body size in the house mouse, *Genetics* **34,** 194–209.

ROBERTSON, F. W. (1955) Selection response and the properties of genetic variation, *Cold Spring Harbor Symposia Quant. Biol.* **20,** 166–177.

SCHULTZE, F. (1953) Concurrent inbreeding and selection in the domestic fowl, *Heredity* **7,** 1–21.

SKALLER, F. (1956) The Hagedoorn ' nucleus-system ' of breeding—a critical evaluation on an experiment with poultry, *Proc. Australian An. Prod.* **1,** 165–176.

THE ESTIMATION OF VARIANCE COMPONENTS IN CERTAIN TYPES OF EXPERIMENT ON QUANTITATIVE GENETICS

By J. A. Nelder

National Vegetable Research Station, Wellesbourne, Warwick, England

INTRODUCTION

The type of experiment considered in this paper is one fully developed by Mather (1949) and concerns the generations derived from the crossing of two breeding lines of self-compatible diploid plants. The generations may be obtained from selfing (the F generations) or by back-crossing to the parents (the B generations), or by other means. The analysis is primarily concerned with first and second-order statistics (means, variances and covariances) derived from the various generations. The model used implies that the expectations of the second-order statistics can be written as linear functions (with known coefficients) of certain unknown variance components which it is desired to estimate. The variance components may include the environmental variance, the additive genetic variance (Mather's D), the non-additive genetic variance due to dominance (Mather's H), and also, if required, components representing the interaction of alleles at different loci (Hayman and Mather's I, J and L).

The analysis used by Mather for the second-degree statistics is that of unweighted least squares. This will be fully efficient only when all the statistics are independent and have the same variance. In practice neither of these provisos holds and in this paper we consider how the analysis may be modified to allow for unequal variances of the statistics and the presence of correlation between them. The paper falls into two parts. In the first we evaluate, for the additive system, the actual variances and covariances of the second-order statistics for the F_3 and F_4 generations and compare them with the values obtained from a simplified model. In the second part we consider the application of these results to the analysis of some data of Mather and Vines given in Mather and Vines (1952).

THE DISPERSION MATRIX OF SOME SECOND-ORDER STATISTICS

We now proceed to evaluate the variances and covariances of all the F_3 second-order statistics and some of those for F_4 expressing them in terms of *compound cumulants* which we define below. These expressions are quite general and can be applied to any genetic system. Examples are then given of the values they take for the general additive system, assuming independent segregation of factors. Family size is assumed constant throughout; this assumption considerably simplifies the algebra and is close enough to the truth in well carried out experiments for the results to be generally applicable.

The general statistical situation can be summed up as follows: we have in some generation (say F_2) a number of genotypes each with a certain expected frequency. A plant of this generation is a sample of 1 from this population of genotypes, and on being, say, selfed gives rise to a population whose cumulants are functions of the parental genotype. Thus if we denote the measurement of the F_2 plant by Y_i, the cumulants of the F_3 family derived from it may be written κ_{ri}. These κ_{ri} have themselves a joint distribution over the F_2 genotypes. Cumulants of this distribution of within-family cumulants I call *compound cumulants of the 2nd degree*.† The notation will be clear from the following examples:

$$\kappa_{1\,.\,2} = \kappa_1\,(\kappa_{2i}), \quad \kappa_{2\,.\,1} = \kappa_2(\kappa_{1i}), \quad \kappa_{\binom{2}{1}\cdot\frac{1}{2}} = \kappa_{21}(\kappa_{1i}, \kappa_{2i})$$

and so on. The order of a compound cumulant corresponding to the orders of ordinary cumulants is obtained by multiplying suffices separated by a dot, and adding at any stage where a bracket occurs, thus writing O for 'order of' we have

$$\mathrm{O}\left[\kappa_{\binom{2}{1}\cdot\frac{1}{1}}\right] = \mathrm{O}\left[\kappa_{\binom{2\times 1}{1\times 1}}\right] = 2+1 = 3$$

For the cumulants of the covariances between, for example, F_2 parents and F_3 means, we need compound cumulants of the joint distribution of κ_{ri} and λ_{ri} where λ_{ri} is the rth cumulant of the distribution of genotype *i*. These we write with a horizontal bar separating the suffices referring to λ_{ri} from those referring to κ_{ri}, thus $\kappa_{111}\,(\kappa_{2i}, \kappa_{1i}, \lambda_{1i})$ is written as

$$\kappa_{\begin{pmatrix}1\\1\\1\end{pmatrix}\cdot\begin{smallmatrix}2\\1\\\overline{1}\end{smallmatrix}}$$

The main usefulness of the compound cumulants to us is that independently segregating factors contribute additively to them, in the same way that independent random variates contribute additively to the cumulants of their sum. This may be proved quite simply by considering the moment generating function of the κ_{ri} and λ_{ri}, noting each can be expressed as the sum of cumulants due to the individual factors. Thus to obtain the results for the general additive system we evaluate the κ's for one factor and sum.

† Robson in a paper on the estimation of these quantities has named them 'cumulant components', on the analogy of 'variance components'. 'Compound cumulants' seems etymologically more satisfactory for quantities which are cumulants of a distribution of cumulants.

Table 1 gives the results for the F_3 generation where n_2 F_2 plants each give families of size n_3 in the F_3. Ordinary k-statistic formulae may be used to go part of the way, as Robson (1956) has pointed out. Thus $V_{1F3} = k_2(x_i.)$ where x_{ij} denotes the jth member of the ith family, so that

$$\text{Var}(V_{1F3}) = \frac{\kappa_4(x_i.)}{n_2} + \frac{2\kappa_2^2(x_i.)}{n_2 - 1}.$$

The derivation of the formula

$$\kappa_4(x_i.) = \frac{1}{n_3^3}\kappa_{1\,.\,4} + \frac{4}{n_3^2}\kappa_{\binom{1}{1}\,.\,\frac{3}{1}} + \frac{3}{n_3^2}\kappa_{2\,.\,2} + \frac{6}{n_3}\kappa_{\binom{1}{2}\,.\,\frac{2}{1}} + \kappa_{4\,.\,1}$$

may be made quite easily algebraically, though it is tempting to speculate whether some extension of Fisher's combinatorial rules for k-statistics might be found for this case, particularly when we notice that V_{1F3} etc. are compound k-statistics, so that with an obvious notation we may write $V_{1F3} = k_{2\,.\,1}$, $V_{2F3} = k_{1\,.\,2}$, Cov $(V_{1F3}, V_{2F3}) = \kappa(1\,.\,2,\, 2\,.\,1)$, etc.

In the F_4 generation compound cumulants of the third degree, and of the second and fourth orders are required. One of the more complicated-looking fourth-order cumulants is

$$\kappa_{\binom{1}{1}\,.\,\binom{1}{1}\,.\,\frac{2}{1}}^{\qquad 1\;\;.\,1} = \text{Cov}\left[{}_i\text{Cov}(\kappa_{2j}, \kappa_{1j}),\, {}_i\kappa_1(\kappa_{1j})\right]$$

where κ_{rj} is the rth cumulant in F_4 arising from an F_3 plant of genotype j, and the prefix i denotes that the mean or covariance following is taken over the population generated by an F_2 plant of genotype i. Finally the covariance is taken over all F_2 genotypes. Tables 2a and 2b give the complete dispersion matrix of the variance statistics V_{1F4}, V_{2F4}, and V_{3F4} together with the important terms involving the covariances.

Robson (1956 and 1957), has considered how to evaluate unbiased estimates of some of these 4th-order quantities, using generalized 4th-order k-statistics. For the purposes of estimation of D and H etc. it may not be necessary, for practical purposes, to have unbiased estimates of the weights in the least-square equations, provided that we can use estimates not differing too greatly from the real values. The most obvious way of deriving simplified weights is to approximate the true weights by using a model in which, for example in F_3, we write

$$x_{ij} = \mu + \eta_i + \varepsilon_{ij},$$

where η_i has mean zero and cumulants λ_r, ε_{ij} has mean zero and cumulants κ_s, and η_i and ε_{ij} are independent. This model differs from the correct genetic model in that the cumulants of ε_{ij} are independent of i, the F_2 genotype, instead of being a function of it. If η_i and ε_{ij} are further taken as normally distributed (i.e. $\lambda_r = 0\ r>2$, $\kappa_s = 0\ s>2$) then the dispersion matrix of the F_3 second-order statistics will be

$$\begin{bmatrix} \dfrac{2V_1^2}{n_2-1} & 0 & \dfrac{2V_1W}{n_2-1} \\ 0 & \dfrac{2V_2^2}{n_2(n_3-1)} & 0 \\ \dfrac{2V_1W}{n_2-1} & 0 & \dfrac{1}{n_2-1}(W^2+V_1V_1') \end{bmatrix} \tag{1}$$

where $V_1 = E(V_{1F3})$, $V_1' = E(V_{1F2})$, $V_2 = E(V_{2F3})$, $W = E(W_{1F3})$.

Comparisons of the values given by (1) with the true values obtained from the formulae of Table 1 have been made for two models. Each model assumes 100 families of 5 members each in the F_3, a number m of equal genetic factors having $\sum d^2 = 1$ and an environmental variance σ^2 superimposed. The two models are (i) no dominance and (ii) complete dominance (note that the direction of dominance is irrelevant, i.e. only h^2 enters into the calculations); for each model all combinations of $m = 1$, 4, 16, 64 and $\sigma^2 = 0.1$ and 0.4 were used. The complete tables of results will not be reproduced here but Table 3 gives a portion of them. In all cases model (i) gives smaller differences between the true and approximate formulae than model (ii), and of course the larger σ^2 is the better (1) is as an approximation. Table 3 shows the results for model (ii), with $\sigma^2 = 0.1$ (i.e. environmental variance about 12% of the F_2 variance) and $m = 1$, 4, and 16.

It will be seen that when $m = 16$, the true values are trivially different from those given by the simplified model, and that the latter would be quite adequate for use in estimation procedures. When $m = 4$, differences of 15% may occur in the dispersion matrix for case (i) with $\sigma^2 = 0.1$, and rather larger differences for case (ii), the principal culprit being var (V_{2F3}) where the ignoring of the term in $\kappa_{2.2}$ is responsible for the low value given by the approximate normal term. On the other hand var (V_{1F3}) and var (W_{1F23}) are over-estimated by the normal term so that the biases in the weights are not all in one direction. With $m = 1$, the errors become substantial, but this situation is barely relevant to quantitative genetics since the genotypes are almost identifiable. Various complications may now be considered; if factors are unequal in effects the mean number of factors as far as biases in these variances and covariances are concerned will be less than the nominal m by an amount depending on the amount of inequality. The effects of linkage are exceedingly complex in detail since 4th order cumulants for linked factors depend on the recombination fractions of all the linked loci in sets of 4. The simple case of linkage of two equal factors with $p = \frac{1}{4}$ gives values intermediate between two independent factors and a single factor of twice the

TABLE 1. DISPERSION MATRIX OF F_3 SECOND-DEGREE STATISTICS

4th-order term	Coefficient in Var V_{1F3}	Cov $[V_{1F3}V_{2F3}]$	Cov $(V_{1F3}W_{1F23})$	Var V_{2F3}	Cov $[V_{2F3}W_{1F23}]$	Var W_{1F23}	Value for one factor
$\kappa_{1.4}$	$n_2^{-1}n_3^{-3}$	$n_2^{-1}n_3^{-2}$	0	$n_2^{-1}n_3^{-1}$	0	0	$-\frac{1}{8}d^4-\frac{1}{16}h^4$
$\kappa_{\binom{1}{1}\cdot\frac{3}{1}}$	$4n_2^{-1}n_3^{-2}$	$2n_2^{-1}n_3^{-1}$	0	0	0	0	$-\frac{3}{32}d^2h^2$
$\kappa_{2.2}$	$3n_2^{-1}n_3^{-2}$	$n_2^{-1}n_3^{-1}$	0	$(n_3+1)n_2^{-1}(n_3-1)^{-1}$	0	0	$\frac{1}{4}(\frac{1}{2}d^2+\frac{1}{4}h^2)^2$
$\kappa_{\binom{1}{2}\cdot\frac{2}{1}}$	$6n_2^{-1}n_3^{-1}$	n_2^{-1}	0	0	0	0	$-\frac{1}{4}d^2(\frac{1}{2}d^2+\frac{1}{4}h^2)$
$\kappa_{4.1}$	n_2^{-1}	0	0	0	0	0	$-\frac{1}{4}d^4-\frac{1}{128}h^4$
$\kappa_{\binom{1}{2}\cdot\frac{2}{1}}$	0	0	0	0	0	$n_2^{-1}n_3^{-1}$	$-\frac{1}{4}d^2(\frac{1}{2}d^2+\frac{1}{4}h^2)$
$\kappa_{\binom{2}{2}\cdot\frac{1}{1}}$	0	0	0	0	0	n_2^{-1}	$-\frac{1}{4}d^4-\frac{1}{32}h^4$
$\kappa_{\binom{1}{1}\cdot\frac{3}{1}}$	0	0	$n_2^{-1}n_3^{-2}$	0	$n_2^{-1}n_3^{-1}$	0	$-\frac{3}{16}d^2h^2$
$\kappa_{\left(\begin{smallmatrix}1\\1\\1\end{smallmatrix}\right)\frac{2}{1}\frac{1}{1}}$	0	0	$3n_2^{-1}n_3^{-1}$	0	n_2^{-1}	0	$-\frac{1}{4}d^2(\frac{1}{2}d^2+\frac{1}{4}h^2)$
$\kappa_{\binom{3}{1}\cdot\frac{1}{1}}$	0	0	n_2^{-1}	0	0	0	$-\frac{1}{4}d^4-\frac{1}{64}h^4$

Second-order terms

Var V_{1F3} $\quad \dfrac{2}{n_2-1}\left[\kappa_{2.1}+\dfrac{\kappa_{1.2}}{n_3}\right]^2$

Cov $[V_{1F3}\,V_{2F3}]$ nil

Cov $[V_{1F3}\,W_{1F23}]$ $\quad \dfrac{2}{n_2-1}\kappa_{\binom{1}{1}\cdot\frac{1}{1}}\left[\dfrac{\kappa_{1.2}}{n_3}+\kappa_{2.1}\right]$

Var V_{2F3} $\quad \dfrac{2}{n_2(n_3-1)}\kappa_{1.2}^2$

Cov $[V_{2F3}\,W_{1F23}]$ nil

Var W_{1F23} $\quad \dfrac{1}{n_2-1}\left[\kappa^2_{\binom{1}{1}\cdot\frac{1}{1}}+\left(\kappa_{2.1}+\dfrac{\kappa_{1.2}}{n_3}\right)(\lambda_2)\right]$

Notation: n_2 = no. of F_3 families

n_3 = no. in each F_3 family

λ_2 = Total F_2 variance of previous generation.

The environmental component is assumed normally distributed.

effect, and one may expect in general that linkage will reduce the effective number of factors.

A similar investigation on the normal approximation has been made for the F_4 statistics using the formulae of Table 2. The results, which will not be given here, are essentially similar to those for the F_3 statistics.

It seems reasonable to assume from these results that provided the effective number of factors is not very small (and such cases may be detectable by examination of frequency curves of the F_2 etc.), approximations based on the normal model may be used to provide weights for the second-order statistics for estimation purposes. One further point needs to be made, however. If the environmental component is markedly non-normal then a term in its fourth cumulant enters into the variances of the variances. Its effect will be most marked in terms like Var (V_{2F3}) and Var (V_{3F4}), but slight in terms like Var V_{1F3} where the taking of a mean involves the division of $\gamma_2 = \kappa_4/\kappa_2^2$ by n, which in general will reduce it to insignificance. Where data from parents and F_1 s are substantial enough, k_4 can be estimated from them, then in terms like Var V_{2F3}, κ_2^2 can be replaced by $\kappa_2^2(1+\frac{1}{2}\gamma_2)$ to allow for the kurtosis, where γ_2 is estimated as the mean k_4 for parents and F_1 divided by the square of the second-order statistic in question.

Possible Methods of Estimation of Variance Components

Consider first the situation where we have a number of sample variances v_i based on n_i degrees of freedom and that

$$E(v_i) = V_i = \sum_j \xi_{ij}\theta_j$$

where ξ_{ij} are known and θ_j require to be estimated. Assuming the Γ-type of distribution for v_i gives maximum likelihood equations of the form

$$\sum \frac{n_i \xi_{ij}}{v_i^2}(v_i - V_i) = 0 \qquad (2)$$

with information matrix $$I_{ij} = \sum_\kappa \frac{n_\kappa \xi_{\kappa i}\xi_{\kappa j}}{2V_\kappa^2}$$

In the type of genetic experiment we are considering the assumption of the Γ-type distribution is not exactly true and it is a difficulty that the true likelihood function depends on the genetic structure which we do not know. In addition we also have to deal with covariances, and the joint likelihood of a covariance and *one* of its corresponding variances is not, even in the normal case, expressible in terms of simple functions. In this situation it seems best to resort to a least-squares approach and to consider minimizing $\sum w_{ij}(v_i - V_i)(v_j - V_j)$ where w_{ij} is the inverse of the variance matrix of the v_i. When all the v_i are sample variances (i.e. sample covariances are omitted)

TABLE 2A. DISPERSION MATRIX OF F_4 VARIANCES

4th-order cumulant	Coefficient in Var V_{1F4}	Cov$(V_{1F4}V_{2F4})$	Cov$(V_{1F4}V_{3F4})$	Var V_{2F4}	Cov$(V_{2F4}V_{3F4})$	Var V_{3F4}	Value for one factor
	$n_2^{-1}\times$	$n_2^{-1}\times$	$n_2^{-1}\times$	$n_2^{-1}\times$	$n_2^{-1}\times$	$n_2^{-1}n_3^{-1}$	
$\kappa_{1.1.4}$	$n_3^{-3}n_4^{-3}$	$n_3^{-2}n_4^{-3}$	$n_3^{-2}n_4^{-2}$	$n_3^{-1}n_4^{-3}$	$n_3^{-1}n_4^{-2}$	n_4^{-1}	$-\frac{1}{16}d^4-\frac{1}{32}h^4$
$\kappa_{1\cdot\binom{1}{1}\cdot\substack{3\\1}}$	$4n_3^{-3}n_4^{-2}$	$4n_3^{-2}n_4^{-2}$	$2n_3^{-2}n_4^{-1}$	$4n_3^{-1}n_4^{-2}$	$2n_3^{-1}n_4^{-1}$	0	$-\frac{3}{64}d^2h^2$
$\kappa_{\binom{1}{1}\cdot\substack{1\\1}\cdot\substack{3\\1}}$	$4n_3^{-2}n_4^{-2}$	$2n_3^{-1}n_4^{-2}$	$2n_3^{-1}n_4^{-1}$	0	0	0	$-\frac{3}{128}d^2h^2$
$\kappa_{1.2.2}$	$3n_3^{-3}n_4^{-2}$	$3n_3^{-2}n_4^{-2}$	$n_3^{-2}n_4^{-1}$	$3n_3^{-2}n_4^{-1}$	$n_3^{-1}n_4^{-2}$	$\frac{n_4+1}{n_4-1}$	$\frac{1}{8}[\frac{1}{2}d^2+\frac{1}{4}h^2]^2$
$\kappa_{2.1.2}$	$3n_3^{-2}n_4^{-2}$	$n_3^{-1}n_4^{-2}$	$n_3^{-1}n_4^{-1}$	$n_4^{-2}\frac{n_3+1}{n_3-1}$	n_4^{-1}	$n_3+\frac{2}{n_4-1}$	$\frac{1}{16}[\frac{1}{2}d^2+\frac{1}{4}h^2]^2$
$\kappa_{1\cdot\binom{1}{2}\cdot\substack{2\\1}}$	$6n_3^{-3}n_4^{-1}$	$6n_3^{-2}n_4^{-1}$	n_3^{-2}	$6n_3^{-1}n_4^{-1}$	n_3^{-2}	0	$-\frac{1}{8}d^2(\frac{1}{2}d^2+\frac{1}{4}h^2)$
$\kappa_{\binom{1}{1}\cdot\substack{1\\2}\cdot\substack{2\\1}}$	$6n_3^{-2}n_4^{-1}$	$2n_3^{-1}n_4^{-1}$	n_3^{-1}	$\frac{2(n_3+1)}{n_3-1}n_4^{-1}$	1	0	$\frac{1}{8}(\frac{1}{2}d^2+\frac{1}{4}h^2)(\frac{1}{2}d^2+\frac{1}{16}h^2)$
$\kappa_{\binom{1}{2}\cdot\substack{1\\1}\cdot\substack{2\\1}}$	$6n_3^{-1}n_4^{-1}$	n_4^{-1}	1	0	0	0	$-\frac{1}{8}d^2(\frac{1}{2}d^2+\frac{1}{4}h^2)$
$\kappa_{1.4.1}$	n_3^{-3}	n_3^{-2}	0	n_3^{-1}	0	0	$-\frac{1}{8}d^4-\frac{1}{256}h^4$
$\kappa_{\binom{1}{1}\cdot\substack{\binom{1}{1}\\1}\cdot\substack{2\\1\\1}}$	$12n_3^{-2}n_4^{-1}$	$6n_3^{-1}n_4^{-1}$	$2n_3^{-1}$	0	0	0	$\frac{1}{128}h^2(\frac{1}{2}d^2+\frac{1}{4}h^2)$
$\kappa_{\binom{1}{1}\cdot\substack{3\\1}\cdot\substack{1\\1}}$	$4n_3^{-2}$	$2n_3^{-1}$	0	0	0	0	$-\frac{3}{128}d^2h^2$
$\kappa_{2.2.1}$	$3n_3^{-2}$	n_3^{-1}	0	$\frac{n_3+1}{n_3-1}$	0	0	$\frac{1}{4}(\frac{1}{2}d^2+\frac{1}{16}h^2)^2$
$\kappa_{\binom{1}{2}\cdot\substack{2\\1}\cdot\substack{1\\1}}$	$6n_3^{-1}$	1	0	0	0	0	$-\frac{1}{4}d^2(\frac{1}{2}d^2+\frac{1}{16}h^2)$
$\kappa_{4.1.1}$	1	0	0	0	0	0	$-\frac{1}{4}d^4-\frac{1}{2048}h^4$

Second-order terms

V_{1F4} $\frac{2}{n_2-1}\left[\kappa_{2.1.1}+\frac{1}{n_3}\kappa_{1.2.1}+\frac{1}{n_3n_4}\kappa_{1.1.2}\right]^2$ V_{2F4} $\frac{2}{n_2(n_3-1)}\left[\kappa_{1.2.1}+\frac{\kappa_{1.1.2}}{n_3}\right]^2$ V_{3F4} $\frac{2}{n_2n_3(n_4-1)}\kappa_{1.1.2}^2$

Notation: n_i $(i=2, 3, 4)$ = no. of individuals in F_i with common parent in F_{i-1}.
Second-order cumulants contain environmental variance component, assumed normal.

TABLE 2B. OTHER IMPORTANT TERMS IN THE DISPERSION MATRIX OF F_4 SECOND-ORDER STATISTICS

$$\text{Var } W_{1F34} = \frac{1}{n_2-1}\{[E(W_{1F34})]^2+E(V_{1F4})E(V'_{1F3})\}$$

$$+ \frac{1}{n_2}\left\{\kappa_{\binom{2}{2}\cdot\frac{1.1}{1}}+\frac{1}{n_3}\kappa_{\binom{1}{2}\cdot\frac{2.1}{1}}+\frac{1}{n_3 n_4}\kappa_{\binom{1}{2}\cdot\frac{1.2}{1}}\right\}$$

$$\text{Var } W_{2F34} = \frac{1}{n_2(n_3-1)}\{[E(W_{2F34})]^2+E(V_{2F4})E(V'_{2F3})\}+\frac{1}{n_2 n_3 n_4}\kappa_{1\cdot\binom{1}{2}\cdot\frac{2}{1}}$$

$$+\frac{1}{n_2 n_3}\kappa_{1\cdot\binom{2}{2}\cdot\frac{1}{1}}+\frac{1}{n_2(n_3-1)n_4}\kappa_{\binom{1}{1}\cdot\frac{1.2}{2.1}}$$

$$+\frac{1}{n_2(n_3-1)}\kappa_{\binom{1}{1}\cdot\frac{2.1}{2.1}}+\left[1+\frac{1}{n_2(n_3-1)}\right]\kappa_{2\cdot\binom{1}{1}\cdot\frac{1}{1}}$$

$$\text{Cov }(W_{1F34}\ V_{1F4}) = \frac{2}{n_2-1}\{E(W_{1F34})E(V_{1F4})\}+\frac{1}{n_2 n_3^2 n_4^2}\kappa_{\binom{1}{1}\cdot\frac{1.3}{1}}$$

$$+\frac{3}{n_2 n_3^2 n_4}\kappa_{\binom{1}{1}\cdot\frac{\binom{1}{1}\cdot\frac{2}{1}}{1}}+\frac{1}{n_2 n_3^2}\kappa_{\binom{1}{1}\cdot\frac{3.1}{1}}$$

$$+\frac{3}{n_2 n_3 n_4}\kappa_{\begin{pmatrix}1\\1\\1\end{pmatrix}\frac{\substack{1.2\\1.1}}{1}}+\frac{3}{n_2 n_3}\kappa_{\begin{pmatrix}1\\1\\1\end{pmatrix}\frac{\substack{2.1\\1.1}}{1}}+\frac{1}{n_2}\kappa_{\binom{3}{1}\cdot\frac{1.1}{1}}$$

$$\text{Cov }(W_{2F34}, V_{2F4}) = \frac{1}{n_2}\left\{\frac{\kappa_{1\cdot\binom{1}{1}\cdot\frac{3}{1}}}{n_3 n_4^2}+\frac{3}{n_3 n_4}\kappa_{1\cdot\begin{pmatrix}1\\1\\1\end{pmatrix}\frac{\substack{2\\1}}{1}}+\frac{1}{n_3}\kappa_{1\cdot\binom{3}{1}\cdot\frac{1}{1}}\right\}$$

$$+\frac{1}{n_2}\left(1+\frac{2}{n_3-1}\right)\left[\frac{1}{n_4}\kappa_{\binom{1}{1}\cdot\binom{1}{1}^{1.2}\cdot\frac{1}{1}}+\kappa_{\binom{1}{1}\cdot\binom{1}{1}^{2.1}\cdot\frac{1}{1}}\right]$$

$$+\frac{2}{n_2(n_3-1)}\{E(W_{2F34})E(V_{2F4})\}$$

Notation: primes (as in V'_{1F3}) refer to the fact that V_{1F3} is measured in the previous generation. Genotype × 'year' interaction is ignored.

this leads to the same equations as (2) provided that the v_i are all independent and come from normal populations. That this is approximately true in many cases is shown by the investigations above. At this stage we are faced with the familiar difficulty that the w_{ij} depend on the unknown V_i; thus we can either resort to iterative methods of solution or use empirical weights in place of fitted weights. The use of empirical weights may be expected to lead to

TABLE 3. COMPARISON OF THE EXACT VARIANCE MATRIX OF F_3 STATISTICS WITH THE APPROXIMATION (I) FOR A NUMBER OF EQUAL FACTORS WITH COMPLETE DOMINANCE, $\Sigma d^2 = 1$, $\sigma^2 = 0.1$, AND 100 FAMILIES OF 5 MEMBERS EACH

	V_{1F3}	V_{2F3}	W_{1F23}
		1 factor	
approximate	*0.873*	*0*	*0.830*
exact	0.391	−0.261	0.445
		0.113	*0*
		0.286	−0.225
			0.959
			0.640
		4 factors	
approximate	*0.873*	*0*	*0.830*
exact	0.753	−0.065	0.734
		0.113	*0*
		0.156	−0.056
			0.959
			0.879
		16 factors	
approximate	*0.873*	*0*	*0.830*
exact	0.843	−0.016	0.806
		0.113	*0*
		0.124	−0.014
			0.959
			0.939

some loss of efficiency in estimation, though Berkson's work (1955) on estimating the parameters of the logistic function appears to indicate that this need not always be so. In the present situation, where 6 or more non-orthogonal parameters may need to be fitted, the iterative method would be exceedingly tedious and it is somewhat doubtful whether the results would be worth while except where the data gave an initially good fit and further refinement was thought necessary. If the model used is clearly inappropriate, as shown by the fitting using empirical weights, further cycles are unlikely to be worth doing. Further information on the efficiency of using empirical weights in this situation would be valuable.

Application to Actual Data

Professor Mather has kindly allowed me access to the data on *Nicotiana rustica* which were presented in Mather and Vines (1952), and I have re-analysed some of these making use of the results discussed above.

For full details the reader is referred to Mather and Vines' paper, but briefly the experiment consisted of two blocks each containing plots of both parents, F_1's, F_2's, F_3's, F_4's, and first backcrosses. Each plot held 5 plants, and 5 was the family size in the F_3 and F_4. The layout was in randomized blocks and height and flowering time were recorded and used for analysis.

We have two checks on the applicability of the simplified model. One depends on the fact that Var (V_{3F4}), Var (V_{2F3}), and Var (V_{2F4}) can be estimated from the data and these estimates compared with those obtained from the simplified model. The other arises from the differences of the duplicates in the two blocks which may be compared with their theoretical variance by an approximate χ^2 test. Thus if x_1 and x_2 are values in the two blocks of a variance estimate based on ν d.f. we put $\chi_1^2 = \nu(x_1 - x_2)^2/(x_1 + x_2)^2$. The assumption made here is that the variance in the two blocks differs by no more than might be expected on the normal model. This assumption needs empirical verification, and indeed may well not always be true. Thus if one block is on more homogeneous land than another, or if one block is planted by a more careful person than another, real differences in error variance may occur, and these might lead to differences in genetic variance as well. Suitable models for this situation (which is best avoided experimentally if at all possible) cannot be conjured *a priori*, but must depend to some extent on the information given by the data themselves.

We discuss in detail the analysis for flowering time in the 1947 experiment and then present the results for 1948 in shortened form.

The Analysis for Flowering Time in 1947

The steps in the analysis may be set out as follows:

(i) Preliminary checks on adequacy of weights and kurtosis in parents and F_1's.
(ii) Construction of the approximate variance matrix of the statistics.
(iii) Inversion of the variance matrix to give the weighting matrix.
(iv) Solution of the weighted least square equations in the form $\hat{\boldsymbol{\theta}} = (\mathbf{a}'\mathbf{w}\,\mathbf{a})^{-1}\,\mathbf{a}'\mathbf{w}\,\mathbf{x}$, where $\boldsymbol{\theta}$ is the vector of unknowns, $\mathbf{x}$ the vector of 2nd order statistics and $\mathbf{a}$ is the matrix of coefficients given by $E(\mathbf{x}) = \mathbf{a}\boldsymbol{\theta}$, linkage assumed absent. This solution involves the successive calculation of $\mathbf{a}'\mathbf{w}$, $\mathbf{a}'\mathbf{w}\,\mathbf{a}$ and $(\mathbf{a}'\mathbf{w}\,\mathbf{a})^{-1}$.
(v) Repetition of (iv) using the new $\mathbf{a}$ given by assuming linkage present.
(vi) Construction of the analysis of variation and tests of linkage and residual heterogeneity.
(vii) Calculation of increase in efficiency over the unweighted analysis.

STEP (i)

The mean value within plots of g_2, the sample estimate of

$$\gamma_2 = \frac{\kappa_4}{\kappa_2^2},$$

was 0.88 for the parent and F_1 generation, with a standard error of ± 0.312. It is, therefore, significantly positive and hence we must adjust the weights for V_{2F3}, V_{3F4}, V_{1F2}, and V_{1B} by a factor $[1+(\lambda/2)g_2]$ where λ is the square of the ratio of E_1 to the variance in question. The data themselves give a sample estimate of the variances of V_{2F3}, V_{2F4} and V_{3F4}. These are compared in Table 4 below with the values given by the approximate model considered above, (all values are on a per-family basis).

TABLE 4

	Var (V_{2F3}) Sample	Var (V_{2F3}) Predicted	Var (V_{2F4}) Sample	Var (V_{2F4}) Predicted	Var (V_{3F4}) Sample	Var (V_{3F4}) Predicted
Block I	84.7	65.8	65.1	53.2	78.0	52.9
II	123.1	78.0	48.0	44.5	166.9	96.6
Mean	103.9	71.7	56.6	48.8	122.4	73.1

While all the predicted values are less than the sample values, weights based on the former will clearly be a good approximation to the relative weights which are all that are required for efficient estimation. When all the sample variances are underestimated by the predicted values, it might be necessary to introduce a ' heterogeneity factor ', similar to that used in probit analysis (6), for adjusting the variances of the final estimates, although in this case this is not found to be necessary.

STEP (ii)

The variance matrix, using the approximate model, is diagonal except for 3 non-zero covariances, namely those of V_{1F3}, W_{1F23}; V_{1F4}, W_{1F34}; and V_{2F4} and W_{2F34}. For E_1, V_{1F2}, B_1, V_{2F3}, V_{3F4} the ' normal ' variance $2m^2/v$ must be multiplied by $(1+\frac{1}{2}\lambda g_2)$. In the formula m is the expected value of the variance and v the degrees of freedom on which the sample value is based. In this particular experiment the same families of F_3 and F_4 were used in each block, so that the sampling variance due to choice of parents and grand-parents is not divided by 2 in taking the mean of the two blocks. Since this is the major part of the sampling variance, the degrees of freedom are taken as those of one block instead of two, though this procedure admittedly makes the estimated variance rather too high. For the variance of the covariances we use the normal formula Var $k_{11}=v^{-1}(\kappa_{11}^2+\kappa_{02}\kappa_{20})$ with the usual notation and for the non-zero covariances

$$\text{Cov}\,(k_{11}, k_{02}) = \frac{2}{v}\kappa_{11}\kappa_{02}.$$

Another slight complication arises from losses in F_3 and F_4 families; these were small in number and no adjustments have been made to the d.f. for V_{1F3} and V_{1F4}. For V_{2F4} the appropriate harmonic mean of family size has been used and for V_{3F4} the exact total number of d.f. Following these rules we get the following approximate variance matrix for the statistics.

APPROXIMATE VARIANCE MATRIX OF 2ND-ORDER STATISTICS (V)

E_1	1.09020											
E_2		0.2281										
V_{1F2}			5.6145									
B_1				24.4983								
V_{1F3}					2.6714		2.2631					
V_{2F3}						1.9050						
W_{1F23}					2.2631		4.5924					
V_{1F4}								5.3940			3.4214	
V_{2F4}									0.4874			0.2462
V_{3F4}										0.1556		
W_{1F34}								3.4214			7.1024	
W_{2F34}									0.2462			0.8093

The blank spaces are to be read as zero; the wide range of the variances, the extremes differing by a factor of more than 100, should be noted.

STEP (iii)

The inverse of the variance matrix **V** may easily be obtained since **V** itself is nearly diagonal and contains non-diagonal sub-matrices of order 2 only. The inverse of the variance matrix is given below.

INVERSE OF VARIANCE MATRIX (**w**)

0.5258											
	4.3840										
		0.1781									
			0.0408								
				0.6426		-0.3167					
					0.5249						
				-0.3167		0.3738					
							0.2670			-0.1286	
								2.4242			-0.7375
									6.4278		
							-0.1286			0.2027	
								-0.7375			1.4600

STEP (iv)

For the additive model with linkage assumed absent we have 4 unknowns to estimate, D, H, E_1 and E_2. The matrix of coefficients **a** is given below. It should be noted that when the family size is small we cannot safely ignore in the expectation of a quantity such as V_{2F4} the contribution from the variance within groups, so that we must put

$$E(V_{2F4}) = \left(\frac{1}{4}D+\frac{1}{32}H\right)+\frac{1}{n}\left(\frac{1}{8}D+\frac{1}{16}H\right)+E_2.$$

Thus when $n=5$ as is here the case, the contribution to the coefficient of H from the second term is 1/80 and from the first 1/32 so that the two contributions are of comparable size. The matrix **a** is given below and from **a** and **w**, we calculate successively by standard methods, **a′w**, **a′w a** and $(\mathbf{a'w\,a})^{-1}$. We omit the intermediate steps and give only $(\mathbf{a'w\,a})^{-1}$.

Matrix of coefficients (**a**)
Linkage assumed absent

	D	H	E_1	E_2
E_1	0	0	1.0000	0
E_2	0	0	0	1.0000
V_{1F2}	0.5000	0.2500	1.0000	0
$V_{B1}+V_{B2}$	0.5000	0.5000	2.0000	0
V_{1F3}	0.5500	0.0875	0	1.0000
V_{2F3}	0.2500	0.1250	1.0000	0
W_{1F23}	0.5000	0.1250	0	0
V_{1F4}	0.5550	0.0244	0	0.2000
V_{2F4}	0.2750	0.0438	0	1.0000
V_{3F4}	0.1250	0.0625	1.0000	0
W_{1F34}	0.5500	0.0438	0	0
W_{2F34}	0.2500	0.0625	0	0

Matrix
$(\mathbf{a'w\,a})^{-1}$

−7.423389	−20.692205	0.451865	−0.476047
	97.345864	−4.063111	0.918110
		0.353532	−0.000082
			0.168763

Finally using the values given by Mather and Vines (Table 8) for the statistics, we calculate **a′w x**, and then $(\mathbf{a'w\,a})^{-1}\,\mathbf{a'w\,x}$ to give the estimates themselves. These turn out to be

$$\hat{D} = 17.95$$

$$\hat{H} = -14.04$$

$$\hat{E}_1 = 8.66$$

$$\hat{E}_2 = 2.58.$$

We defer for the moment the allocation of standard errors to these estimates.

STEP (v)

The inclusion of linkage results in new parameters being introduced; these are fully described by Mather (1949) and will not be elaborated here. We need two D's and two H's to describe the components of additive and dominance variance occurring in quantities V_{1F2}, V_{1F3}, W_{1F23}, V_{1F4} and W_{1F34} on the one hand, and V_{2F3}, V_{2F4}, W_{2F34} on the other, and a fifth parameter we call G to describe the genetic part of the variance V_{3F4}. The backcross generation variance has yet another parameter in its expectation but since this occurs nowhere else, it is omitted from the analysis. The analysis now proceeds as before, though with a 7×7 matrix to invert it is now more tedious to perform. The relevant matrices and estimates are given below.

MATRIX **a**, LINKAGE ASSUMED PRESENT

	D_1	H_1	D_2	H_2	G	E_1	E_2
E_1	0	0	0	0	0	1.0000	0
E_2	0	0	0	0	0	0	1.0000
V_{1F2}	0.5000	0.2500	0	0	0	1.0000	0
V_{1F3}	0.5000	0.0625	0.0500	0.0250	0	0	1.0000
V_{2F3}	0	0	0.2500	0.1250	0	1.0000	0
W_{1F23}	0.5000	0.1250	0	0	0	0	0
V_{1F4}	0.5000	0.0156	0.0500	0.0062	0.0400	0	0.2000
V_{2F4}	0	0	0.2500	0.0312	0.2000	0	1.0000
V_{3F4}	0	0	0	1.0000	1.0000	1.0000	0
W_{1F34}	0.5000	0.0312	0.0500	0.0125	0	0	0
W_{2F34}	0	0	0.2500	0.0625	0	0	0

$(\mathbf{a}'\mathbf{w}\,\mathbf{a})^{-1}$

12.176440	−34.927677	4.716345	−21.813154	−1.063218	1.060171	−0.370645
−34.927677	182.782792	−24.504484	115.885613	7.847350	−7.817727	1.087004
4.716346	−24.504492	32.205494	−112.577552	−4.205204	4.030722	−1.111762
−21.813154	115.885613	−112.577552	494.438570	20.121214	−19.619783	3.039267
−1.063218	7.847349	−4.205204	20.121214	1.842598	−1.680504	0.037825
1.060172	−7.817729	4.030721	−19.619780	−1.680504	1.673588	0.040755
−0.370645	1.087004	−1.111762	3.039269	0.037825	−0.040755	0.189489

$\mathbf{a}'\mathbf{w}\,\mathbf{x}$	Estimates
3.188984	$\hat{D}_1 = 12.26$
0.741365	$\hat{H}_1 = -15.10$
6.393704	$\hat{D}_2 = 44.06$
1.334292	$\hat{H}_2 = -98.50$
67.843697	$\hat{G} = 1.04$
77.843697	$\hat{E}_1 = 10.98$
30.624449	$\hat{E}_2 = 1.80$

STEP (vi)

The total sum of squares is $\mathbf{x}'\mathbf{w}\,\mathbf{x}$, obtained by multiplying the vector $\mathbf{x}$ by columns of the weighting matrix and then multiplying the resulting vector by $\mathbf{x}'$. The sum of squares due to fitting constants is obtained by multiplying the vector $\mathbf{a}'\mathbf{w}\,\mathbf{x}$ by the vector of estimates in the usual way. In the analysis where linkage is assumed present we must add to the S.S. for constants wx^2 for the term due to fitting $V_{B1}+V_{B2}$ where w is the appropriate weight and x is the mean value of the variance. As usual the term for linkage is obtained as the difference between the S.S. for constants when it is assumed present and when it is assumed absent. If the model is adequate the residual S.S. should be a χ^2 with 4 d.f. (12 statistics—8 constants fitted). Further evidence on homogeneity is obtained by considering block differences. By analysing half the block difference as we have analysed the mean we obtain S.S. for blocks × components, linkage, and remainder. In this way we obtain the following analysis of variation for flowering time in 1947:

	S.S.	D.F.
Components	1001.749	4
Linkage	31.547	4
Remainder	5.428	4
Components × blocks	19.096	4
Linkage × blocks	2.120	4
Remainder × blocks	0.398	4

The remainder S.S. is not different from its expectation as a χ_4^2 so that the model including the terms for linkage may be said to fit well enough. The linkage S.S. is significantly too large for a χ_4^2, but there are difficulties, discussed below, in regarding this as definite evidence for linkage. The analysis of block differences presents rather a puzzle, in that the components S.S. is significantly large but the other two are not; this heterogeneity makes the allocation of standard errors to the variance components somewhat hazardous. Evidence for this heterogeneity can be seen in the block differences for the original statistics $\mathbf{x}$; thus if we list their contributions individually we get the following values.

Statistic(s)	S.S.	D.F.
E_1	0.90	1
E_2	2.64	1
V_{1F2}	0.32	1
$V_{B1} + V_{B2}$	0.09	1
V_{1F3} and W_{1F23}	0.04	2
V_{2F3}	0.07	1
V_{1F4} and W_{1F34}	0.12	2
V_{2F4} and W_{2F34}	0.36	2
V_{3F4}	17.08	1

V_{3F4} is clearly different from the remainder. Its block difference is far greater than the model predicts. On the other hand the remainder have rather smaller χ^2 than the model would suggest and this may indicate subnormal variation between blocks.† No explanation is offered for the high χ^2 for V_{3F4}, the presence of which must cast some doubt on the validity of estimates of variance components obtained from the inclusion of V_{3F4}. In the absence of heterogeneity between blocks and with a non-significant remainder S.S., variances and covariances for the estimates of components can be obtained from the matrix $(\mathbf{a}'\mathbf{w}\,\mathbf{a})^{-1}$. Thus for instance we have that the standard error of D_1 is $\sqrt{(12.1764)} = \pm 3.49$.

† Professor Mather has pointed out to me that this sub-normal variation between blocks may have resulted from the use of a common seedbox for the propagation of all the plants in any one family.

STEP (vii)

The efficiency of an unweighted analysis as regards the estimates of variance components can be evaluated by standard least-squares. Using the notation established previously, and denoting the unweighted estimates by $\breve{\theta}$, we have $\breve{\theta} = (\mathbf{a}'\mathbf{a})^{-1}\,\mathbf{a}'\mathbf{x}$, and var $\breve{\theta} = (\mathbf{a}'\mathbf{a})^{-1}\,\mathbf{a}'\mathbf{v}\,\mathbf{a}\,(\mathbf{a}'\mathbf{a})^{-1}$ where $\mathbf{v}$ is the variance matrix of $\mathbf{x}$. As an example we consider the fitting of D, H, E_1 and E_2 only, ignoring for the moment the inadequacies of the model. The actual computation of var involve the successive calculation of $\mathbf{a}'\mathbf{a}$, $(\mathbf{a}'\mathbf{a})^{-1}$, $\mathbf{v}\,\mathbf{a}$, $\mathbf{a}'\mathbf{v}\,\mathbf{a}$, $(\mathbf{a}'\mathbf{v}\,\mathbf{a})(\mathbf{a}'\mathbf{a})^{-1}$, and finally the complete expression. We omit the intermediate stages and give the result for flowering time in 1947 in Table 5.

TABLE 5. THE ESTIMATED VARIANCE MATRIX OF THE UNWEIGHTED ESTIMATES

D	13.12	-34.31	0.97	-1.70
H		158.23	-7.28	3.26
E_1			0.90	-0.12
E_2				0.53

The main quantities of interest here are the variances of the estimates of D and H. In Table 6 below we compare for 1947 and 1948 the estimates for the unweighted analysis as obtained by Mather with those in Table 5 and also with the estimates for the weighted analysis. The table shows that weighting has appreciably improved the efficiency of estimation and also that the values for the variance derived from the unweighted analysis are considerably too low. A similar situation was noted by Nelder (1953) in his reanalysis of Mather and Philip's barley experiment, though the method of analysis was somewhat different. More data are needed to show whether this effect is a general one.

The Analysis for 1948 *and Methods of Combined Analysis*

The data for 1948 have also been analysed by the methods given above and the relevant results are as follows:

MATRIX $\mathbf{a}$

	D_1	H_1	D_2	H_2	G	E_1	E_2
E_1						1.0000	
E_2							1.0000
V_{1F2}	0.5000	0.2500				1.0000	
V_{1F3}	0.5000	0.0625	0.0500	0.0250			1.0000
V_{2F3}			0.2500	0.1250		1.0000	
W_{1F23}	0.5000	0.1250					
V_{1F4}	0.5000	0.0156	0.0125	0.0012	0.0100		0.0500
V_{2F4}			0.2500	0.0312	0.2000		1.0000
V_{3F4}					1.0000	1.0000	
W_{1F34}	0.5000	0.0312	0.0500	0.0125			
W_{2F34}			0.2500	0.0625			

$$(\mathbf{a}'\mathbf{w}\,\mathbf{a})^{-1}$$

$$\begin{bmatrix} 8.160420 & -22.037012 & 0.597144 & -2.951284 & -0.182307 & -0.181530 & -0.032595 \\ -22.037012 & 145.278489 & -6.302661 & 29.600134 & 2.645978 & -2.636021 & -0.145043 \\ 0.597144 & -6.302663 & 10.208018 & -39.779980 & -1.492714 & 1.430632 & -0.448090 \\ -2.951284 & 29.6000138 & -39.779980 & 191.443467 & 6.898588 & -6.693458 & 1.467685 \\ -0.182306 & 2.645977 & -1.492713 & 16.898585 & 0.713218 & -0.663811 & 0.015383 \\ -0.181530 & -2.636021 & 1.430631 & -6.693455 & -0.663811 & 0.661513 & -0.016148 \\ -0.032595 & 0.145043 & -0.448090 & 1.467685 & 0.015384 & -0.016148 & 0.063167 \end{bmatrix}$$

a′w x	Estimates
2.831577	$\hat{D}_1 = 7.67$
0.718674	$\hat{H}_1 = 14.86$
16.751295	$\hat{D}_2 = 24.02$
2.670249	$\hat{H}_2 = -28.04$
171.479661	$\hat{G} = 1.06$
176.610765	$\hat{E}_1 = 6.46$
77.248772	$\hat{E}_2 = 1.09$

ANALYSIS OF VARIATION

	S.S.	D.F.
Components	1778.929	4
Linkage	16.373	4
Remainder	2.228	4
Comp. × blocks	16.892	4
Linkage × blocks	3.098	4
Rem. × blocks	1.388	4

TABLE 6. ESTIMATED VARIANCES OF D AND H

Component		Apparent variance as given by unweighted analysis (from Mather and Vines (1952))	Variance of unweighted estimates as obtained from weighted analysis	Variance of weighted estimates as obtained from weighted analysis
1947	D	1.3	13.4	7.5
	H	13.5	168.1	102.3
1948	D	4.5	8.9	3.6
	H	49.8	114.5	61.0

Kurtosis in parent and F_1 distributions was very similar to that in 1947 giving an average g_2 of 0.82 as compared with 0.88. The agreement of sample variances with estimated weights for V_{2F3}, V_{2F4} and V_{3F4} was good, and better than in 1947. The analysis of variation is remarkably similar to that for 1947, and again block differences are heterogeneous. This time E_1 and V_{3F4} account for 15.33 out of the total S.S. of 20.17. The apparent differences in E_1 is unlikely to be a real block difference since V_{1F2} and $V_{B1}+V_{B2}$ show a trend in the opposite direction while V_{3F4} has a much smaller fall than E_1. No obvious explanation of these results suggests itself.

Before making a combined analysis of the two years some test of homogeneity is needed. This is best carried out on the original variance statistics;

if x_{i1} and x_{i2} are values taken by the statistics in year i, with weight w_i, then $\dfrac{(x_{11}+x_{12}-x_{21}-x_{22})^2}{2/w_1+2/w_2}$ (between years) and $2w_1(x_{11}-x_{12})^2+2w_2(x_{21}-x_{22})^2$ (within years) are approximately χ_1^2 and χ_2^2 variates respectively. Where the within-years S.S. is significantly large for a χ_2^2 we may use the F-ratio with 1 and 2 d.f. The results of this applied to the 1947–48 flowering time data are shown in Table 7.

TABLE 7. TEST OF HOMOGENEITY BETWEEN YEARS

Statistics	Between years S.S. (χ_1^2)	Within years S.S. (χ_2^2)
E_1	6.411	9.034
E_2	0.304	2.639
V_{1F2}	0.253	2.136
$V_{B1}+V_{B2}$	0.012	0.905
V_{1F3}	0.781	0.441
V_{2F3}	0.591	0.067
V_{1F4}	9.947	0.160
V_{2F4}	18.575	2.471
V_{3F4}	28.775	24.891

Among the variances with genetic components none of those for the B_1, F_2 and F_3 generations shows any significant deviation from homogeneity. In F_4 however the difference between years for V_{1F4} and V_{2F4} are large and highly significant for a χ_1^2 whereas the within years differences are not significantly above expectation. The position with regard to V_{3F4} is less clear, both between- and within-years sums of squares being greater than expected, while the F ratio though greater than unity is not significantly so. In this situation a combined analysis seems barely justified, but had all the genetic variances shown no departure from homogeneity, a combined analysis could be carried out using common weights for the two years, and leading to an analysis similar to that shown in Mather and Vines' Table 14.

DISCUSSION

The introduction of weights into the analysis undoubtedly increases the amount of computing necessary in analysing the type of experiment we have been considering. Its justification must therefore lie in the increased ' sharpness ' it brings to the analysis. Mather and Vines, in their original analysis, concluded that there was no detectable heterogeneity within and between years, and no mean residual deviation from additivity after allowing for linkage. On the other hand the linkage term was significant. The analysis presented in this paper gives strong indication of heterogeneity between years in some of the statistics, and also pinpoints anomalies like the large block-to-block variation of V_{3F4} in both years. In particular the data in Table 7 suggest quite strongly that the F_4 generation is in some way different from the others; perhaps some form of selection is acting here, a possibility which Mather and Vines themselves discuss in their paper when dealing with the scaling tests on the means. Evidence that the apparent significance of the linkage term does not necessarily mean what it at first appears to mean is provided by the values of H_2. In 1947 this was -98.5 ± 22.2 and in 1948 -28.0 ± 13.8. Thus the good fit with 8 constants has been obtained by giving H_2 a significantly negative value in both years. Since H_2 is essentially positive in the model used, it cannot be taken as certain that the better fit using 8 constants is a positive indication of the existence of linkage.

The increase in efficiency brought about by the use of weights has been mentioned. The possibility arises of designing the experiment in such a way that weighting would be unnecessary, thus allowing the ordinary least-squares technique to be used without appreciably losing efficiency. Before this could be done rough estimates of the various variances would have to be available, and even if these were available some situations might arise in which it would be impossible to equalize the weights. Thus if V_{2F3} were less than V_{1F3} equalization of weights would imply that V_{2F3} must be based on fewer degrees of freedom than V_{1F3}, but this is impossible since even with families of 2, V_{2F3} has one more d.f. than V_{1F3}. Since, whenever E and H are small compared with D, we shall have (in the absence of linkage at least) inequalities like $V_{1F4} > V_{2F4} > V_{3F4}$ it is obvious that often even the smallest of families will leave V_{3F4} more accurately estimated than V_{2F4}, and V_{2F4} than V_{1F4}. In this situation the most we can do is to keep family size as small as possible and attempt at least to keep the weights attached to the overall variances of generations as nearly equal as other considerations (such as time spent in making crosses etc.) allow. Some compromise may also have to be made between the not necessarily consonant requirements of having the means of such accuracy that scaling tests are as sensitive as possible, and having the variances with equal weights. It would seem, then, that difficulties would often arise in attempts to adjust family size in this type of experiment in order to eliminate weighting in the analysis and that such adjustment might be impossible.

A more general, and more important, problem concerns the allocation of material from the various generations in experiments of this kind. The difficulty lies in deciding on the priorities to be given to the various preliminary tests to be made and parameters to be estimated. Thus we want simultaneously accurate scaling tests on the means, sensitive tests of linkage and interaction in the variances and accurate estimates of whatever parameters the preliminary tests indicate as being required. The approximate weights used in this paper would probably suffice in practice to work out the statistical characteristics of different allocations of material as they affect the variances (the means present no new problem), but application of these results to the problem of experimental design must await further investigation.

To sum up, the chief advantages of weighting are the increase in efficiency in estimation, and the possibilities it gives of detailed tests of homogeneity between and within years. These tests are very necessary because of the rather long chain of assumptions implicit in the analysis and the consequent importance of designing as many checks as possible on their validity. A disadvantage is the increase in computing time necessary, though this increase is likely to be a small part of the total time spent on an experiment of this kind.

SUMMARY

1. In genetical experiments dealing with the generations derived from the cross of two true-breeding lines, the possibility of analysing the second order statistics by weighted instead of unweighted least squares is considered.

2. The exact dispersion matrices for F_3 second order statistics and F_4 variances are obtained in a general form using compound cumulants.

3. Values of these matrices for a general additive system are obtained and compared with an approximation based on a simplified normal model. It is concluded that the approximation will usually provide sufficiently accurate weights.

4. A weighted analysis is made of data on flowering time in *Nicotiana rustica* obtained by Mather and Vines, and the results compared with the original (unweighted) analysis. It is concluded that the weighted analysis gives more sensitive tests of homogeneity of the data between and within years, and an improvement in the efficiency of estimation.

5. The interpretation of the results given by the analysis is considered and the possibility of designing experiments of this kind to avoid weighting is discussed, also whether ' optimum ' designs in any sense exist.

Acknowledgement: I am most grateful to M. J. R. Healy of Rothamsted Experimental Station for programming the weighted least-squares analysis on the Rothamsted electronic computer.

REFERENCES

BERKSON, J. (1955) Maximum likelihood and minimum χ^2 estimates of the logistic function, *J. Am. Statist. Assoc.* **50,** 130–162.
FINNEY, D. J. (1952) *Probit Analysis,* Cambridge Univ. Press, England.
MATHER, K. (1949) *Biometrical Genetics,* Methuen, London.
MATHER, K. & VINES, A. (1952) The inheritance of height and flowering time in a cross of *Nicotiana rustica, Quantitative Inheritance,* H.M.S.O., London.
NELDER, J. A. (1953) Statistical Models in biometrical genetics, *Heredity* **7,** 111–119.
ROBSON, D. S. (1956) Applications of the F_4 statistic to genetic variance component analyses, *Biometrics* **12,** 433–444.
ROBSON, D. S. (1957) Application of Multivariate *polykays* to the estimation of genetic variance components. Abstract in *Biometrics.*

IMPORTANCE OF GENOTYPE–ENVIRONMENT INTERACTIONS IN RANDOM SAMPLE POULTRY TESTS†

By A. W. Nordskog and O. Kempthorne
Iowa State College, Ames

So-called random sample poultry tests are popular in the U.S. as a means of demonstrating the productive performance of various strains and varieties of poultry offered for sale by commercial breeders. The test is not unlike a corn yield test. Currently there are in operation some eighteen random sample performance tests for chickens in the United States and one here in Ottawa. Eleven of these, including the one in Canada, are tests of egg laying strains and eight are tests of broiler or meat-type chickens. In addition, five random sample turkey performance tests are being conducted in the United States.

All of these tests have in common the principle that a random sample of chicks is obtained from each of the commercial strains which are then tested under a similar set of conditions. The typical sample consists of fifty pullet chicks selected from a hatchery or breeder. Randomization if properly done ensures that no bias due to sample selection enters into comparisons between entries. Entries are tested for approximately a 16 month period starting with the baby chicks. During this time records are kept on each entry as to egg production, mortality, feed consumption, etc., and at the end of the test entries are ranked on the basis of net income.

Most of the random sample tests are conducted at a single location or test farm in single or duplicate pens. If genotype × environment, i.e. strain × farm interactions, are important the average genetic differences between strains would be over-estimated. At the same time duplicate pen differences would not be a valid estimate of experimental error. Inconsistent rankings of the same strains entering a single test location from year to year is a possible consequence of real genotype × environment interactions.

Very little experimental work has been undertaken for the purpose of obtaining information which might be used to design valid and efficient tests of genetic differences between strains of poultry. Local poultry geneticists with the Dominion Experiment Station in Ottawa have recognized the importance of this problem. Experiments conducted by Dr. R. S. Gowe and co-workers utilizing branch experiment stations have led them to conclude that genotype × environment interactions are probably not important and

† Journal Paper No. J-3574 of the Iowa Agriculture and Home Economics Experiment Station, Ames, Iowa. Projects 1385 and 890.

accordingly that comparisons of different varieties of poultry at a single location are entirely adequate. On the other hand, the results we have obtained in Iowa would seem to indicate that strain $\times$ farm interactions may be important.

In January of 1957 a random sample poultry test set up on a multiple farm basis was started in Iowa under the supervision of the Iowa Poultry Improvement Supervisory Board. Although the primary purpose of the Iowa test is to compare commercial strains of egg-laying chickens, an equally important purpose at the moment is to provide for adequate research data which will allow evaluation of factors influencing the reliability of test results.

The Iowa test is conducted on typical midwest farms. For this reason it is felt that results should more truly reflect what poultry raisers can expect from a strain.

In the first Iowa Multiple Unit Poultry Test just completed, an entry consisted of a total of 625 to 1200 pullet chicks divided over 5 farms. Chicks were produced in 5 hatches. Hatch effects were confounded with farm effects. Similar brooding, feeding, housing, disease control and management conditions were the same for all entries at any one farm. No attempt was made to control conditions between farms, with the exception that all farms were required to feed an all-mash diet. Farms used both floor-type (pens) and cage management. At housing time, entries on floor-type management were placed in duplicate pens at random. In the case of a cage farm operation, the cages were arranged in rows and tiers. Entries were assigned to duplicate cage rows at random. Each farm was provided with a control strain entry to permit between farm comparisons.

Twelve entries plus controls were placed on eleven farms involving more than 14,000 pullet chicks in the first test. The farms were set up as farm units. The latter consisted of ten pens which accommodated five entries including the control in duplicate pens or the equivalent number of pullets in cages. Nine farms had single units. One farm had four units and one had two.

The Model

The interpretation of the results of the Iowa Multiple Unit Poultry Test is based on the following linear model, in which Y represents the mean performance of a single pen:

$$Y = \mu + s_i + f_j + (sf)_{ij} + p_{ijk}$$

where: μ = an over-all mean

s_i = average effect of the ith strain

f_j = average effect of the jth farm

$(sf)_{ij}$ = interaction effect of the ith strain on the jth farm

p_{ijk} = an effect of the kth pen (or cage row) at the jth farm where the ith strain is tested.

We impose the restriction that $\sum s_i = \sum f_j = \sum (sf)_{ij} = 0$. Further, we assume that p_{ijk} is a random variable with mean zero and variance σ_p^2.

It follows that the variance among pen means is,

$$\sigma_Y^2 = \sigma_s^2 + \sigma_f^2 + \sigma_{sf}^2 + \sigma_p^2.$$

In the first Iowa Test the twelve entries were divided into three groups of four each. Each group plus a control entry was placed on $m = 5$ farm test units. A farm test unit consists of $mn = 10$ pens. For each group of $s-1$ entries plus the control placed on m farms, the following analysis of variance was used:

	d.f.	Expectation of mean squares.
Strains	$s-1$	$\sigma_p^2 + n\sigma_{sf}^2 + m\sigma_s^2$
Farms	$m-1$	$\sigma_p^2 + n\sigma_{sf}^2 + s\sigma_f^2$
Strains × farms	$(s-1)(m-1)$	$\sigma_p^2 + n\sigma_{sf}^2$
Pens	$sm(n-1)$	σ_p^2

Possible Comparisons

The design of the test permits an evaluation of the validity and accuracy of four possible kinds of comparisons:

(*a*) Between pen means of two entries tested at the same farm. This corresponds to a typical single-location random sample test.

(*b*) Between two entries each of which are tested on m different farms.

(*c*) Between two entries each of which are tested on m different farms but having a control entry in common.

(*d*) Between two entries each tested on the same m farms.

The experimental errors for the different comparisons are as follows:

	Element in the model tested	Experimental error
(*a*) Entries on one farm	$\{s_i + (sf)_{ij}\}$	$\dfrac{\sigma_p^2}{n}$
(*b*) Entries on different farms	(s_i)	$\dfrac{\sigma_p^2}{mn} + \dfrac{\sigma_{sf}^2}{m} + \dfrac{\sigma_f^2}{m}$
(*c*) Same as (*b*) with common control entry	(s_i)	$2\left(\dfrac{\sigma_p^2}{mn} + \dfrac{\sigma_{sf}^2}{m}\right)$
(*d*) Entries on the same farms	(s_i)	$\dfrac{\sigma_p^2}{mn} + \dfrac{\sigma_{sf}^2}{m}$

A single location test is valid only if strain × farm interaction effects are negligible, because in this case the elements of the model actually tested are the $\{s_i + (sf)_{ij}\}$ effects.

Comparisons between entries under (*d*) are, of course, most efficient. The experimental error for comparisons under (*c*) is just twice as large as that under (*d*).

An alternative procedure for evaluating different methods of comparison is to use estimates of so-called repeatabilities of entries. These are simply intra-class correlations. We may, therefore, consider four kinds of intra-class correlations which parallel the four methods of making comparisons:

	Intra-class correlation
(*a*) Between means of entries at a single test farm	$\dfrac{\sigma_s^2 + \sigma_{sf}^2}{\sigma_s^2 + \sigma_{sf}^2 + \dfrac{\sigma_p^2}{n}}$
(*b*) Between means of entries each tested on *m* different farms	$\dfrac{\sigma_s^2}{\sigma_s^2 + \dfrac{\sigma_{sf}^2 + \sigma_f^2}{m} + \dfrac{\sigma_p^2}{mn}}$
(*c*) Same as (*b*) but with control entry in common	$\dfrac{\sigma_s^2}{\sigma_s^2 + 2\left(\dfrac{\sigma_{sf}^2}{m} + \dfrac{\sigma_p^2}{mn}\right)}$
(*d*) Between means of entries all tested on the same farms	$\dfrac{\sigma s^2}{\sigma_s^2 + \dfrac{\sigma_{sf}^2}{m} + \dfrac{\sigma_p^2}{mn}}$

RESULTS AND DISCUSSION

Variance Component Estimates

Table 1 shows the percentage variance components for a number of performance characteristics from pooled analyses of variance.

TABLE 1. PERCENTAGE VARIANCE COMPONENTS

	d.f.	Maturity (Age at 50% production)	Egg production to May 1st	Mortality to May 1st	Egg weight at 355 days	Egg quality (Haugh units)
Entries	12	35†	22†	0	30†	32†
Farms	11	47†	61†	15*	34†	38†
Entries × Farms	44	9†	9†	31†	10†	4
Pens	70	9	8	53	9†	26
Pen samples	140	—	—	—	17	—

* $P<0.05$. † $P<0.01$.

Of particular interest are the interaction effects which proved to be highly significant for maturity, egg production and egg weight, but not for mortality nor for the egg quality measure.

We are now in a position to consider the accuracy of some of the possible comparisons. First, it should be pointed out that comparisons of entries at the same farm (Method (*a*)) are not strictly valid for characteristics which show interaction effects. Hence, this method will not be considered here.

Table 2 shows the expected size of the experimental error as a ratio of the variance of a single pen ($\sigma_p^2+\sigma_{sf}^2$) for different testing situations with respect to the variance estimates obtained for egg production.

TABLE 2. EXPERIMENTAL ERRORS AS A PERCENTAGE OF THE VARIANCE ($\sigma_p^2+\sigma_{sf}^2$) FOR DIFFERENT TESTING SITUATIONS IN THE CASE OF EGG PRODUCTION TO MAY 1ST.

Number farms (m)	Pen replications (n)	Methods of comparing entries		
		B	C	D
2	1	225%	100	50
5	1	90	40	20
10	1	45	20	10
22.5	1	20		
2	2	213	76	38
5	2	86	30	15
10	2	43	15	7.5

The results show that for egg production testing birds on different sets of farms (Method (*b*)) is rather inaccurate, except where fairly large numbers of farms are used. In such a case, however, it is shown that using more than one pen per entry adds very little to the precision of the test. When controls are used (Method (*c*)) then testing entries on five farms is about equal in accuracy to testing without controls on ten farms. If entries are all tested on the same farms (*d*) then, of course, controls are no longer needed. The dotted line indicates the cases of equal accuracy for $n = 1$. Thus, when entries are all tested on the same five farms, the precision of the test is equal to Method (*b*) using ten farms or Method (*a*) using 22 or 23 farms.

Repeatability

Table 3 gives the expected repeatabilities for the four methods of comparison.

The repeatability of means of replicate pens of the same entry at a single test (*a*) approaches one as a limit as the number of pens per entry is increased. If genetic–environmental interactions are at all important, repeatabilities obtained from data at a single location can be quite misleading.

As pointed out Method (*a*) shows that the repeatability of replicate pens of the same entry at a single location is rather substantial for egg rate, egg number and age at maturity. The repeatability of strain means tested at the same five farms (*d*) shows that this method of testing should lead to reasonably consistent results from the three traits considered. The intraclass-correlations range from 0.89 to 0.93. However, when strain means are tested at each of

TABLE 3. REPEATABILITIES (INTRA-CLASS CORRELATIONS)

	Maturity	Egg production	Egg size
(*a*) Replicate pens of same entry at one test	0.83	0.79	0.66
(*b*) Between strain means each tested on five different farms	0.74	0.60	0.81
(*c*) Same as (*b*) but with control entry in common	0.87	0.81	0.82
(*d*) Between strain means all tested at five farms	0.93	0.89	0.90

five different farms (*b*) we find that the repeatabilities now range from 0.60 to 0.81. Method (*c*) shows that when a control entry is included with the various farms on which the strains are being tested under (*c*) that the repeatability of hypothetical sets of the same entry are made considerably larger.

Source of Interaction Variance

The farm test units were operated under two general types of environment or management, namely floor pens and cages. If this management difference is incorporated into our linear model, then the farm effect (f) may be separated into a management effect (m) and an effect associated with farm differences of the same management (f/m), or $f = m + (f/m)$, and the farm variance may be partitioned into two parts, $\sigma_f^2 = \sigma_m^2 + \sigma_{f/m}^2$.

The question may be raised, therefore, whether the interaction effects presented arise from cage versus pen management or from farm differences of the same type of management. Since the interaction effects (sf) can be partitioned likewise into $sf = sm + (sf/m)$ the interaction variance may be partitioned into $\sigma_{sf}^2 = \sigma_{sm}^2 + \sigma_{sf/m}^2$.

Analysis of our data with regard to these two sources of interaction effects yields the following percentage variance components:

	σ_{sm}^2	$\sigma_{sf/m}^2$
Maturity age	− 1.	10.*
Egg production	5.*	4.*
Adult mortality	−16.	47.*
Egg weight	− 6.	12.*
Egg quality (Haugh Units)	0.3	3.

* $P<0.01$.

The results show that only in the case of egg production did we find a statistically significant interaction involving strains and cage versus pen management. This is in agreement with Gowe (1956) who reported a similar highly significant interaction for survivor's egg production but not for mortality, egg weight or sexual maturity.

The results show that the interaction of strains with farm differences independent of cage or pen management is highly significant statistically for each of the performance factors except the egg quality measure. Hill and Nordskog (1956) also found significant interaction effects for strains × farms for adult mortality and for strains × farms and strains × years for both adult mortality and rate of egg production. On the other hand, Gowe (1954) found little evidence for genotype–environment interaction with respect to egg production and only a slight indication of interaction for laying house mortality from laying tests on five widely scattered farms in Canada. Gowe's experiment was based on considerably less data than that involved in the present study; and furthermore, he imposed standard management and feeding procedures between his test farms. This would tend to minimize possible strain × farm interaction effects.

Fixable and Non-fixable Environmental Factors

In any consideration of genotype–environment interactions it is useful to distinguish two types of environmental factors, namely those which are fixable and those which are non-fixable. A fixable factor of environmental classification is one in which the levels can be controlled or can be recreated at will. For example, in testing the performance of genotypes, the geographical area may be controllable by the worker; he can decide whether the genotypes are to be used in the state of Iowa or the state of Minnesota. Again, the poultryman can decide whether to use cages or floor pens. He must decide what sort of feeding program he shall provide. Non-fixable factors of classification are ones which cannot be repeated at will. For example, any set of data will contain year effects, but the poultryman will not know the year effect which will occur next year. Year effects are entirely out of his control. Again, a poultry breeder who produces stock for a particular geographical area will not be able to produce stock ideally suited to each particular farm. For his purposes, he may regard farms within a geographical area as a source of random variation which will render his tests less precise than if there were no farm differences.

The breeder may choose to regard what we have termed fixable factors as non-fixable in that he may produce stocks which are to perform in a population of farms some of which have one level of a fixable factor, and others another level. It has not been the practice for instance to produce strains specifically bred for one type of management, though one can imagine a large breeding enterprise which produces a stock which performs at an optimum for one particular set of management procedures, and a different stock for another set of management procedures.

As regards non-fixable factors, however, the breeder has no alternative but to treat them as random factors.

It was with this background of reasoning that the small investigation of cage versus floor pens was made. If we suppose there are two factors of classification of environment, say A and B, and the environmental contribution from the ith level of A and the jth level of B is E_{ij}, then we can write for the genotype–environment interaction contribution

$$GE_{ij} = \text{constant} + GA_i + GB_j + G(AB)_{ij}$$

and

$$\sigma^2_{GE} = \sigma^2_{GA} + \sigma^2_{GB} + \sigma^2_{GAB}.$$

If the factor of classification A is fixable and is fixed, the new environmental variance would be

$$\sigma'^2_{GE} = \sigma^2_{GB} + \sigma^2_{GAB}.$$

The gain from fixing a particular aspect of the environment associated with factor A is, therefore, indicated by the ratio

$$\frac{\sigma^2_{GA}}{\sigma^2_{GA} + \sigma^2_{GB} + \sigma^2_{GAB}}.$$

If this ratio is 'large' one would be obliged to consider the possibility of selecting stocks for particular A levels, e.g. for particular geographical regions.

An Alternative Design

The design system by which entries were assigned to the farms in the above study has some shortcomings. Most important is the fact that the difference of a pair of entries not on the same farm has twice the variance of two entries on the same farm. For this reason and because it was thought desirable to examine other aspects of field testing, an alternative design has been selected for the second year's test. This design is represented as follows:

Block	Farm unit	Entry and flock number					Hatch
W	1	Q1, 1	A1, 1	B1, 2	C1, 2	D2, 2	
Cage	2	Q1, 1	E1, 2	F2, 2	G1, 1	H1, 2	1
	3	Q1, 1	I2, 2	J1, 2	K1, 2	L1, 1	
	4	Q1, 1	M1, 2	N1, 1	O2, 2	P1, 2	
X	5	Q1, 1	A1, 2	E2, 2	I1, 1	M1, 2	
Floor	6	Q1, 1	B1, 2	F1, 1	J2, 2	N1, 2	2
	7	Q1, 1	C2, 2	G1, 2	K1, 2	O1, 1	
	8	Q1, 1	D1, 1	H1, 2	L1, 2	P2, 2	
Y	9	Q1, 1	A1, 2	F1, 2	K2, 2	P1, 1	
Floor	10	Q1, 1	B2, 2	E1, 1	L1, 2	O1, 2	3
	11	Q1, 1	C1, 1	H2, 2	I1, 2	N1, 2	
	12	Q1, 1	D1, 2	G1, 2	J1, 1	M2, 2	
Z	13	Q1, 1	A2, 2	H1, 1	J1, 2	O1, 2	
Floor	14	Q1, 1	B1, 1	G2, 2	I1, 2	P1, 2	4
	15	Q1, 1	C1, 2	F1, 2	L2, 2	M1, 1	
	16	Q1, 1	D1, 2	E1, 2	K1, 1	N2, 2	

in which Q is the control and A, B, C, D, ... O, P represent 16 entries. On each farm there are 10 pens in all. Each entry including the control is represented twice. An additional factor examined by having two pens for each entry is its origin or source as to parent breeding flock. A1, 1 designates two pens with entry A both produced at source 1 for that entry. C1, 2 indicates that the two pens for entry C originated from two sources or parent flocks of that entry denoted by 1 and 2.

The structure of the design is that of a quadruple lattice (cf. Cochran and Cox, 1957; or Kempthorne, 1952), in which the four replicates are four groups of farms. Of the four groups of farms, one group has cages and the other three have pens. This asymmetry is a property of the farms which were available. The confounding of hatch effects with groups or blocks of farms was intentional, there appearing to be no easy way to incorporate this factor in any other way.

This design will permit better comparison of all entries, it will permit examination for effects of the source of the entries, and will permit rather precise comparison of all entries with the control which will be maintained over the years. It will allow evaluation of the magnitude of interactions with farm over and above interactions with pen which would certainly be regarded as non-fixable. Also, since the control population is ‘random bred’, it should make possible the estimation of yearly effects. The design is not necessarily optimal, but is included here to give an idea on how aspects subsidiary to the purely testing aspects may be examined in a testing program with very little extra effort.

SUMMARY

The results obtained from the first Iowa Multiple Unit Poultry Test indicate that strain–farm interactions, hence genotype–environmental effects, are of importance and need to be taken into account in order to make unbiased comparisons between strains of egg laying chickens. Interactions for age, at sexual maturity, rate of egg production, mortality and egg weight were all highly significant, statistically. The fraction of total variance among pen means due to such interactions amounted to 9, 9, 31 and 10%, respectively, for these various traits.

Comparisons were made between the efficiency of testing strains on the same farms with testing strains on different farms when a common control entry was used and was not used.

The nature of the genotype–environment interaction is discussed. A portion of this due to fixable environmental effects such as geographical differences and management differences, can be controlled by the breeder. The other portion, due to non-fixable environmental factors such as that associated with years, cannot be controlled by the breeder. This must be regarded purely as a stochastic process, and its magnitude can be controlled only by increasing the number of testing units.

REFERENCES

COCHRAN, W. G. & COX, GERTRUDE M. (1957) *Experimental Designs*, 2nd ed., Wiley, New York.

GOWE, R. S. & WAKELY, W. T. (1954) Environment and poultry breeding problems. *Poultry Science* **33**, 691–703.

GOWE, R. S. (1956) Environment and poultry breeding problems. 2. *Poultry Science* **35**, 430–435.

HILL, J. F. & NORDSKOG, A. W. (1956) Efficiency of performance testing in poultry. *Poultry Science* **35**, 256–265.

KEMPTHORNE, OSCAR (1952) *Design and Analysis of Experiments*, Wiley, New York.

EXPERIMENTAL RESULTS

STUDIES ON ESTIMATION OF DOMINANCE VARIANCE AND EFFECTS OF LINKAGE BIAS†

By H. F. Robinson, C. Clark Cockerham and R. H. Moll

Professor and Head, Department of Genetics; Associate Professor of Experimental Statistics and Genetics; and Assistant Professor of Genetics and Experimental Statistics

North Carolina State College, Raleigh, North Carolina

Investigations of the inheritance of quantitative characters in corn by the statistical genetics personnel at the North Carolina Experiment Station have been devoted in part to estimation of the components of genetic variance with interpretations of level of dominance of genes based on the magnitude of the ratio of dominance variance to the additive genetic variance. The initial studies by Robinson *et al.* (1949) and Gardner *et al.* (1953) used material of the F_2 generation of crosses of two inbred lines and the results gave indications that genes concerned with yield were in the range of over-dominance. The suggestion was made in the report of these early results that repulsion phase linkage could provide sufficient upward bias in the estimates of dominance variance to result in indications of over-dominance, whereas the genes may actually have only partial to complete dominance.

The level of dominance of genes for yield in open pollinated varieties, obtained by Robinson *et al.* (1955) from extensive experimentation providing estimates of the additive genetic and dominance variance, has been in the range of partial-to-complete dominance. Linkage combinations have had sufficient opportunities to become dissipated in reproduction of the open-pollinated varieties, affording a possible explanation of the difference in level of dominance estimates in F_2 generation material from hybrid populations compared with open-pollinated varieties.

The earlier estimates of additive genetic variance, σ_g^2, and dominance variance, σ_d^2, that have been obtained for two hybrid populations and three open-pollinated varieties are given in Table 1.

The estimates presented for a population are averages of estimates obtained from the various tests with each kind of material. Each test of the hybrid material contained 810 plots and variety population tests each consisted of

† Contribution from the Departments of Genetics and Experimental Statistics, North Carolina Agricultural Experiment Station, Raleigh, North Carolina, and published with the approval of the Director of Research as paper no. 965 of the Journal Series. The research was supported in part by a grant from the Rockefeller Foundation.

TABLE 1. PREVIOUS ESTIMATES OF ADDITIVE GENETIC AND DOMINANCE VARIANCE FOR YIELD IN THE F_2 GENERATION OF HYBRID POPULATIONS AND IN OPEN-POLLINATED VARIETIES

Population	No. of tests	$\hat{\sigma}_g^2$	$\hat{\sigma}_d^2$	$\hat{\sigma}_d^2/\hat{\sigma}_g^2$
Hybrids				
CI21 × NC7	3	0.0016	0.0032	2.00
NC33 × K64	3	0.0024	0.0024	1.00
	Means	0.0020	0.0028	1.40
Varieties				
Jarvis	6	0.0030	0.0005	0.17
Weekley	6	0.0037	0.0018	0.49
Indian Chief	2	0.0023	0.0010	0.35
	Means	0.0030	0.0011	0.37

512 plots. Different experimental procedures were used with the different kinds of material, accounting for difference in number of plots involved.

It is from the ratio of dominance variance to additive genetic variance, σ_d^2/σ_g^2, that information is gained on the level of dominance of the genes. This ratio has an expected value of 0.5 where the gene frequency in the population is 0.5 and dominance is complete, assuming the absence of linkage and epistasis. While the F_2 generation of a hybrid population of a cross from homozygous lines can be assumed to have gene frequency of 0.5 this is not the case with the open-pollinated varieties. However, the ratio, σ_d^2/σ_g^2, is interpretable at varying gene frequencies and levels of dominance as has been done in an earlier report of results from the variety populations.

The two important issues from the earlier results with hybrid and open-pollinated variety populations are:

(1) $\hat{\sigma}_d^2/\hat{\sigma}_g^2$ is almost four times as large, in the average, for hybrid populations as it is for open-pollinated varieties.

(2) This evidence for hybrid populations indicates overdominance in contrast to partial-to-complete dominance for open-pollinated varieties.

The objective of the study reported here was to determine the effects that recombination had on the components of genetic variance by studying simultaneously F_2 and advanced generation material of hybrid populations of corn. The results contained in this report are from only a portion of the work in progress or planned on this issue. It is intended that this represent a progress report of the results to date and provide the reader with a knowledge of the experimental research being devoted to the question of linkage bias in the dominance variance estimates which we have suggested as a factor in overdominance estimates for genes concerned with yield of corn.

Similar type studies involving corn belt material have been in progress at the Nebraska Agriculture Experiment Station under the direction of Dr. C. O. Gardner. A report of this research by Gardner and Lonnquist is in the process of being published.

EXPERIMENTAL PROCEDURE

The experimental material is produced from backcross matings of plants of a segregating generation of a population to the two long time inbred lines from which the population was derived. The plants of the segregating generations are generally designated pollen parents, with each randomly chosen male plant being crossed to enough plants (usually 2–4) of both parent-inbred lines to insure sufficient seed for replicated testing of the progenies. The backcross families are produced in pairs where a single plant of the segregating generation material is mated to plants of each of the inbred line parents. This procedure has been designated Design III whereas the procedure in genetic variance studies with the variety populations used half- and full-sib families and has been designated Design I.

The field design consists of approximately nine (9) random backcross pairs of progenies in each of a sufficient number of sets to accommodate the total experimental material for a population. The nine backcross pairs or 18 progenies allocated to each set are arranged in three contiguous replications forming a ‘ block ’ of the experiment.

Design III material was prepared for a simultaneous test of the F_2 and F_8 generation of each of two hybrid populations, where the F_8 material resulted from six generations advance of the F_2 with random sib matings. Sets of the F_2 and F_8 backcross progenies were intermingled throughout the studies with each population. Approximately 135 backcross progeny pairs or 15 sets of material of each generation was contained in each test. This requires 810 plots for a Design III (D-III) study of each generation or 1620 plots for a population. The F_2–F_8 D-III progenies of one population, CI21 × NC7, were tested in 1956 and 1957. Approximately two-thirds of the same entries tested in 1956 were repeated in the 1957 test. The first year test of a second population, NC33 × K64, with F_2–F_8 material was conducted in 1957. The data for each generation of each population were analyzed separately for each year's results. Analyses for individual year results with CI21 × NC7 were pooled for a two-year analysis.

The form of the statistical analysis used for the variance analysis of data collected from a Design III study is shown in Table 2. The expectations of the mean squares of interest are shown in the right-hand column of the table.

TABLE 2. THE FORM OF THE ANALYSIS OF VARIANCE OF A DESIGN III STUDY CONDUCTED IN ONE ENVIRONMENT AND IN ONE YEAR

Source of variation	d.f.	M.S.	Expectation of M.S.
Blocks	$s-1$		
Replications in blocks	$s(r-1)$		
Inbred parents	1		
Inbred parents × blocks	$s-1$		
F_n parents in blocks	$s(n-1)$	M_1	$\sigma^2+2r\sigma_m^2$
F_n parents × lines in blocks	$s(n-1)$	M_2	$\sigma^2+r\sigma_{ml}^2$
Remainder among plots (error)	$s(2n-1)(r-1)$	M_3	σ^2

s is the number of blocks
r is the number of replications in each block
n is the number of pairs of backcross progenies in each set
σ^2 is the error variance among plots of the same progeny
σ_m^2 is the progeny variance arising from genetic differences among F_n (variable) parents
σ_{ml}^2 is the progeny variance arising from interaction of genotypes of F_n and inbred parents

Estimates of the variance components are obtained by equating the mean squares to their expectations. The definitions of the abbreviated letters and symbols used are given at the bottom of the table.

The genetic interpretation of σ_m^2 and σ_{ml}^2, arising as a result of genetic differences among progenies of a population, is given in Table 3.

TABLE 3. GENETIC INTERPRETATION OF VARIANCE COMPONENTS

$$\sigma_m^2=\tfrac{1}{2}\sum_i q_i(1-q_i)u_i^2u_i \quad +\sum_{ij}(pt-rs)_{ij}u_iu_j$$

$$\sigma_{ml}^2=\sum_i q_i(1-q_i)a_i^2u_i^2+2\sum_{ij}^{c}(pt-rs)_{ij}a_iu_ia_ju_j+2\sum_{ij}^{r}(rs-pt)_{ij}a_iu_ia_ju_j$$

where: u_i = one-half the difference between the means of the homozygous genotypes at the ith locus.

a_iu_i = the deviation of the mean of the heterozygous genotype from the mean of the two homozygous genotypes at the ith locus.

q_i = the frequency of the favorable allele.

$\tfrac{1}{2}\sum_i q_i(1-q_i)u_i^2=\tfrac{1}{4}\sigma_g^2$ at $q_i=0.5$

$\sum_i q_i(1-q_i)a_i^2u_i^2=\sigma_d^2$ at $q_i=0.5$

p = frequency of B_iB_j gametes, that is, with the favorable allele at both the ith and j^{th} locus.

r = frequency of B_ib_j gametes.

s = frequency of b_iB_j gametes.

t = frequency of b_ib_j gametes.

$\sum_{ij}^{c}$ indicates summation over pairs of loci at which favorable genes were in the coupling phase in pure-line parents.

$\sum_{ij}^{r}$ indicates summation over pairs of loci at which favorable genes were in the repulsion phase in pure-line parents.

These expressions were given by Comstock and Robinson (1952) where considerations were given to the possible magnitude of the linkage bias on the level of dominance estimates. With the population at linkage equilibrium, the linkage terms in equations for σ_m^2 and σ_{ml}^2 will disappear. Under this condition $\sigma_m^2 = \sigma_g^2/4$ and $\sigma_{ml}^2 = \sigma_d^2$ when the gene frequency, q, of the population is 0.5. If linkage is present and equilibrium has not been reached, $(pt-rs)$ will be positive if the initial linkage phase (the linkage phase of the inbred parents) is coupling. Some cancellation of the linkage bias in σ_m^2 is expected; however, the linkage bias in σ_{ml}^2 in this design is positive regardless of the linkage. The bias here is a function of $(pt-rs)$ for coupling and $(rs-pt)$ for repulsion, both of which are positive.

When q_i's are 0.5, as may be assumed for an F_2 of a cross of two homozygous lines of corn or the nth generation of material produced from random breeding of such material with no selection, a measure of level of dominance, $\bar{a}$, can be computed from the ratio of the two genetic components of variance. This measure of level of dominance is shown in Table 4 where

$$\frac{\sigma_{ml}^2}{2\sigma_m^2} = \frac{\sum_i a_i^2 u_i^2}{\sum_i u_i^2} = \bar{a}^2.$$

TABLE 4. MEASURE OF LEVEL OF DOMINANCE

$$\bar{a} = \sqrt{\left[\frac{\sum_i a_i^2 u_i^2}{\sum_i u_i^2}\right]} = \sqrt{\left[\frac{\sigma_{ml}^2}{2\sigma_m^2}\right]}$$

Magnitude of a_i	*Degree of dominance*
$a_i=0$	No dominance
$0<a_i<1$	Partial dominance
$a_i=1$	Complete dominance
$a_i>1$	Over-dominance

The $\bar{a}^2$ is a weighted mean of the a_i^2's and weighted relative to associated u_i^2's. Thus

$$\bar{a} = \sqrt{\left[\frac{\sigma_{ml}^2}{2\sigma_m^2}\right]} = \sqrt{\left[\frac{2\hat{\sigma}_d^2}{\hat{\sigma}_g^2}\right]}.$$

The scale on which the a_i is measured, relative to the degree of dominance is shown in the lower part of Table 4.

RESULTS AND DISCUSSION

The results for the D-III studies with the two hybrid populations are given in Table 5.

TABLE 5. COMPARISON OF ESTIMATES OF GENETIC VARIANCE FOR YIELD IN F_2 AND F_8 GENERATIONS IN TWO HYBRID POPULATIONS

Population	Year	Estimated value	F_2	F_8
CI21 × NC7	1956	σ_d^2	0.0022	0.0014
		σ_g^2	0.0019	0.0012
		$\bar{a}$	1.54	1.52
	1957	σ_d^2	0.0015	0.0004
		σ_g^2	0.0015	0.0012
		$\bar{a}$	1.41	0.81
	Pooled Two Year	σ_d^2	0.0019	0.0009
		σ_g^2	0.0017	0.0012
		$\bar{a}$	1.49*	1.24
NC33 × K64	1957	σ_d^2	0.0009	0.0002
		σ_g^2	0.0037	0.0029
		$\bar{a}$	0.68	0.38*

* Indicates that the observed deviation from the hypothesis of complete dominance ($\bar{a}=1$) has a probability of occurrence of 0.01 or less.

The estimates of additive genetic variance in the F_2 of CI21 × NC7 made in 1956 and 1957 are quite consistent with previous estimates for this population. The dominance variance of F_2 reported here is somewhat less than previously obtained values. In general, however, agreement is as good as might be expected in view of sampling errors and the possible effects of genotype–environmental interactions since the comparison is with estimates obtained in different years. The 1957 estimate of additive genetic variance in the F_2 of NC33 × K64 was considerably larger than the previously obtained values. However, much less dominance variance was indicated in the estimate here for F_2 than was the case in the studies of earlier years. The level of dominance found in the F_2 generation of this population is not significantly different from complete dominance whereas $\bar{a} = 0.38$ for the F_8 generation is a significant departure from $\bar{a} = 1.0$ and is indicative of partial dominance.

Consistent and appreciable reduction in dominance variance was obtained in advanced generation material in each test with both populations. However in every instance there has been a decrease in estimated additive genetic variance in F_8 compared with F_2. The percentage decrease in additive genetic variance has, in general, not been as great as is the case for dominance variance which results in some reduction in the level of dominance, $\bar{a}$, in F_8 compared with F_2.

The expected change in the components of variance and level of dominance following the dissipation of linkage effects if a linkage bias did exist is given in Table 6.

TABLE 6. TRENDS OF VARIANCES AND $\bar{a}$ TO BE EXPECTED FOLLOWING RECOMBINATION UNDER VARIOUS LINKAGE PHASE ASSUMPTIONS

Initial linkage phase	σ^2_{ml}	σ^2_m	$\bar{a}$
Cancellation of effects due repulsion and coupling	decrease	no change	decrease
Predominantly repulsion	decrease	increase	decrease
All coupling	decrease	decrease	no change
Predominantly coupling	decrease	decrease	$\frac{\sigma^2_{m}, F_2}{\sigma^2_{m}, F_n} > \frac{\sigma^2_{ml}, F_2}{\sigma^2_{ml}, F_n}$ = increase; $\frac{\sigma^2_{m}, F_2}{\sigma^2_{m}, F_n} < \frac{\sigma^2_{ml}, F_2}{\sigma^2_{ml}, F_n}$ = decrease.

The dominance variance, estimated from the σ^2_{ml}, if biased due to linkage effects, is expected to be reduced following recombinations regardless of the type of linkage in the initial phase. This is not the case for σ^2_m which provides a measure of additive genetic variance. There might be no change in additive genetic variance following recombination opportunities if the repulsion and coupling linkage of the initial phase tended to balance each other. An increase in additive genetic variance could occur with predominately repulsion phase linkages in the parent lines. With initial phase coupling linkages, the additive genetic variance would be expected to decrease, the rate of decrease being dependent upon the predominance of the coupling linkages.

The results to date with F_2 and advanced generations of hybrid populations tend to support the hypothesis that linkage bias is a factor in dominance estimates with the hybrid populations. The reduction in dominance variance following recombination is consistent with the suggestion of linkage effect associated with a multiplicity of loci. A downward trend in σ^2_g suggests a preponderance of coupling linkages in the F_2 generation of the hybrid populations used here. It is reasonable to expect that other hybrid populations might have initial phase repulsion linkages and an increase in additive genetic variance be found in advanced generation material as was the case with Gardner and Lonnquist.

REFERENCES

COMSTOCK, R. E. & ROBINSON, H. F. (1952) Estimation of average dominance of genes. *Heterosis*, pp. 494–516, Ames, Iowa, Iowa State College Press.

GARDNER, C. O. & LONNQUIST, J. H. Linkage and the degree of dominance of genes controlling quantitative characters in maize (In press).

GARDNER, C. O., HARVEY, P. H., COMSTOCK, R. E. & ROBINSON, H. F. (1953) Dominance of genes controlling quantitative characters in maize, *Agron. J.* **45,** 186–191.

ROBINSON, H. F., COMSTOCK, R. E. & HARVEY, P. H. (1949) Estimates of heritability and the degree of dominance in corn, *Agron. J.* **41,** 353–359.

ROBINSON, H. F., COMSTOCK, R. E. & HARVEY, P. H. (1955) Genetic variances in open-pollinated varieties of corn, *Genetics* **40,** 45–60.

AN EXPERIMENTAL CHECK ON THE ACCURACY OF PREDICTION OF RESPONSE DURING SELECTION†

By G. A. MARTIN‡ and A. E. BELL

Population Genetics Institute, Purdue University
Agricultural Experiment Station, Lafayette, Indiana, U.S.A.

INTRODUCTION

THE APPLICATION of statistics to the problems of predicting genetic response to selection has been extensively developed during the last four decades. Very recent studies have tended to concentrate on intensive refinement of design and analysis to further separate effects that were formerly confounded (Horner, 1952; Anderson and Kempthorne, 1954; Kempthorne, 1955; Cockerham, 1956). The basic problem of application of population genetics to animal improvement is one of choice of the most efficient breeding plan. Theoretical considerations point to type of gene action, association of traits, influence of environment, and interactions of these phenomena as major determiners of the efficiency of breeding plans. However, relatively few experiments in animal breeding have been reported that were extensive enough in terms of numbers of observations and generations to provide an adequate test of the predictability of population changes during selection. Clayton *et al.* (1957) have published an experiment with *Drosophila* that gave both long and short range tests of the adequacy of genetic theory for explanation of response of the selected trait. The selected lines were replicated so that conclusions regarding repeatability of results could be drawn. The effects on non-selected traits were observed but were not subjected to prediction and thereby a very important aspect of selection in economic species was omitted.

Extensive selection experiments with laboratory species have revealed some inconsistencies of expected and observed results. This is vividly illustrated by such occurrences as the asymmetry of response to selection for large and small body weight in mice (Falconer, 1953) and the ' plateaus ' reached while genetic variance was still present in *Drosophila* (Mather, 1943; Bell *et al.*, 1953 and 1955; Rasmuson, 1955; and others). Elucidation of

† Journal Paper No. 1338 of the Purdue University Agricultural Experiment Station. Supported in part by grants from the Rockefeller Foundation and the National Science Foundation.

‡ Present address: North Carolina State College, Raleigh, N.C., U.S.A.

the problem seems to require the simultaneous examination of as many as possible of the determiners of breeding plan efficiency. A series of experiments were conducted in 1954 and 1955 to (1) provide estimates of parameters needed for predicting response to selection and inbreeding, (2) test predictions by imposing selection and inbreeding on a population and comparing predicted to observed changes, and (3) observe repeatability of selection experiments.

MATERIALS AND METHODS

The traits to be studied needed to parallel, as closely as possible, those of economic value in economic species. Only when this requirement is met can similar physio-genetic control of the traits in pilot and economic species attain a maximum probability. *Drosophila melanogaster* was chosen as the experimental species because of its known adaptability for genetic studies plus the fact that techniques were available for the measurement in this species of several quantitative traits similar to important traits in economic species. Adult weight is of importance in most economic species and was considered an appropriate trait to expose to selection in these pilot experiments. As unselected traits, egg size, fecundity and adult emergence were measured in order to check on correlated responses. Weight was recorded to the nearest microgram on a ' Micro-Gramatic ' balance. Egg size was measured in eyepiece micrometer units as described by Bell *et al.* (1955). The measure of fecundity was number of eggs produced on three consecutive days. Adult emergence in these studies refers to the percentage of eggs yielding adult flies. Thus was observed a highly heritable trait, egg size, that is not directly related to fitness and two traits which are major indicators of reproductive fitness.

Prediction of change of selected and non-selected traits during selection is dependent upon reliable estimates of such parameters as means, heritability, genetic correlations among traits, rate of inbreeding, and variances associated with groups and individuals. The parameters were estimated from inbred lines, their crosses, and two experiments involving the mating of several dams to each of several sires. Effects of high-low selection for body weight over fifteen generations and changes in the other traits were predicted. A replicated experiment was conducted and observed measurements compared to those that had been predicted.

In order to impose constant inbreeding pressure upon the selected lines, family selection was used to choose the superior six families each generation. Within these families a maximum of eighteen flies of each sex were weighed and the superior six selected to reproduce the line. Single pair matings of the selected flies were made as shown in Table 1 to provide the permutations taken two at a time for the six selected families plus the six full-sib matings. Such a mating plan produces a high probability of perpetuation of any genetic combination contributing to the desirability of the selected family.

It also insures a distinctly higher level of in-breeding for the progeny of the six full-sib matings than for the other 30 progenies. A more detailed description of these experiments is given by Martin (1959) and will be published elsewhere.

TABLE 1. MATING SYSTEM WHEREBY A MALE FROM EACH SELECTED FAMILY IS MATED TO A FEMALE FROM EVERY SELECTED FAMILY.

For example mating 11 is a male from family 1 mated to a full sib, mating 12 is another male from family 1 mated to a female from family 2, etc.

		Male parent					
	Selected family	1	2	3	4	5	6
Female parent	1	11	21	31	41	51	61
	2	12	22	32	42	52	62
	3	13	23	33	43	53	63
	4	14	24	34	44	54	64
	5	15	25	35	45	55	65
	6	16	26	36	46	56	66

PARAMETER ESTIMATION AND PREDICTION

The variance of body weights of adults from the 12 inbred lines was determined. The variance component between inbred lines is an unbiased estimate of $2fA$, where f is inbreeding coefficient and A denotes additive genetic variance, and variance within inbred lines is an unbiased estimate of $(1-f)A+E$, where $E=$ environmental variance (Lerner, 1950). Only the assumption that inbreeding is approximately 100% is necessary to estimate heritability as (variance between lines)/(variance between + variance within lines). By using the ‘ modified diallel ’ analysis (Griffing, 1956), independent estimates of additive, (A), and non-additive, (D), genetic variance were obtained from weights of all combinations of crosses from the 12 inbred lines. Effects of sex-linkage were avoided by using only weights of female flies. The estimates of heritability from these sources are shown in Table 2. These estimates are made from the entire gene pool of a ‘ synthetic population ’ produced by free interbreeding of the 12 lines and should more accurately depict the genetics of the population than would sample inbred lines drawn from the population. Of the total genetic variance between crosses, 0.98 was additive and only 0.02 was non-additive.

After four generations of free interbreeding of the inbred lines to form a random mating ‘ synthetic ’ population, data were obtained from two trials in which 4–7 dams were mated to each of 20 sires. The per cent emergence from each dam's egg production was determined and transformed to arc-sine for analysis. Body weight, egg size, and fecundity were measured on the offspring from each mating. Analysis of variance of these data provided estimates of components of variance due to sires, dams and full-sib deviations from which the heritability values shown in Table 2 were derived.

Genetic correlations of non-selected traits with body weight were calculated in each of the nested experiments. The independent estimates of these correlations ranged from +0.75 to −0.63 for fecundity, from +0.50 to −0.47 for egg size, and from +0.16 to +0.71 for adult emergence. Since each estimate was based on more than 100 observations, the fluctuations in the correlations from large negative to large positive values are greater than would be expected from sampling variation alone. Evidence will be presented elsewhere to support the hypothesis that transient linkage was present between genes for body weight and those determining the other traits. Thus the erratic estimates of genetic correlations were, at least in part, a function of genetic recombination. The average genetic correlations given in Table 2 obviously have large standard errors; however, they are the best estimate available for predicting the correlated responses of the non-selected traits.

TABLE 2. ESTIMATES OF GENETIC PARAMETERS FOR VARIOUS TRAITS IN THE FOUNDATION POPULATION.

	Parameters estimated		
Traits	h^2	r^G with body weight	Effect of 1% inbreeding
Body weight—Inbreds	0.190	—	—
—Crosses	0.193	—	−0.65 μg
—Sib r	0.214	—	—
ze	0.584	0.133	0.00 units
Fecundity	0.071	0.139	−0.37 eggs
Adult emergence	0.512	0.236	—

Data for use in calculating an estimate of inbreeding depression upon adult emergence were not available. For the other three traits inbreeding depression can be predicted if one is willing to assume that this depression is a function of the non-additive (D) variance. Straus (1942) found that heterosis for fecundity in *Drosophila melanogaster* was due to dominance effects of chromosomes rather than to interaction between chromosomes. The assumptions for predicting inbreeding depression are: (1) that the depression is due to reduction of heterozygosity at loci having dominance effects, (2) that the mean is due entirely to the action of segregating genes, (3) that there are two genes per locus with each at 0.5 frequency, and (4) that additive with additive gene interactions vs. interactions involving dominance bear the same ratio as additive vs. dominance gene action. Under these conditions the equation, $f2q(1-q)\sqrt{D}/(\sqrt{D}+\sqrt{A})$ is simplified to $f.5\sqrt{D}/(\sqrt{D}+\sqrt{A})$, and may be used to predict the reduction in the mean at any value of f. The predicted values shown in Table 2 reveal the expected change in each trait per 1% of inbreeding.

The rate of inbreeding resulting from the mating plan in Table 1 can be calculated if selection is assumed to be at random relative to inbreeding. This rate predicts a total of 41% inbreeding after fifteen generations of selection. If inbreeding depression is pronounced and genes for large size are dominant, the small-body-size lines would become inbred at a greater rate and the large-body-size lines at a lesser rate than that predicted. Conversely, if effects of additive genes are the predominant influence upon body weight, lines selected large and lines selected small would become inbred at a greater than predicted rate due to selection of more than a random number of cousins. Thus comparison of predicted and observed inbreeding rates can be used to supplement other evidence on the type of gene action involved.

Selection of the superior one-sixth of the families and the superior one-third of the individuals weighed in the family permits a family selection differential of 0.97 standard deviations of the family means and 0.42 standard deviations selection differential within families in the initial generation. Unequal population density in different culture bottles which was due to the dam's phenotype for reproductive rate accounted for 0.486 of the deviations of family mean body weights. Since this fraction was due to environmental correlation with the dam's phenotype for a non-selected trait, it had to be removed in predicting the effective selection differential. The effective family selection differential for any generation was predicted as

$$Sd_F = 0.514\,(0.97)\sigma_F(1-0.514h^2f)$$

where σ_F is the standard deviation of family means. The selection differential within families was predicted as

$$Sd_w = 0.42\sigma_w(1-h^2f)$$

where σ_w is the standard deviation of weights within the family.

The predicted selection differentials were calculated and multiplied by the appropriate heritabilities (corrected for predicted inbreeding) to provide the ' predicted weight ' response plotted in Fig. 1. When the observed selection differentials for each generation were used instead of those predicted, the ' expected weight ' response of Fig. 1 was obtained.

Changes in egg size, fecundity, and adult emergence were predicted as

$$\Delta_i = r^G_{iw}\, Sd_{wt}\sigma_i/\sigma_w + \Delta f\,(\text{inbreeding effect on } i)$$

where Δ_i is change in the indicated trait, r^G_{iw} is the genetic correlation of the indicated trait with body weight, Sd_{wt} is the effective selection differential for weight and Δf is the change in inbreeding coefficient. The predicted changes are shown in Table 3.

TABLE 3. PREDICTED AND OBSERVED CHANGES IN VARIOUS TRAITS PER GENERATION OF SELECTION FOR BODY WEIGHT

Traits	Large lines		Small lines	
	Predicted	Observed	Predicted	Observed
Body weight (μg)	14	12	-18	-19
Egg size (units)	0.26	-0.05	-0.33	-0.20
Fecundity (eggs)	-0.69	-1.27	-1.65	-1.07
Adult emergence %	0.63	-1.02	-0.81	-0.68

RESULTS AND DISCUSSION

The response of body weight to high-low selection in the two replications of the experiment is shown in Fig. 1. The observed asymmetry of response is treated fully elsewhere (Martin, 1959) and is attributed largely to greater effects of population density in the large lines. In both replications the observed selection differentials were larger than predicted and thus led to the ' expected ' response being larger than the ' predicted ' response. Table 3

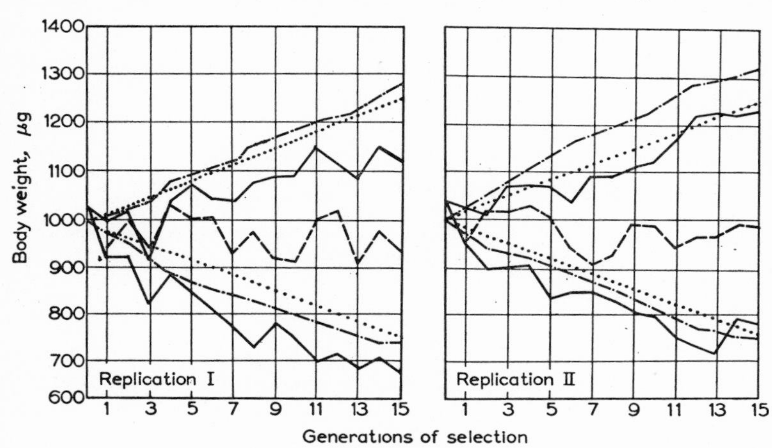

FIG. 1. Theoretical and observed response during selection for large and small body weight.

——— observed weight .... predicted weight
-·-·-· expected weight ----- weight of controls.

shows that the average predicted and observed response per generation of selection are in reasonably good agreement for body weight. The realized heritability for the large, (L), and small, (S), lines is shown in Table 4. Since estimates of heritability within a generation actually estimate heritability of divergence for high-low selection rather than heritability of response in one direction, the mean h^2 of 0.18 should be compared with the predicted level of 0.19 to 0.21 from Table 2. Therefore, response to selection for body weight over fifteen generations was more accurately predicted from the inbreds and their crosses than from half-sib correlations in samples of random matings from the population.

Genetic correlations of the other traits with body weight were calculated in all selected lines in early, middle, and late generations of selection. There was little indication of trends in the correlations of egg size with body weight and each selected line had both negative and positive correlations. However, correlations in adjacent generations were of the same sign in 75% of the pairs examined. Thus the correlations displayed some short-range predictive value. The average correlation of 0.01 was slightly smaller than the initial value of 0.133. Correlations of fecundity with body weight tended toward positiveness but showed less consistency in adjacent generations than those of egg size. The average correlation shown in Table 4 is the mean of large negative and large positive correlations with the latter predominating. The average correlation of adult emergence with body weight (Table 4) was negative during selection although it had been estimated at 0.24 in the population before selection was initiated. Eighty per cent of these correlations in the large lines were negative whereas 70% were positive in the small lines. This produced an average correlation of −0.51 in the large lines and 0.30 in the small lines. A definite tendency for low emergence to become associated with the selected trait is indicated so that the correlation before selection was not useful for predicting change in the trait. Thus the genetic correlations in the unselected population were of little value in predicting mean of unselected traits after fifteen generations of selection.

TABLE 4. HERITABILITY, GENETIC CORRELATIONS AND EFFECTS OF INBREEDING ON VARIOUS TRAITS DURING SELECTION FOR BODY WEIGHT

Trait	Observed statistics		
	Realized h^2	r_G with body weight	Effect of 1% inbreeding
Body weight—*L*	0.12	—	0.02 μg
,, ,, —*S*	0.23	—	−0.28
,, ,, mean	0.18	—	−0.13
Egg size	—	0.01	−0.01 units
Fecundity	—	0.26	−0.36 eggs
Adult emergence	—	−0.10	−0.21%

Effects of inbreeding upon each trait in each generation were calculated as the difference in the mean of the progenies of the full-sib matings and that of their less inbred cousins for each 1% difference in inbreeding coefficient. The averages for each line and trait are shown in Table 5 and the overall means are recorded in Table 4. Inbreeding effects on body weight were of the order of one three-thousandth part of the mean and were inconsequential and variable in direction. Those for egg size are of a similar general magnitude but are consistently negative. Thus definite but small inbreeding depression of egg size is indicated. Fecundity was depressed by about one-third of a per cent for each per cent increase in inbreeding. This indicates that approximately

TABLE 5. AVERAGE EFFECT OF ONE PER CENT INCREASE IN INBREEDING ON BODY WEIGHT, DAILY EGG PRODUCTION, EGG LENGTH, AND PER CENT EMERGENCE FOR THE SELECTED LINES.

Line	Effect of one percent inbreeding on:			
	Weight	Fecundity	Egg size	Emergence
Large 1	+0.33	-0.45 eggs	-0.012 units	-0.18%
Small 1	+0.31	-0.23	-0.020	-0.31
Large 2	-0.28	-0.35	-0.012	-0.12
Small 2	-0.88	-0.39	-0.014	-0.25

36% of the mean egg production of a non-inbred population would be lost when inbreeding reached 100%. This result agrees with that predicted from the initial population and thus agrees with Straus' (1942) observation that heterosis of fecundity is due to dominance. Adult emergence was consistently depressed by inbreeding. The average depression of the mean as shown in Table 4 was about 60% as great as it was for fecundity. It may be stated that where data were available, the effect of inbreeding was predicted with reasonable accuracy on the assumption that heterosis is due to dominance effects.

The overall fit of predicted and observed changes in the means of non-selected traits was not very good as shown in Table 3. The failure of prediction is attributed largely to the transient nature of the genetic association of these traits with the selected trait. If genetic correlations in general are similar to those observed in the present data, their inclusion in selection indexes is of questionable value.

The predicted coefficient of inbreeding in the fifteenth selected generation was 0.41 and the observed values were 0.44 in the large lines and 0.50 in the small lines. All lines became inbred at a rate greater than that predicted with a ratio of additional inbreeding approximating the ratio of realized heritability in the two directions of selection. This result indicates additive rather than dominance or epistatic gene action influencing the selected trait and agrees with the absence of important inbreeding effects upon body size.

Finally, the repeatability of results was high for divergence of the selected trait (Fig. 2) and for effects of inbreeding (Table 5). Repeatability of genetic correlations and of response of the selected trait in a given direction was, in general, not nearly so high. Heritability as estimated in a random-bred population is heritability of divergence and it seems to have more value for predicting divergence than for predicting response to selection in a given direction. Repeatability and predictability seem closely associated so that phenomena that were less repeatable were also more difficult to predict.

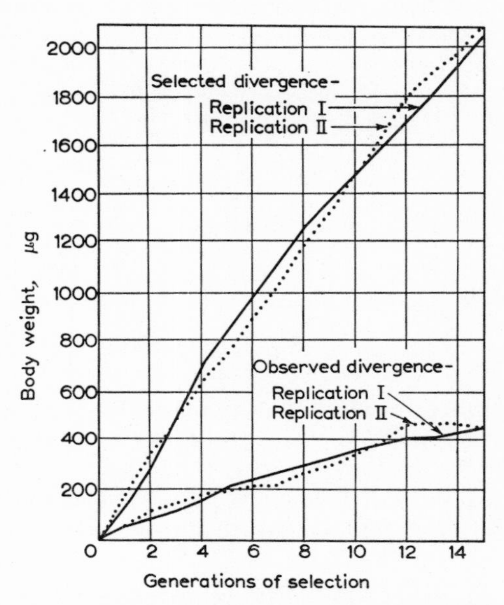

FIG. 2. Selected and observed total divergence between lines selected for large and small body weight.

SUMMARY

Population parameters needed for the prediction of response to high-low selection for body weight with inbreeding and changes in egg size, fecundity, and adult emergence during selection for body weight were estimated from twelve inbred lines, their crosses, and random samples drawn from a population synthesized from the inbred lines. Two samples were drawn from the synthetic population and a replicated experiment selecting for large and small body weight was carried through fifteen generations of selection. A breeding plan that imposed inbreeding at about 3% per generation was used. The three unselected traits were measured in most generations.

Slightly larger selection differentials were obtained than had been predicted whereas realized heritability of body weight was slightly below preselection estimates. Genetic correlations of the unselected traits with body weight were highly transitory both before and during selection and were of little value for predicting association with the selected trait or change in the means of unselected traits.

Effects of inbreeding were predicted on the assumption that heterosis is due to dominance effects of genes. The predicted values were in close agreement with those calculated independently in each line and generation. Inbreeding depression was most severe for fecundity, less severe but still large for adult emergence, definite but very small for egg size, and of little consequence for body weight.

Coefficient of inbreeding was predicted on the assumption of its independence from the selected trait. It exceeded prediction in all lines by a pattern that indicated additive gene action.

Divergence of body weight was highly repeatable over replications whereas response to selection in a given direction was less repeatable and less predictable.

REFERENCES

ANDERSON, V. L. & KEMPTHORNE, O. (1954) A model for the study of quantitative inheritance, *Genetics* **39,** 883–898.

BELL, A. E., MOORE, C. H. & WARREN, D. C. (1953) A biological evaluation with *Drosophila melanogaster* of four methods of selection for the improvement of quantitative characteristics, *Proc. 9th Intern. Genetics Congr., Caryologia* **6,** Suppl. 851–853.

BELL, A. E., MOORE, C. H. & WARREN, D. C. (1955) The evaluation of new methods for the improvement of quantitative characters, *Cold Spring Harbor Symposia Quant. Biol.* **20,** 197–212.

CLAYTON, G. A., MORRIS, J. A. & ROBERTSON, A. (1957) An experimental check on quantitative genetical theory, *J. Genetics* **55,** 131–180.

COCKERHAM, C. CLARK, (1956) Effects of linkage on the covariation between relatives. *Genetics* **41**, 138–141.

FALCONER, D. S. (1953) Selection for large and small size in mice, *J. Genetics* **51,** 470–501.

GRIFFING, BRUCE (1956) A generalized treatment of the use of diallel crosses in quantitative inheritance, *Heredity* **10,** 31–50.

HORNER, T. W., COMSTOCK, R. E. & ROBINSON, H. F. (1955) Non-allelic gene interactions and the interpretation of quantitative genetic data, *N. Carolina State College, Agr. Exp. Sta. Tech. Bull.* 118, pp. 1–117.

KEMPTHORNE, OSCAR (1955) The theoretical values of correlations between relatives in random mating populations, *Genetics* **40,** 153–167.

LERNER, I. M., (1950) *Population Genetics and Animal Improvement*, Cambridge Univ. Press.

MARTIN, G. A., (1959) Selection for body weight in *Drosophila melanogaster*, Ph. D. Thesis, Purdue University Library, Lafayette, Indiana.

MATHER, K., (1943) Polygenic inheritance and natural selection, *Biol. Revs.* **18,** 32–64.

RASMUSON, M., (1955) Selection for bristle members in some unrelated strains of *Drosophlia melanogaster*, *Acta Zool.* **36,** 1–49.

PREDOMINANCE OF HYBRID LOSSES OR NEGATIVE HETEROSIS IN MOUSE CROSSES*†

By R. W. MASON, H. H. NICHOLSON, RALPH BOGART and HUGO KRUEGER
Oregon Agricultural Experiment Station, Corvallis, Oregon

ANIMAL production, as plant production, is successful only when the total production per square foot of factory space is high. Plant yields are logically related to a per acre basis and hybrid vigor as measured in plants is dependent upon a series of heterotic effects acting upon many individual plants through a complete developmental process. Animal yields are most logically related to a per cow, per ewe or per sow basis since the most costly and limiting item in animal production is the female of the breeding herd. Total yield is a resultant of fertility and growth. Because individual animals are more prominent than individual plants and because man is more closely associated with animals for longer periods of time, the importance of all phases of a life cycle are not given appropriate emphasis. Thus, one might observe faster growth rates and conclude that heterosis existed. A complete life cycle broken into nine parts is considered in this study.

MATERIALS AND METHODS

Four strains of mice—Oregon State College strains *A*, *C*, *O* and *V*—were crossed via a diallel mating plan. Characteristics measured in the 6 cross, 6 reciprocal cross and 4 purebred offspring groups were: growth, food consumed and grams of food consumed per gram of growth from 21 to 45 days of age, 45-day body weight, number of mice born per litter from the crossbred and pure strain mice, 12-day litter weights of offspring of the crossbred and pure strain mice, thyroid weights, micrograms of thyroid per gram of body weight and gram-minutes of survival during asphyxiation.

The diallel mating plan was to mate each of 7 males of each strain to a female of each strain, that is to have 7 litters born in each of the 16 possible frames of a 4×4 diallel table. Ideally, 28 females of each strain would have been used and no female would have had more than one litter. In reality, the *C* strain was so low in fertility that fewer than 7 litters were born in each frame involving *C* and several of the *C* females were used more than once.

* This study was conducted in cooperation with the Agricultural Research Service, U.S. Dept. of Agriculture, and State Experiment Stations under Western Regional Project W-1 on Beef Cattle Breeding Research. Oregon Agricultural Experiment Station, Corvallis, Oregon.

† Technical Paper No. 1170, Oregon Agricultural Experiment Station.

The mating plan for obtaining litters from the F_1 mice born from the first mating plan was originally a 16×16 diallel plan to produce the 256 possible genotypes of the F_2 generation. Since there were not enough mice produced by the original matings to satisfy this objective, an incomplete 16×16 diallel plan was used wherein male mice of one of the 16 genotypes were mated to as many as possible of the 16 female genotypes as follows:

MALES	FEMALES															
	a	b	c	d	e	f	g	h	i	j	k	l	m	n	o	p
a.	X	X	X			X	X		X	X	X	X				X
b.	X	X	X		X	X	X	X	X		X		X	X		X
c.	X	X	X		X	X	X	X	X		X		X			X
d.		X	X			X				X	X	X	X			
e.	X						X	X				X				
f.	X	X	X	X		X	X	X	X	X	X			X	X	X
g.	X	X	X			X	X	X	X		X	X	X			X
h.						X	X	X	X						X	
i.	X	X	X	X		X	X		X	X	X		X		X	X
j.	X	X	X	X	X	X	X	X	X	X	X		X		X	X
k.	X	X	X	X	X	X	X		X		X					X
l.	X	X				X	X		X				X			
m.	X	X	X		X						X					X
n.										X	X					
o.			X													X
p.	X		X	X						X			X		X	X

The position that an individual female of genotype z ($z = a, \ldots, p$) occupied was random with the restriction that all frames a–p be filled before duplication was made, as was the position of an individual male of type z, and thus missing frames were at random. In this way it was hoped that the level of fertility in one group would not be reflected in the fertility of any other group.

It had previously been shown that a sex difference in fertility existed among three of the four pure strains, the females being more fertile than the males in two of the strains and the males more fertile than the females in a third strain (Bogart *et al.*, 1958).

Two methods of analyzing the diallel table were used. The first was a modification to include two sexes of offspring, of method 1, model I, for combining ability analysis as outlined by Griffing (1956). In this analysis, the model used was:

$$y_{ijkl} = u + g_i + g_j + s_{ij} + r_{ij} + K + g_{ki} + g_{kj} + s_{kij} + r_{kij} + e_{ijkl}$$

$i = 1, \ldots, 4$

$j = 1, \ldots, 4$

$k =$ male or female

$l = 1, \ldots, n$, the individual

where y_{ijkl} is an individual of genotype Y_{ijk}; u is the effect common to all animals, the mean; g_i is the general combining ability (g.c.a.) effect of the ith parent strain, that is, the effect common to parents of strain i regardless of parental sex; s_{ij} is the specific combining ability (s.c.a.) effect for the cross between the ith and j^{th} parents such that s_{ij} is equal to s_{ji}; r_{ij} is the reciprocal effect involving the reciprocal crosses between the ith and j^{th} parents such that r_{ij} equals $-r_{ji}$; K is the sex effect such that K for females equals $-K$ for males; g_{ki} is the general combining ability effect for offspring of sex k of the ith parent strain not accounted for by g.c.a. or by sex; s_{kij} is the specific combining ability effect of the ith and j^{th} parent as expressed in sex k and not accounted for by s_{ij}, g.c.a., sex or sex × g.c.a.; r_{ijk} is the reciprocal effect of sex k not accounted for by r_{ij} such that r_{ijk} for males equals $-r_{ijk}$ for females; and e is the remaining discrepancy of an individual of genotype y_{ijk} from the mean of genotype Y_{ijk}.

The second method of analyzing the diallel table was a factorial analysis in which the following model was used:

$$y_{ijkl} = u+K+s_j+d_i+s_jd_i+s_{jk}+d_{ik}+(s_jd_i)_k+e_{ijkl}$$

where y_{ijkl}, u, e and K are as previously defined, s_j is the effect of the jth strain sire, d_i is the effect of the ith strain dam, s_jd_i is the effect of mating the j^{th}strain males with i^{th} strain females not accounted for by the effects of the jth sire and the i^{th}dam, s_{jk} is the effect of the j^{th}strain sire on the kth sex not accounted for by s_j or K, d_{ki} is the effect of the i^{th}strain dam on the kth sex not accounted for by d_i or K, $(d_is_j)k$ is the remaining discrepancy of the Y_{ijk} means from Y_{ij} means, e is the deviation of the individual y_{ijkl} fro m Y_{ijk}.

Since there were disproportionate subclass numbers, the analyses were run on the unweighted means using the within subclass sum of squares divided by the harmonic mean of subclass numbers for the error sum of squares (Snedecor, 1956).

Finally gross correlation coefficients, for the mean of males and the mean of females of corresponding genotypes, were calculated for each trait and the gross correlation coefficients for each trait with each other trait were calculated within sexes using the subclass means as the observations.

The methods of housing and caring for the animals have been described previously by Mason *et al.* (1956) and Mason *et al.* (1958).

RESULTS AND DISCUSSION

The pertinent data are tabulated in Tables 1 through 6. From these tables which summarize the effects as determined from model I, the nine diallel tables can be reconstructed. In presenting the results and discussing them, the diallel tables were studied extensively but are not included in the text because they require much space.

TABLE 1

General combining ability effects of the four strains A, V, O and C as expressed by the average of the male and female offspring, male offspring deviations (negative female deviations), general mean of each characteristic (u) and male sex effect K (negative female) for each characteristic.

Characteristic	Strain				
	O	*V*	*A*	*C*	*u*
Growth; 21–45 days of age	0.79	−0.72	0.39	−0.45	10.68
45-day body weight	1.47	−0.52	0.09	−1.04	19.46
Food consumed; 21–45 days of age	5.13	−2.19	−0.59	−2.35	64.54
Feed per g gain; 21–45 days of age	0.08	0.13	−0.24	0.03	5.31
Number of mice born per litter	0.64	−0.34	0.20	−0.50	5.54
12-day litter weight	2.24	−0.92	0.60	−1.92	25.90
Thyroid weight	0.27	0.36	−0.13	−0.50	2.72
μg thyroid per g body weight	2.73	16.38	−5.77	−13.34	105.43
Gram-minutes of survival	1.01	41.17	−13.70	−28.48	805.77

Characteristic	MALE DEVIATIONS Strain				
	O	*V*	*A*	*C*	*K*
Growth; 21–45 days of age	0.11	−0.13	0.06	−0.05	0.95
45-day body weight	0.19	−0.10	−0.06	−0.03	1.03
Food consumed; 21–45 days of age	−1.44	−0.05	0.26	1.23	1.62
Feed per g gain; 21–45 days of age	−0.11	0.22	−0.15	0.04	0.71
Number of mice born per litter	0.25	0.04	−0.56	0.27	0.17
12-day litter weight	0.99	1.28	−2.04	−0.23	0.87
Thyroid weight	−0.03	−0.06	−0.08	0.17	−0.43
μg thyroid per g body weight	0.44	−2.09	−3.08	4.73	−15.98
Gram-minutes of survival	11.54	0.10	−2.38	−9.26	−16.29

TABLE 2

Specific combining ability effects of the ten combinations of the strains *A*, *V*, *O* and *C* as expressed by the average of the two sexes of offspring and deviations as expressed by male offspring. Female offspring deviations are male offspring deviations multiplied by −1.

Characteristic	STRAIN COMBINATIONS									
	OO	*OV*	*OA*	*OC*	*VV*	*VA*	*VC*	*AA*	*AC*	*CC*
Growth	1.73	−1.00	−0.57	−0.16	0.81	0.56	−0.37	−0.38	0.40	0.14
45-day weight	0.80	−0.58	0.33	−0.54	−0.07	0.15	0.50	−0.04	−0.44	0.47
Food consumed	3.20	−1.41	4.34	−6.13	3.05	−0.26	−1.38	−2.02	−2.06	9.57
Feed per g gain	−0.44	0.53	0.52	−0.61	0.05	−0.49	−0.08	0.11	−0.14	0.83
Number born per litter	0.17	−0.50	−0.04	0.37	−0.51	1.14	−0.15	−1.66	0.54	−0.76
12-day weight	−0.22	0.88	−0.33	−0.33	−6.59	3.19	1.81	−8.91	5.33	−6.81
Thyroid weight	−0.03	0.10	0.04	−0.11	0.40	−0.22	−0.28	0.07	0.12	0.27
μg thyroid/g b.w.	−7.71	8.45	−1.94	1.20	7.74	−8.98	−7.21	5.42	5.51	0.50
Gram-minutes	−18.91	6.84	33.65	−21.58	16.24	−18.67	−4.41	28.16	−43.14	69.13

Characteristic	MALE DEVIATIONS									
	OO	*OV*	*OA*	*OC*	*VV*	*VA*	*VC*	*AA*	*AC*	*CC*
Growth	−0.09	−0.15	0.27	−0.04	0.20	0.21	−0.26	0.11	−0.61	0.89
45-day weight	−0.11	−0.45	0.24	0.31	0.01	0.24	0.19	0.68	−1.17	0.67
Food consumed	−4.01	3.88	1.60	−1.47	−5.40	0.93	−0.59	−0.39	−2.15	3.03
Feed per g gain	−0.59	0.75	−0.05	−0.11	−0.98	−0.11	0.32	0.26	−0.10	−0.12
Number born per litter	−0.84	0.31	0.83	−0.29	−0.60	0.19	0.13	−0.26	−0.74	0.91
12-day weight	−3.29	4.10	1.65	−2.46	−5.02	0.02	0.89	−0.12	−1.56	3.13
Thyroid weight	−0.37	0.34	−0.02	0.05	−0.53	0.11	0.07	0.07	−0.17	0.05
μg thyroid/g b.w.	−12.95	8.95	−0.40	4.40	−13.10	−5.12	−0.97	0.46	−5.18	1.76
Gram-minutes	41.44	−9.15	−14.77	−17.53	−24.25	−47.99	−14.59	−58.21	24.99	7.13

TABLE 3

Reciprocal effects of the four strains A, V, O and C in each of their six combinations as expressed by the average of male and female offspring and deviations as expressed by male offspring. Female offspring deviations are male offspring deviations times −1. Six reciprocal crosses are omitted and the effects of these six are equal to the respective cross given times −1.

Characteristic	Strain combinations, female strain × male strain					
	$O\times V$	$O\times A$	$O\times C$	$V\times A$	$V\times C$	$A\times C$
Growth	1.54	−0.35	0.03	−0.43	0.58	0.42
45-day weight	1.53	0.75	1.80	1.28	1.90	2.56
Food consumed	4.03	2.93	8.94	4.56	4.38	3.85
Feed per g gain	−0.66	0.29	0.81	0.55	0.21	−0.37
Number born per litter	1.03	−0.21	−0.25	0.29	2.38	0.63
12-day litter weight	2.17	1.57	1.53	−1.97	7.16	6.54
Thyroid weight	−0.24	−0.01	0.18	0.19	0.37	−0.02
μg thyroid/g b.w.	−15.76	−4.11	−2.20	3.21	5.67	−8.86
Gram-minutes	−4.14	−33.92	6.22	−10.43	13.76	21.24

Characteristic	$O\times V$	$O\times A$	$O\times C$	$V\times A$	$V\times C$	$A\times C$
Growth	0.69	0.20	0.46	0.25	−0.13	0.76
45-day weight	0.47	0.00	0.85	0.52	0.50	1.49
Food consumed	2.85	−1.76	1.18	4.10	−0.38	3.44
Feed per g gain	−0.51	−0.21	−0.11	0.24	−0.06	0.38
Number born per litter	−1.93	−0.44	0.37	−0.30	−0.54	−0.21
12-day litter weight	−11.69	−0.60	−0.96	−2.13	−1.14	−3.33
Thyroid weight	−0.29	0.22	0.02	0.31	−0.17	−0.10
μg thyroid/g b.w.	−6.13	6.30	−6.48	−11.60	10.48	1.98
Gram-minutes	12.93	18.97	2.01	6.85	27.14	18.26

Example: Number born per litter

$u \quad +g_o \quad +g_v \quad +g_{ok} \quad +g_{vk} \quad +K \quad +s_{ov} \quad +s_{ovk} \quad +r_{ov} \quad +r_{ovk}$

5.54 + 0.64 − 0.34 + 0.25 + 0.04 + 0.17 − 0.50 + 0.31 − 1.03 + 1.93 VO♂

5.54 + 0.64 − 0.34 + 0.25 + 0.04 + 0.17 − 0.50 + 0.31 + 1.03 − 1.93 OV♂

5.54 + 0.64 − 0.34 + 0.25 + 0.04 + 0.17 − 0.50 + 0.31 − 1.03 − 1.93 VO♀

5.54 + 0.64 − 0.34 + 0.25 + 0.04 + 0.17 − 0.50 + 0.31 + 1.03 + 1.93 OV♀

Method of visualizing interaction of sex with reciprocal effects

	$O\times V$	$V\times O$
♂	−1.93*	+1.93
♀	+1.93	−1.93

* tabulated value.

TABLE 4. CORRELATION COEFFICIENTS OF RELATIONSHIPS BETWEEN THE NINE TRAITS STUDIED IN CROSSBRED MICE.

	TRAITS																	
	1 Growth		2 Feed per g gain		3 45-day weight		4 Food consumed		5 Number born		6 12-day weight		7 Thyroid weight		8 μg thyroid body weight		9 gram-minutes of survival	
	♂	♀	♂	♀	♂	♀	♂	♀	♂	♀	♂	♀	♂	♀	♂	♀	♂	♀
1.			−0.61*	−0.02	0.69	0.55	0.52	0.47	0.23	0.68	−0.18	0.56	−0.21	0.24	−0.52	−0.03	0.20	−0.54
2.					0.02	0.27	0.31	0.70	0.12	−0.17	0.38	−0.23	0.58	0.37	0.52	0.21	0.23	0.11
3.							0.79	0.79	0.43	0.62	0.13	0.62	0.23	0.50	−0.19	0.01	0.42	−0.29
4.									0.35	0.27	0.08	0.24	0.18	0.55	−0.23	0.19	0.42	−0.10
5.											0.73	0.90	0.42	0.24	0.26	−0.06	0.39	−0.51
6.													0.60	0.05	0.43	−0.23	−0.33	−0.56
7.															0.88	0.89	0.65	0.11
8.																	0.46	0.48

* Values larger than 0.50 or less than −0.50 are statistically significant at the 5% point of probability.

TABLE 5A. MEAN SQUARES OF THE VARIOUS EFFECTS AS DETERMINED FROM TWO SEPARATE ANALYSES. SEX IS COMMON TO BOTH ANALYSES.

Source	Degrees of freedom	M.S. growth	M.S. 45-day wt.	M.S. food consumed	M.S. feed per g. gain	M.S. no. mice born
g.c.a.	3	8.0062†	18.8261†	196.8458†	0.4216	4.3482
s.c.a.	6	2.5719†	1.0911	81.5299†	1.0886*	2.5608
r	6	2.1214†	11.9963†	106.2389†	1.1001*	4.8913*
sex	1	28.7471†	34.2378†	83.3340	15.9189†	0.9906
s × g.c.a.	3	0.1872	0.2544	19.2903	0.4497	2.4695
s × s.c.a.	6	0.6706	1.5261*	35.2392	0.9307	1.6283
s × *r*	6	0.9306	2.4329†	27.6138	0.3494	2.9893
dams	3	8.8423†	34.8695†	346.6503†	1.5257*	5.7352*
sires	3	1.1290	3.6253	44.9431	0.2497	2.2651
sires × dams	9	2.4738†	2.1686†	60.2633†	1.0078*	3.7506
sex × sires	3	0.2756	1.6653*	24.7867	0.2050	3.0320
sex × dams	3	1.0591	4.2357†	2.8969	0.6880	1.2902
sex × sires × dams	9	0.6850	0.7571	39.1042	0.7056	2.4609
error	405	0.4534	0.5569	23.9088	0.4386	
error	334					1.7853

* Probability<0.05.
† Probability<0.01.

TABLE 5B. MEAN SQUARES OF THE VARIOUS EFFECTS AS DETERMINED FROM TWO SEPARATE ANALYSES. SEX IS COMMON TO BOTH ANALYSES

Source	Degrees of freedom	M.S. 12-day weight	M.S. thyroid weight	M.S. µg thyroid/g B.W.	M.S. gram minutes
g.c.a.	3	52.8420	2.5182†	2597.39†	14370.79†
s.c.a.	6	88.3729*	0.1875	209.43	4647.12*
r	6	71.7397	0.1769	260.54	1303.80
sex	1	24.3253	5.8141†	8167.70†	8496.22*
s × g.c.a.	3	36.5349	0.2249	194.81	1198.41
s × s.c.a.	6	34.4841	0.2559	216.66	4414.99
s × *r*	6	103.1026*	0.1731	244.94	1098.96
dams	3	135.7180*	2.1782†	1919.36†	9096.79†
sires	3	22.7550	0.6637†	1073.32†	7630.62*
sires × dams	9	71.5282	0.1350	181.53	3181.27
sex × sires	3	67.4226	0.2192	208.49	114.90
sex × dams	3	61.2077	0.0484	37.58	2383.16
sex × sires × dams	9	61.0233	0.2718*	290.64	3242.31
error	334	41.5759			
error	359		0.1242	188.01	2168.42

* Probability < 0.05.
† Probability < 0.01.

TABLE 6. PARENTAL MEANS $\hat{p}$ AND AVERAGE OF THE CROSSBREDS $\hat{y}$ AND VALUES REQUIRED FOR SIGNIFICANCE (LSD) AT THE FIVE PER CENT LEVEL BETWEEN $\hat{y}$ AND $\hat{p}$.

Strains crossed	Characteristic									
	45-day weight		Growth		Food consumed		Feed per g gain		Number born	
	$\hat{y}$	$\hat{p}$	$\hat{y}$	$\hat{p}$	$\hat{y}$	$\hat{p}$	$\hat{y}$	$\hat{p}$	$\hat{y}$	$\hat{p}$
OV	19.8*	20.9	9.8*	12.0	61.1*	70.6	6.1*	5.3	5.3	5.7
OA	21.4	21.4	11.3*	12.5	74.4	69.7	5.7	5.0	6.4	5.6
OC	19.4*	20.5	10.9*	11.9	61.2	73.7	4.8	5.6	6.0	5.4
VA	19.2	19.0	10.9	10.6	61.5	62.3	4.7	5.3	6.6	4.8
VC	18.4	18.1	9.1*	10.0	58.6*	66.3	5.4	5.9	4.6	4.1
AC	18.1	18.7	11.0	10.5	59.5*	65.4	5.0	5.6	5.8	4.0
LSD		0.8		0.9		6.8		0.9		1.9
	12-day weight		Thyroid weight		μg thyroid body weight		gram-minute of survival			
OV	28.1	23.8	3.5	3.5	133	129	855	847		
OA	28.4	29.2	2.9	2.9	100	101	824	798		
OC	25.9	22.7	2.4	2.6	96	91	757	804		
VA	29.5	27.8	2.7	3.2	107*	123	815	855		
VC	24.9	16.4	2.3*	2.9	101	113	814	861		
AC	29.9*	16.7	2.2	2.3	92	89	720	812		
LSD		9.0		0.5		19		137		

* Probability less than 0.05.

Growth from 21–45 *Days of Age*

Strains *O*, *V* and *C* were superior to their crossbred offspring in ability to grow after weaning. Two crosses of strain *A*, those with *V* and *C*, were the only crosses which exhibited superior growing ability that could not be accounted for by the general combining ability of the parent strains. There was a sex difference in the offspring of 1.90 g in total growth for the period which was essentially constant over all genotypes as evidenced by the lack of interaction of sex with any of the other sources of variation studied in the two analyses.

Most of the differences in general combining ability can be accounted for by maternal effects since the mean square for differences between strains of dam (general combining ability of the female strains) is about the same as the mean square for general combining ability, whereas the mean square for differences between sires is very small and not statistically significantly larger than the error mean square, Table 5. After removal of the general combining ability and specific combining ability effects, offspring of strain *O* females are superior in post-weaning growth of their reciprocal crosses only to offspring of strain *V* females. As reported previously by Mason *et al.* (1957) and by Bogart *et al.* (1958) *OV* mice born from *V* females suffered from a severe, inherited vitamin deficiency before weaning from which they apparently did not recover.

In pure strain matings, *O* females are adapted to raising litters of around nine mice or about two more than they raise in crossbred litters which, since the *O* females are extremely good mothers as indicated by the 12-day weights of their offspring, would leave little room for post-weaning compensatory growth. Thus, the superior post-weaning growing ability of offspring of *A* females and *C* females in the crosses *OA* and *OC* is most likely compensatory growth.

In pure strain matings, *A* females are adapted to raising only about five mice per litter, whereas in crossbred litters they had to attempt to raise one to four extra mice (Bogart *et al.*, 1958). Thus it can be expected that compensatory growth would occur in their crossbred offspring and this is borne out by the fact that in each cross *AO*, *AV* and *AC* the reciprocal effect is in favor of the *A* female.

Crossbred offspring of strain *C* females were never superior to their reciprocal cousins and this can not be explained by maternal effects since *C* females had litters of about the same size in cross or pure strain matings and the 12-day litter weights were generally low. Individuals of strain *C* were smaller than those of the other three strains (see below) and the small size predominates in all of their crossbred offspring. Thus, the genes for *small size* in strain *C* are *dominant* as are the genes (see below) for increased oxygen consumption, and the latter may be one causal factor of the former.

Partial support of this statement is provided by the fact that 12-day weights of offspring in the second generation from *C* females are still small even when the line of descent is through the male crossbred sons, which might indicate sex linkage.

Strain *V* had poor general combining ability for post-weaning growth and combined better with itself than with any of the other three strains. Strain *V* imparted to its offspring a relatively inactive thyroid gland as evidenced by greater gram-minutes of survival, and by the heavier thyroid weights which were correlated with gram-minutes of survival. This would be expected to increase growth because it should increase efficiency of growth. However, the lower thyroid activity apparently led to decreased food consumption because of the lesser activity associated with hypo-thyroidism. Further, the food consumed, or at least the food utilized, was not sufficient to provide for growth (anabolism) at a rate exceeding catabolism to the extent of other mice in the population. The cross of *VA*, which had superior growing ability, also had optimum thyroid activity, and apparently other factors which would affect efficiency such as the digestive system and the kidneys were working well.

Forty-five-Day Body Weight

In many ways 45-day body weight is the most important item for consideration because it is comparable to a weight at slaughter age in farm animals as well as weight at first mating in farm animals. Thus, when using mice as a tool for developing agricultural philosophy it is well to consider thoroughly the relationship between this characteristic, the importance of which is most apt to be overemphasized, with all previous and future characteristics which will have an effect on the economic well-being of farmers.

Forty-five-day body weight is positively correlated with growth from 21 to 45 days of age in both sexes ($r = 0.55$ for females and 0.69 for males), it is even more highly correlated with food consumed from 21 to 45 days of age ($r = 0.79$ for both sexes); there is however, no correlation between efficiency of growth and 45-day body weight. The correlation between 45-day body weight and the number of mice born per litter is 0.62 for females and 0.43 for males. The latter correlation coefficient is not significant at the 5% level of probability. Forty-five-day body weight of females is correlated with the 12-day weights of their offspring with a coefficient of 0.62, while the 45-day body weight of males has no significant correlation with the 12-day litter weights of their offspring.

In general combining ability, strain *C* was low; however, this was largely because offspring from strain *C* females were much smaller than other mice. There is some evidence that sex linkage may be involved in the genes determining 45-day body weight of *C* mice since the male and female offspring of *C* females and the female offspring of *C* males are especially small. Since

45-day body weights were not obtained on the F_2 mice it can only be surmised that sex linkage is involved and that the same sex linked genes for small size affecting 45-day body weights are also affecting 12-day litter weights.

Strain *O* was superior in general combining ability for 45-day weight but a lot of the superiority was due to the female parent and occurred prior to weaning.

There were no significant specific combining ability effects in 45-day body weight although there were some significant interactions involving sex of the offspring and specific combining ability which involved strain *A* and *C* and the cross *AC*. The males of strains *A* and *C* had larger 45-day body weights than could be accounted for by specific combining ability and the crossbred males were smaller than expected. Of course, the opposite can be said of females in each case. The net effect of all factors provided *AC* with the highest metabolic rates of all mice observed. Thus, results of this increased metabolism were especially striking if the *C* females were the mothers. The growth after weaning was good in males of both crosses, but the mothers, and particularly the *C* mothers, could not meet the nutritional needs of the males during the nursing period. Assuming that there was a sex difference in birth weight, the females would have been smaller and consequently would have required somewhat less milk which would allow them to grow more normally than did their brothers. This is borne out by the satisfactory weaning weights of female offspring. In strain by strain matings, *A* mothers are adapted to raising male offspring with the thyroid activity of the females of the cross *AC*, whereas in strain by strain matings the *C* mothers are not even adapted to raising males of the high thyroid activity of the crossbreds, p. 207.

Reciprocal effects and the interaction of sex with reciprocal effects were both statistically significant. Offspring of *O* females were larger in all crosses than their reciprocal cousins and in the crosses *OV* and *OC* sons were larger to a greater extent than were daughters. The superior mothering ability of the *O* females should explain this effect since in unpublished investigations we have found that the males are somewhat more variable than females even when the coefficient of variation is considered. The consequences of this difference in variation were discussed by Mason *et al.* (1958) and briefly mean that sex differences in body size increase as body size increases.

Offspring of *V* mothers were larger at 45 days of age than the reciprocal crosses from either *A* or *C* females and again the male offspring were larger to a greater extent than female offspring. This effect had to be due to a greater weaning weight of the offspring of *V* mothers since post-weaning growth was less. It is doubtful that the *V* females gave more milk than the *A* or *C* females since there is a positive correlation (−0.56 with gram-minutes of survival) between thyroid activity of the mothers and 12-day litter weights of the offspring. What is more likely is that the nutritive requirements of the offspring of *V* females were less since they had lower rates of metabolism than their reciprocal cousins. This is supported by the fact that 12-day weights of *V* females when mated to a random sample of the 16 genotypes of the F_1 population were intermediate between 12-day weights of offspring of *A* and *C* females when mated in the same way.

A mothers were superior to *C* mothers in the cross *AC*. This cross has been discussed in detail above and it is only necessary to remark again on the apparent sex linkage of small size dominant genes of strain *C* which, acting in this cross, decreased the body weights of *CA* males in contrast to *AC* males.

Forty-five-day body weight was chosen as a characteristic to measure which would be relatively free of maternal effects as discussed by McArthur (1944) and by Falconer (1953). Maternal influences were acting on 45-day body weights of mice in this study as discussed above. In part this is explainable on the basis of conflicting metabolic patterns which are inherited. Aside from this it should be fruitful to examine the past history of the strains. Strain *O* had been maintained, unused, for a number of years in the laboratory in which this study was conducted. During this time only three or four breeding animals of each sex were kept at any time. Selection was for large size and healthy animals. Litters were weaned at 28 days of age or later. Matings were not made until females were 90 days old or older and thus were well grown. Females which did not raise large litters of big, healthy individuals were discarded. In this way, selection was for large size as well as for favorable maternal effects which would accumulate even in a constant genotype. These maternal effects might take several generations to eliminate under the conditions of this experiment.

Strain *V*, on the other hand, was used for diagnostic work in its previous history. A large colony of mice was maintained in one cage and, when mice were needed for diagnostic purposes, large and healthy males and large and healthy females were removed. Thus, the mice that had the greatest chance of being mothers were either young or very old, and in this way unfavorable maternal effects had a chance to accumulate, in addition to there being selection for small size. The surviving mice of diagnostic tests were replaced in the colony and in this way selection for inactive thyroids may have occurred. Maintaining the *V* mice as they were maintained would create a feeding problem and mice which did not require large amounts of food would have the best chance of survival. That there could have been selection for decreased daily food consumption is indicated by the general combining ability of strain *V* for less food consumption, and of course 45-day body weights are positively associated with food consumption after weaning.

Strain *A* was maintained in much the same way as strain *V* except that it was used in insecticide studies which may have induced a selection for high thyroid activity since survivors of these tests were also returned to the colony. Food consumption would again be a problem but since the mice had high rates of metabolism, large amounts of food in relation to body size had to be eaten. The only way the strain could cope with the problem was to develop small body size and about average food consumption. Since the females required large amounts of food for the maintenance of their own bodies, and since food was a limiting factor, it is only logical that there would be selection for small litter size. In $A \times A$ matings only 4.4 mice are born per litter on the average, and surprisingly, the male is largely responsible (Bogart *et al.*, 1958).

The history of strain *C* is not known; however, the effects of strain *C* on 45-day body weight seem to be well explained on purely genetic grounds. Finding maternal effects so outstanding in the mice of this study as compared to those of other published reports is not surprising after the previous history of the strains is known.

As expected, 45-day weight is less subject to maternal influences than growth as is indicated by the significance of differences between strains of sire for 45-day body weight. In other words, true genetic differences have some chance to express themselves in 45-day body weight and thus it would seem that strain *V* is genetically smaller than the other strains and that these genes are essentially additive with those of the other strains.

Food consumed from 21–45 *Days of Age*

Food consumption has been discussed above in relation to growth and 45-day body weight. The general combining ability effect of strain *O* was to increase food consumption by about 5 g and most of this effect was maternal since differences between strains of sires were not significant. Since 45-day body weight is comparable to the weight at marketing age of meat producing animals and since the correlation between 45-day weight and food consumption is the highest correlation ($r = 0.79$) observed, it is well to consider how food consumption for this period might be increased. Large size at weaning is probably the most important influence on a mouse's ability to eat during this growing period as indicated by the relationship of (1) general combining abilities of the strains for food consumption and 12-day litter weight as measured in their offspring and (2) the relationships of the 12-day weights of the four strains when mated to a random sample of the 16 F_1 genotypes. These are both positive relationships.

The next most important item in increasing food consumption is to avoid matings with strains *V* or *C*, or *A* with strain *O*, or above all to avoid using females of these strains. If one considers that the consumption of large amounts of food from 21–45 days of age is desirable, then crosses involving *V* and *C* were undesirable and exhibited negative heterosis.

Efficiency of Growth from 21–45 *Days of Age*

Efficiency of growth during the post-weaning period is of utmost importance to the livestock feeder who buys weanling animals to develop for the meat market. It is important to both the primary producer and the livestock feeder in the situation where the feeder does not purchase the animals for some considerable time after weaning. And, it is important to the primary producer in connection with the females developed for the breeding herd.

Grams of food consumed per gram of growth is the index of efficiency used, with small values or negative effects being desirable. The failure of differences due to general combining ability and differences due to strains of sire to be statistically significant indicate that additive genes or perhaps even non-additive genes are not important in determining this trait. Differences between strains of dams were significant, with offspring from *A* females being the most efficient. As discussed above, compensatory growth of these mice was probably occurring and this type of growth is generally more efficient than non-compensatory growth (Pomeroy, 1955; Brody, 1945).

Specific combining ability effects were statistically significant with strain *C* particularly outstanding in its low efficiency as compared to its crosses. This increased efficiency in the crossbreds was accomplished through decreased food consumption in excess of the decrease in growth associated with *C* crosses, and was accomplished in spite of very short asphyxiation times. In this case, the increased efficiencies, while heterotic in themselves, must be considered as a result of a general hybrid loss in the *C* mice. Further, although high efficiency is desirable, a livestock man would not profit from it when obtained in this way because of the generally small final weights attained, the reduced fertility as indicated by litter size at birth and the reduced mothering ability as indicated by reduced 12-day litter weights.

Crosses of strains *V* and *A* with *O* resulted in negative specific combining ability for efficiency of growth which was associated with negative specific combining ability for growth and number of mice born per litter.

Reciprocal effects, which were significant, have been mostly explained previously by growth and food consumption. Crossbred offspring from *O* females required more food per gram of growth than the reciprocal crossbreds from *A* and *C* females. These mice were larger at weaning and at 45 days of age, therefore, higher maintenance requirements are expected. The reciprocal cross *OV* was more efficient than *VO*. *OV*, from *O* mothers, were generally healthy throughout their life, whereas the *VO*, from *V* mothers, were stunted badly prior to weaning and had hardly recovered by 45 days of age, although an attempt was made by their consuming large amounts of food. It is probable that efficient use of the food could not be made until first the previously acquired vitamin deficiency had been made up and secondly the damage resulting from the vitamin deficiency had been repaired.

There was a significant difference in sex response to reciprocal effects in the cross *OV* (*VO*) and the cross *AC* (*CA*). In the first case it appears that *VO* females from *V* mothers were not as severely affected by the vitamin deficiency as were their brothers since they ate relatively more food, grew relatively faster and were relatively heavier at 45 days of age.

In the cross *AC*, male offspring from *C* males were relatively less efficient than their sisters when compared with male offspring from *A* males. This is in agreement with previous discussions of sex linkage for small size genes of strain *C* and the effect of strain *C* on efficiency of growth.

Number of Mice Born per Litter in the F_2 Generation

The number of mice born per litter in the F_2 generation was affected mainly by maternal effects of their grandmothers, or it might be said that the number of mice an individual may have is affected to some extent by the individual's mother. Perhaps oddly, the male is affected as well as the female. If strain *O* females were the mothers, crossbred mice had a better chance of having large litters; if strain *C* females were the mothers, crossbred offspring had small litters; litters of intermediate size were born to crossbred offspring of *A* and *V* mothers. Outstanding reciprocal effects were observed if *O* females were mothers rather than *V* females; *V* females rather than *C* females; and *A* females rather than *C* females. The *OV* cross has been discussed previously in detail as to its abnormality. The relationship of *C* females to *V* and *A* females in the crosses *VC* and *VA* is the same as for growth, 45-day body weight and food consumption. The number of mice born per litter was positively correlated with growth from 21–45 days of age in females only ($r = 0.68$); positively correlated with food consumed from 21–45 days of age in females only ($r = 0.70$); positively correlated with 45-day body weight in females only ($r = 0.62$), and negatively correlated with gram minutes of survival in females only ($r = -0.51$). The correlations of these characteristics in male offspring to the number of mice they sired in litters were in the same direction, but were not statistically significant.

Twelve-day Litter Weights

Twelve-day litter weights follow closely the number of mice born per litter, there being a correlation of 0.90 between number of mice born in litters of females and the 12-day weights of these litters, indicating that the same factors, including maternal effects, which endow a female with the ability to give birth to a large number of mice, also endow her with the ability to provide for them after birth. The correlation between 12-day weights of litters sired by males and the number of mice born in the litters is not so high ($r = 0.73$), which would indicate that after birth the maternal influence of the mate, or mothers of the litter, was becoming more prominent. There was a significant interaction of sex of the parents of the litters with reciprocal effects of the parents in the original cross. This was most outstanding in the cross *VO* where female offspring of *V* females were unable to raise large litters and in the cross *AC* where female offspring of *C* males raised much larger litters than those sired by their brothers or in fact than any other group related to strain *C* or to strain *A*, a definite heterotic effect which cannot be explained with the information collected in this experiment.

Thyroid Weight

There is a large sex difference in thyroid weight, thyroids of females being 0.86 mg heavier than those of males. This is a very substantial difference when the mean thyroid weight is only 2.72 mg. Thyroid weights were relatively independent of body weight as indicated by the high correlation between thyroid weight and μg of thyroid per gram of body weight ($r = 0.89$ for females and 0.88 for males). As far as females are concerned thyroid weight is also independent of gram-minutes of survival, and thus presumably of oxygen consumption. However, thyroid weights of females are significantly correlated with food consumed ($r = 0.55$) and with 45-day body weight ($r = 0.50$). In males thyroid weights are significantly correlated with gram-minutes of survival ($r = 0.65$); with 12-day weight of the litters sired by particular males ($r = 0.60$); and with efficiency of growth ($r = 0.58$), but are not significantly correlated with food consumption or 45-day weight.

The non-linearity of the relationships of the various traits studied has not been investigated except for the relationship of thyroid weight of males to growth of males, which is definitely not linear, and growth of males can be described by including a quadratic function of thyroid weight. This relationship was noted in the previous discussion of growth, and has been discussed further by Mason *et al.* (1956).

Efficiency of growth, which is related to thyroid weight in males and not to thyroid weight in females, is related to growth ($r = 0.61$) of males, but not of females; and is related to food consumption of females ($r = 0.70$) but not of males; and food consumed is related to thyroid weight of females ($r = 0.55$) but not of males. In other words, the heavier the thyroids of females, the more food they eat and the less efficient they are because growth is not increased at a sufficiently rapid rate. Thus, it might be expected that upon further investigation a curvilinear relationship would also be found between growth of females and thyroid weight. In contrast to females where the important item contributing to efficiency is food consumption, in males growth is the important determiner and it is known that growth in our mice decreases rapidly and consequently efficiency decreases rapidly after thyroid weights attain 2.4 mg.

Thyroid weights are worthy of the above discussion since they are more highly heritable and less subject to maternal influences than previous items studied. Differences due to general combining ability account for most of the differences in thyroid weights other than sex. The offspring of strain *O* which is superior in general combining ability in most of the traits studied have intermediate thyroid weights, whereas offspring of strain *C* which had mostly poor general combining ability were low in thyroid weights. Differences between strains of dams were somewhat greater than differences between sires. These differences were mainly due to thyroids of offspring of strain *V* (largest thyroids) and strain *C* (smallest thyroids) females being larger and smaller respectively than the average of the reciprocal crosses. There does not seem to be any sex linkage involved and the explanation may be that large and small amounts, respectively, of thyrotropin affect the embryonic thyroids and create a permanent environmental effect.

From the relationships cited above, it would seem that intermediate thyroid weights are heterotic and that these can be obtained and supposedly maintained by selective mating.

Micrograms of Thyroid per Gram of Body Weight

The inheritance of the amount of thyroid tissue per gram of body weight follows the same pattern as the inheritance of thyroid weight. The correlation coefficient between the two characteristics being about 0.89, as stated above, means that if animals have large thyroids they also have large amounts of thyroid in relation to body weight. However, whereas thyroid weight is significantly correlated with gram-minutes of survival only in males, μg thyroid per gram of body weight is significantly correlated with gram-minutes of survival in both sexes; $r = 0.48$ in females and 0.46 in males.

The failure to establish a significant relationship of μg thyroid per gram body weight to growth in females, whereas one was established in males ($r = -0.52$) is logical since the range of μg thyroid per gram body weight covered by females is very small as compared to males. The relationship of μg thyroid per gram body weight to growth is probably independent of sex, since when the female values are plotted on the graph for males which was constructed by Mason *et al*, 1956, the values fit very well, so that growth could be predicted, regardless of sex, by the equation $\hat{y} = 10.68 - 0.04\hat{x}$, where $\hat{y}$ is the average growth of mice of a given genotype and $\hat{x}$ is the average μg thyroid per gram body weight of that genotype.

There is a negative correlation in males, but not in females, between μg thyroid per gram body weight and efficiency of growth ($r = 0.52$ with grams of food consumed per gram of growth). However, this is to be expected since variation in food consumption of females is more important in determining efficiency than is growth, and food consumption is not related in either sex to the amount of thyroid tissue per gram body weight.

Since both large amounts of growth and good efficiency are desirable, small amounts of thyroid per gram of body weight are desirable, but it must be remembered that the growth associated with the smallest amounts of thyroid tissue is compensatory, and that the efficiency of growth attained in the groups with the lesser amounts of thyroid tissue per unit body weight was attained by their eating small amounts of food rather than by large amounts of growth.

Gram-minutes of Survival

Rates of oxygen consumption as measured by gram-minutes of survival followed the same pattern of inheritance as thyroid weight, except that there is specific combining ability. In particular, strain *C* combined with itself to reduce oxygen consumption as compared to its crosses. The generally poor combining ability of strain *C* for all characteristics measured parallels this overdominant effect on oxygen consumption of strain *C* in crosses, and since oxygen consumption does not follow exactly the thyroid characteristics, it is logical that other factors are being inherited through strain *C* which affect oxygen consumption, as indicated by survival time per unit of tissue.

Oxygen consumption was positively correlated with growth in females ($r = -0.54$ with gram-minutes of survival), but not with males, and also with number of mice born per litter ($r = -0.51$) and 12-day litter weights ($r = -0.56$) in females only. Since females, in this group of mice, had lower metabolic rates than males, something can be gained by increasing metabolic rates of females. It should be noted that strain *O* females, which were superior mothers, had higher metabolic rates than their brothers, whereas in nearly all other groups the opposite situation existed. There were only two groups which imply a heterotic effect in this direction: *V* females × *A* males and *A* females × *C* males.

GENERAL DISCUSSION

As a final indication of hybrid vigor the parental means were compared with the average of their crossbreds, Table 6. The significant differences for 45-day weight, *OV* and *OC*, were both in the direction of negative heterosis as were the significant differences for growth *OV*, *OA*, *OC* and *VC*; and considering increased food consumption heterotic, as per the above discussion, the crosses *OV*, *VC* and *AC* exhibited negative heterosis. The cross *OV* was significantly less efficient than the average of the parents, also negative heterosis. Thus all significant differences from parental means for characteristics concerning growth and body weight were negatively heterotic.

There were no significant differences from parental averages in the number of mice born per litter (the crossbred mothers generally had more mice born per litter, but not the required 1.9 extra ones), whereas in 12-day litter weights one cross, *AC*, definitely showed positive heterosis, and again the means were generally in favor of the crossbred mothers.

The mice studied in this problem displayed conflicting physiological patterns. The basic physiological traits studied were mostly additive in their inheritance, and thus there was generally created a conflict between the physiology of the mother and the genotype of her crossbred offspring.

It would seem that if positive heterotic effects are to be attained in crossbreeding of mammals, where maternal effects can be so profound, selection must be toward similar physiology in the parental strains. This physiology of course must be adapted to the environment under which the crossbreds are to perform. Thus as discussed by Dobzhansky (1950) heterosis can be attained by crossing co-adapted groups, but negative heterosis can be attained if selection has been toward different physiological patterns which produce the same phenotype.

SUMMARY

Four strains of mice were crossed via a diallel plan. Characteristics measured in the offspring were post-weaning growth, food consumption and efficiency of growth to 45 days of age; 45-day body weight, fertility as measured by number of mice born per litter and milking ability as measured by 12-day litter weights. The thyroid characteristics, weight and μg thyroid per gram of body weight, and oxygen consumption measured by gram-minutes of survival in a sealed ½ pint Mason jar were studied in an attempt to find a basic explanation for some of the results.

Maternal effects were outstanding for all of the first five traits.

The thyroid characteristics were inherited in an apparently additive manner.

Sex linkage of dominant genes for small size was apparent in the crossbred mice of strain *C*.

The physiological patterns in the parent mice were widely different and the crossbreeding resulted in a conflict between mother and offspring which generally resulted in a negative heterosis, or the inability, in some cases, for offspring to exploit their superior genotypes.

It is concluded that for heterosis to be attained in mammals, where maternal effects can be profound, that selection of parental material must be for similar physiological patterns.

REFERENCES

BOGART, RALPH, MASON, R. W., NICHOLSON, HUGH & KRUEGER, HUGO (1958) Genetic aspects of fertility in mice. *Intern. J. Fertility* **3,** 86.

BRODY, S. (1945) *Bioenergetics and Growth*, Reinhold, New York.

DOBZHANSKY, TH. (1950) Genetics of natural populations. XIX. Origin of heterosis through natural selection in populations of *Drosophila pseudoobscura*, *Genetics* **35,** 288.

FALCONER, D. S. (1957) Milk production in mice, *J. Agr. Sci.* **37,** 224.

FALCONER, D. S. (1953) Selection for large and small size in mice. *J. Genetics* **51,** 470.

GRIFFING, B. (1956) Concept of general and specific combining ability in relation to diallel crossing systems. *Australian J. Biol. Sci.* **9,** 463.

MACARTHUR, JOHN W. (1944) Genetics of body size and related characters. I. Selecting small and large races of the laboratory mouse. *Am. Naturalist* **78,** 142.

MASON, R. W., BOGART, RALPH & KRUEGER, HUGO (1956) Growth rate, feed efficiency and thyroid activity in male mice of different strains and strain crosses. *Proc. West. Sec. Amer. Soc. An. Prod.* **7,** XLIII.

MASON, R. W., BOGART, RALPH & KRUEGER, HUGO (1958) Heritability estimates as affected by sex, genetic-environmental interaction, and type of selection practised. *Proc. West. Sec. Am. Soc. An. Prod.* **9**, XLV.

MASON, R. W., BOGART, RALPH & KRUEGER, HUGO (1958) Methods of adjusting data for differences due to sex. *Proc. West. Sec. Am. Soc. An. Prod.* **9**, XLI.

MASON, R. W., NICHOLSON, HUGH, BOGART, RALPH & KRUEGER, HUGO (1957) Inherited differences in vitamin requirements among mice. *J. Pharmacol. & Exptl. Therap.* **119**, 165.

POMEROY, R. W. (1955) in *Progress in the Physiology of Farm Animals*, Vol. 2, Butterworths, London.

SNEDECOR, G. W. (1956) *Statistical Methods*, 5th ed., Iowa State College Press, Ames, Iowa.

THE USE OF CORRECTION FOR REGRESSION ON A SECOND CHARACTER TO INCREASE THE EFFICIENCY OF SELECTION

By A. F. PURSER

A.R.C., Animal Breeding Research Organisation, Edinburgh

WHEN selective breeding is practised within a population for a single continuous character, the progress expected may be predicted on certain assumptions. For instance, in an additive situation the genetic gain ΔG of a character with heritability $h^2 = \sigma_g^2/\sigma_p^2$ may be shown to be

$$\Delta G = \bar{\imath} h^2 \sigma_p$$

$$= \frac{\bar{\imath}\sigma_g^2}{\sigma_p} = \frac{\bar{\imath}\sigma_g^2}{\sqrt{(\sigma_g^2 + \sigma_e^2)}}$$

where $\bar{\imath}$ is the selection intensity and σ_p^2, σ_g^2 and σ_e^2 are the phenotypic, genetic and environmental variances respectively. Reducing σ_e^2, by making corrections for known environmental effects for example, will increase the genetic gain to be obtained. The use of a second character of the phenotype of the animal to give information on environmental variation will however alter the situation because of the possibility of there also being a genetic association between the two characters. A method of increasing the genetic gain for a single character by means of correction for linear regression on a second character is discussed in this paper. The theory is outlined and some results given from a selection experiment where these ideas were put into practice.

THEORY

Both Rendel (1954) and Osborne (1957) have considered the efficiency of selection of a character when correction is made for its linear regression on a second character. Some of their results are included in the following synthesis.

Suppose we have two characters X_1 and X_2 having a phenotypic correlation r_p and a genetic correlation r_g.

Consider an index of the form

$$I = X_1 - aX_2$$

where a is a constant.

The ratio of the genetic gain in X_1, when selection is based on I, $\Delta G(X_1/I)$, to the gain by direct selection on X_1, $\Delta G(X_1)$, is

$$\frac{\Delta G(X_1/I)}{\Delta G(X_1)} = E = \left[1 - a r_g \frac{\sigma_{g2}}{\sigma_{g1}}\right] \Big/ \sqrt{\left[1 - 2 a r_p \frac{\sigma_{p2}}{\sigma_{p1}} + a^2 \frac{\sigma_{p2}^2}{\sigma_{p1}^2}\right]} \qquad (1)$$

E is a maximum when

$$a = \left[r_p \frac{\sigma_{p1}}{\sigma_{p2}} - r_g \frac{\sigma_{p1}^2}{\sigma_{p2}^2} \frac{\sigma_{g2}}{\sigma_{g1}}\right] \Big/ \left[1 - r_p r_g \frac{\sigma_{p1}}{\sigma_{p2}} \frac{\sigma_{g2}}{\sigma_{g1}}\right] \qquad (2)$$

If $r_g = 0$ then a reduces to the phenotypic regression of X_1 on X_2. E then becomes $1/\sqrt{(1-r_p^2)}$ as would be expected. In any case one may use the phenotypic regression for a even if r_g is not zero, though the efficiency is then less than maximal. Such a course may be adopted when no reliable estimate of the genetic correlation is available. The range of values of a that give some increase in genetic gain for X_1 may be found from Equation 1. For $E > 1$ we find a lies between limits $0 < a < A$ where

$$A = 2\left[r_p \frac{\sigma_{p1}}{\sigma_{p2}} - r_g \frac{\sigma_{p1}^2}{\sigma_{p2}^2} \frac{\sigma_{g2}}{\sigma_{g1}}\right] \Big/ \left[1 - r_g^2 \frac{\sigma_{p1}^2}{\sigma_{p2}^2} \frac{\sigma_{g2}^2}{\sigma_{g1}^2}\right]$$

For a wide range of parameters it is found that A is approximately twice the optimum value of a.

A point to be considered is that if r_g is not zero, selection for I will generally cause a correlated genetic change in X_2. If X_2 is to be kept constant the value of a must be such that the genetic covariance of I and X_2 must be zero.

Thus $$r_g \sigma_{g_1} \sigma_{g_2} - a \sigma_{g_2}^2 = 0$$

and so $$a = r_g \frac{g_1}{g_2}$$

i.e. a is now the genetic regression of X_1 on X_2. In this case the efficiency of selection for X_1 is given by

$$E = [1 - r_g^2] \Big/ \left[1 - 2 r_p r_g \frac{\sigma_{p2}}{\sigma_{p1}} \frac{\sigma_{g1}}{\sigma_{g2}} + r_g^2 \frac{\sigma_{p2}^2}{\sigma_{p1}^2} \frac{\sigma_{g1}^2}{\sigma_{g2}^2}\right]$$

EXPERIMENTAL MATERIAL

A comprehensive selection programme was started in 1954 with a hill flock of Scottish Blackface sheep at Stanhope in Peeblesshire. Part of the experiment was a two-way selection programme, together with a control, to change body conformation of young lambs. Selection of breeding stock was on individual merit and took place at the normal castration time about 2 months of age.

The main aim of the experiment was the provision of information on the genetic parameters of hill sheep. To this end it was thought desirable to have a criterion of selection that was as highly heritable as possible. In the lines selected for conformation, cannon bone length was chosen as the main selection character. A correction for variation in body weight was introduced in order to increase the efficiency of selection. This correction for weight also served a second purpose, that of keeping the average weights of selected animals reasonably similar in all three lines.

The breeding system was such that rams selected in 1954 were used as shearlings to produce the 1956 lamb crop; thereafter ram lambs were used. Thus the three lamb crops in 1956–58 represent three successive generations of selection on the male side.

RESULTS AND DISCUSSION

The parameters required to estimate the value of a to be used in this study were estimated from analysis of variance and covariance among half-sib progeny groups. The numbers of lambs and sire groups involved in each year were:

	1954	1955	1956	1957	1958
No. of lambs	494	563	944	1067	1034
No. of sire groups	35	61	57	56	52

The results obtained from the first year's data were of necessity used as a basis for deriving the index to be used that year. For the sake of uniformity the index has been used unchanged in succeeding years though subsequent data showed that a slightly more efficient index could have been used.

In 1954 the phenotypic regression of cannon length on body weight was 0.076 cm/lb. The value of a as determined from Equation 2 was 0.117 cm/lb. However, the genetic correlation was not very accurately determined so a working value of $a = 0.08$ cm/lb (approximating to the phenotypic regression) was used. Thus the index I, which was in practice called the corrected cannon length, was made up from cannon length (X_1) and body weight (X_2) as follows:

$$I = X_1 - 0.08X_2.$$

Analysis of the full data from 1954–58 enabled the efficiency of selection on the basis of the index to be determined. The analysis of variance and covariance of half-sib groups within years gave the following results:

	Mean squares			Mean product	Degrees of freedom
	X_1	X_2	I	$X_1 X_2$	
Bet. sire groups	0.634	47.8	0.482	2.86	244
Within sire groups	0.313	29.9	0.135	2.31	3841
Total	0.332	31.0	0.156	2.34	4085

The phenotypic regression was 0.076 cm/lb, the same as the estimate from the 1954 data alone and still in close agreement with the working value of $a = 0.08$ cm/lb.

The phenotypic correlation of X_1 and X_2 was 0.73 and the genetic 0.23. As had been assumed, at the beginning of this experiment, the body weight of lambs was a useful indicator of environmental variation of cannon length, in the sense that the environmental correlation was high (actual estimate of $r_e = 0.85$).

Components of variance between and within sire groups were calculated and from these were derived the phenotypic, genetic and environmental variances and corresponding heritabilities.

	X_1	X_2	I
σ_p^2	0.334	31.0	0.156
σ_g^2	0.083	4.6	0.090
σ_e^2	0.251	26.4	0.066
h^2	0.25	0.15	0.57

Correction of cannon length for regression on body weight markedly reduced the environmental variance and increased the heritability from 0.25 to 0.57. This latter figure is in agreement with estimates calculated from the response to two-way selection over three generations in 1956–58. About 200 lambs were produced each year in each of the two selection lines, from these the heritabilities of corrected cannon length were estimated as 0.65, 0.58 and 0.57 for the three successive years.

Though heritability of the index was more than twice as great as that of the cannon length alone, the improvement due to selection is not necessarily in the same ratio. The expected genetic change in cannon length when selection is based on an index may be calculated from the given figures. It was found (using Equation 2) that the maximum genetic gain would have been obtained with $a = 0.066$ cm/lb with the corresponding value of E, $E_{max} = 1.28$. In this optimum case the heritability of the index was estimated as 0.53, rather lower than the value of 0.57 obtained in our experiment. This highlights the fact that with an index based on two characters (or more), maximum heritability does not in general imply maximum genetic advance, though this would be true of a single character. The efficiency of the actual index used (with $a = 0.08$ cm/lb) was 1.26, only slightly less than the maximum possible value. In either case, the response to selection is at least 25% greater than could be expected by direct selection for cannon length alone.

An improvement in the response to selection of the order indicated by these results in long term breeding experiments with livestock is quite an important consideration. The basic principle may be extended to many other characters for which selection is desirable. For example if fleece weight was being selected, a correction for total skin area may be introduced. The phenotypic regression of fleece weight on skin area may be used though genetic progress in selection may be much greater if the optimum value of a (calculated from Equation (2)) is used.

SUMMARY

A method of increasing the efficiency of selective breeding for a character X_1 by the use of an index of the form $I = X_1 - aX_2$ is discussed. An expression for a for which efficiency of selection is maximal is found; this expression reduces to the phenotypic regression of X_1 on X_2, if the genetic correlation of X_1 and X_2 is zero.

An index was used in a selection experiment for body conformation of lambs in a hill flock of Scottish Blackface sheep. The main selection criterion was cannon bone length and a correction for body weight variation was introduced. The results showed that the heritability of the index was about twice as great as that of the primary character and that the genetic gain when selecting on the index was at least 25% greater than could be obtained by direction selection.

REFERENCES

OSBORNE, R. (1957) Correction for regression on a secondary trait as a method of increasing the efficiency of selective breeding, *Austral. J. Biol. Sci.* **10,** 365.

RENDEL, J. M. (1954) The use of regressions to increase heritability, *Austral. J. Biol. Sci.* **7,** 368.

ENDOCRINE VARIATION: HERITABILITY OF IODINE METABOLISM IN THE THYROIDS OF MICE

By C. K. Chai†

Roscoe B. Jackson Memorial Laboratory, Bar Harbor, Maine

Most studies of quantitative variation in laboratory animals have dealt mainly with anatomical characters, such as body size, wing size, number of bristles in Drosophila, and size and skeletal variations in mammals. Their essential purposes are to check the quantitative genetic theories and to elucidate the basic genetic phenomena. Similar studies have been quite extensively carried out in farm animals considering mainly the yield and performance such as milk, meat, wool, and egg production. The purpose of these studies is to improve the economical value of the farm animals. Experimental studies concerning physiological variation of polygenic inheritance are lacking. It is apparent, as Mather, and, more recently, Snyder and some others, have pointed out, that polygenic differences may result in many human aberrations, such as hypertension, resistance and susceptibility to specific infections, and to organic degenerative disease in general, including aging. The physiological systems must play a significant role. It is felt that genetic study of physiological variation may be of interest from both genetic and medical points of view.

We have previously demonstrated differences in thyroid activities between inbred strains of mice (Chai *et al.*, 1957; Chai, 1958). The present study will consider the heritability of iodine metabolism in the thyroid glands of mice.

MATERIALS AND METHODS

The experimental animals were produced by systematic hybridization of 6 inbred lines of mice for the purpose of incorporating a wide range of different genetic backgrounds. The crossbreeding is illustrated in Fig. 1 which is self-explanatory. Mice in the F_3 generation were produced by 8 matings of the F_2 hybrids. Eight males and 20 females from this generation were randomly chosen as breeders, one male being mated with 2 or 3 females, to produce the first generation. Therefore mice in the first generation had

† This study was supported by a research grant C–3108(C1) from the National Cancer Institute of the National Institute of Health, Public Health Service. The author is indebted to Prof. Sewall Wright for criticisms and help in the path coefficient analysis and Charles Ames for assistance in the experiment.

relationships of full-sib, half-sib and non-sib. The genetic structure of this generation was still different from a randombred population in regard to the genetic relationships between individuals. This difference is concerned with genetic variance and will be analyzed.

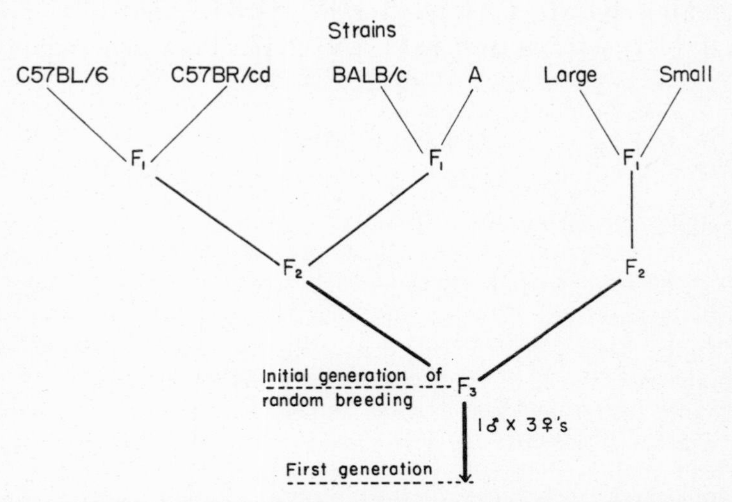

FIG. 1. A diagram illustrates the crossbreeding of the 6 inbred strains of mice. The first generation mice were produced by mating 1 male with 2 or 3 females randomly chosen from the F_3 generation.

Determination of I^{131} retention in the thyroid was made in mice of the first generation at 120–150 days of age. Each mouse was injected subcutaneously with 5–10 μc of I^{131} in 5 ml. of saline. Forty-eight hours were allowed for iodine fixation by the thyroid and the elimination of excess isotope. External thyroid counts were taken at 48 hrs and 72 hrs after the injection by restraining the mouse in a tapered wire chamber with a flat bottom. The thyroid region was centered over a 12 mm opening in the lead shield directly above the window of a Geiger-Müller tube. Body background count was measured over the epigastric region. It was taken at the same time.

The original thyroid counts were corrected by 65% of the body background in addition to physical decay. Then each thyroid count was converted to percentage of total amount of I^{131} injected. The output constant for each mouse was computed using the formula,

$$C_{t_1} = C_t \, e^{-Bt_1}$$

where C_t and C_{t_1} are the percentage counts at time t and t_1, e is the natural logarithm base, and B is the output constant. This formula is rather simplified, but for the present purpose it may be adequate. B is essentially a measure of the rate of iodine turnover in the thyroid gland and is closely related to the rate of thyroid hormone secretion.

RESULTS AND ANALYSIS

The mean output constant of the thyroid glands in these mice was found to be 0.28. The biological half life was 2.5 days according to the formula $0.693/B$. The results of the analysis of variance for these data is given in Table 1. The mean square between sires was significant ($P<0.05$) while that between dams within sire was not. It ought to be mentioned that female mice generally have a higher output than male mice. (More precise analysis of

TABLE 1. ANALYSIS OF VARIANCE FOR IODINE OUTPUT CONSTANT OF THE THYROID

Source of variation	Degree of freedom	Mean squares	Components of mean squares
Between sires	7	0.770	$Q+K_1D+K_2S$
Between dams within sire	11	0.518	$Q+K_1D$
Between full sibs	227	0.325	Q

K_1 = harmonic mean no. of mice in a sire family
K_2 = „ „ „ „ „ „ „ dam family
Q = variance between full sibs
D = variance between means of dam families
S = „ „ „ „ sire families.

these data would follow the method of analysis of disproportionate sub-class numbers. This would involve very cumbersome calculations.) For the sake of simplicity, we have not considered sex differences in the analysis. The variance due to this is therefore left mostly in the within female variance, which undoubtedly causes underestimation of heritability. S, D, and Q are the estimates of variance components associated respectively with sire, dam, and individual within dam.

The different genetic components of variance (Comstock, 1956), in each are given in Table 2, which show a much greater contribution to the total variation from environmental than from genetic source.

Heritability can be estimated in the present experiment, using the formula of

$$\frac{2(D+S)}{S+D+Q}, \quad \frac{4D}{S+D+Q}, \quad \text{or} \quad \frac{4S}{S+D+Q}.$$

In view of the difference in genetic components associated with sire and dam, it is more justifiable to use the sire component of genetic variance than the dam component, or both, for the estimate of heritability. Based on the formula $4S/(Q+S+D)$ we have arrived at a value of 0.10 for the estimate of heritability in these mice, without allowance for inbreeding. The sampling error for the estimate is 0.017. It is computed according to the procedure described by Osborne and Paterson (1957) for computing sampling error of a ratio.†

DISCUSSION

The larger variance between dams than between sires is expected, as maternal influence and dominance contribute nothing to the variance between sires. Even the effect due to non-allelic genic interactions contributes more to the variance for dams than for sires. This is easy to see in Table 2. The relative importance of dominance in comparison with interaction is not determinable in the present experiment, nor is the magnitude of maternal influence. It is possible to compute the effect of maternal influence, if both maternal and paternal half-sibs are provided. However separation of dominance and epistatic effects still remains a difficult problem in animal breeding experiments. If we care to assume that maternal influence and epistasis are negligible, the difference in variance between dam and sire is wholly due to dominance. An estimate of the ratio of dominance to additive genetic effect may be obtained. This ratio is 0.75 ($= D/S - 1$). In any event, it may be safe to say that there was no over-dominance.

Studies of inheritance of any physiological variation have been faced with the problem of obtaining adequate experimental control. Thyroid function is especially so, for it is influenced not only by environmental conditions but also by the internal conditions of the animal. There are also seasonal and possible diurnal variations in thyroid activity. The internal changes affected by other endocrine systems are very difficult to determine in such quantitative experiments. In view of the different sources of error, each of which could reduce the estimate of heritability, we tend to expect a low value. In effect, there has been no information in regard to the magnitude of heritability of

† $$s_{h^2}^2 = \frac{16(Q+D)^2 s_S^2 + S^2\{(s_Q^2 + s_D^2 + 2\,\widehat{\mathrm{Cov}}\,(Q, D)\} - 2S(Q+D)\,\widehat{\mathrm{Cov}}\,(D, S)}{(Q+D+S)^4} = 0.00029680$$

$$s_{h^2} = 0.017$$

where

$$s_Q^2 = 2Q^2/a$$

$$s_D^2 = \frac{2}{k^2}\left\{\frac{(Q+K_1D)^2}{b} + \frac{Q^2}{a}\right\}$$

$$s_S^2 = \frac{2}{k^2}\,2\left\{\frac{(Q+K_1D+K_2S)^2}{c} + \frac{(Q+K_1D)^2}{b}\right\}$$

$$\widehat{\mathrm{Cov}}\,(Q, D) = -s_Q^2/K_1$$

$$\widehat{\mathrm{Cov}}\,(D, S) = \frac{S_Q^2 - n^2 s_D^2}{K_1K_2}$$

$$\widehat{\mathrm{Cov}}\,(Q, S) = 0$$

a, b, and c are the degrees of freedom associated with sire, dam within sire, and full-sibs respectively.

TABLE 2. GENETIC COMPONENTS OF VARIANCE ASSOCIATED WITH SIRE, DAM, AND FULL-SIBS

Variance	Additive	Dominance	Interaction (epistasis)
$S=0.0086$	$(1/4)\sigma^2_G$		$(1/16)\ \sigma^2_{2G}+(1/64)\sigma^2_{3G}+\ldots+(1/4)^n\sigma^2_{nG}$
$D=0.0151$	$(1/4)\sigma^2_G$	$1/4\sigma^2_H$	$(3/16)\ \sigma^2_{2G}+\ldots+[(2n-1)/4n]\sigma^2_{nG}$ $(1/8)\sigma^2_{GH}+(1/16)\sigma^2_{GH}+\ldots+(1/2)^n(1/4)^m\sigma^2_{nGmH}$ $(1/16)\ \sigma^2_{2H}+\ldots+(1/4)^m\sigma^2_{mH}$

$Q=0.325=\sigma^2_E+$The remaining part of the genetic variance

$\sigma^2_G=$variance due to additive genetic effect

$\sigma^2_H=$,, ,, ,, dominance effect

$\sigma^2_{2G}, \sigma^2_{3G} \ldots, \sigma^2_{nG}$ =variance due to 2, 3 ..., n additive genic interactions

$\sigma^2_{GH}, \sigma^2_{2GH} \ldots, \sigma^2_{nGmH}=$,, ,, ,, additive × dominance, additive × additive × dominance ... n additive × m dominance interactions.

$\sigma^2_{2H}, \sigma^2_{3H} \ldots, \sigma^2_{mH}$ =variance due to 2, 3 ..., m dominance genic interactions.

physiological characters. By comparison with anatomical traits in some laboratory animals and yield in farm animals, the present estimate of heritability appears to be in the lower range. But comparison of this sort would be meaningless on account of the differences in species, characters and environmental conditions.

In order to realize the reduction of genetic variance due to genetic correlation between individuals in the first generation, the genetic relationships have been analyzed among mice in the different generations of this breeding system. This was done according to the method of path coefficient (Wright, 1921). This method seems convenient to apply to the present complicated breeding system. It is based on the assumption of neither dominance nor epistasis. As far as the results stand, the dominance and epistasis effect on the thyroid iodine metabolism, if in existence, would be small and would not invalidate the use of this method. The detailed calculations are given in the appendix. We have obtained, in the first generation, an average genetic correlation of 0.5839 for between sibs and 0.3572 for between random individuals. As noted, all of these correlations are relative to a non-existent hypothetical population from which the original inbred lines are supposed to have been derived and the inbreeding is complicated. These correlations need to be considered as approximations. Nevertheless in reference to a randombred population, the genetic variance was reduced in the mice of the first generation. The observed genetic variance is therefore about 64% ($1-m=0.6428$) of that in a hypothetical population from which the present inbred strains are assumed to have been derived. If correction is made for this correlation, a higher value of 0.155 is obtained for the estimate of heritability.

Needless to say, heritability of a character varies from population to population. The present data were obtained from a mouse population by deliberate crossing of 6 inbred strains. A difference in output constant of I^{131} in the thyroid was found to exist between some of these strains (for example the value for C57BL/6 was about twice that for A and BALB/c). It was found later that some other strains such as the DBA's had even higher thyroid activity than the C57BL/6 strain (Chai, 1958). A possible higher heritability may be obtained should the DBA mice be included in the breeding system. Nevertheless, this study has demonstrated quantitative inheritance of thyroid function—a physiological function which plays a significant role in basic metabolism, growth, and development but is extremely liable to environmental variation—and opened possibilities of genetic studies in physiological variations of other characters.

SUMMARY

A study has been made of the heritability of thyroid iodine metabolism in mice. A breeding system was set up by deliberate hybridization of 6 inbred strains of mice, (C57BL/6, C57BR/cd, BALB/c, A, LG and SM). Mice of F_1, F_2, and F_3 hybrids were produced. A further generation was produced by random mating of one male with 2 or 3 females in the F_3 generation so that a mouse population with half-sib, full-sib and non-sib relationships was obtained. Mice in this generation were used for the determination of iodine output constant.

Each animal was injected with 5–10 μc I^{131}. Counts of radiation in the neck of the thyroid region were made at two different times after the injection. The iodine output constant was computed from an exponential equation of biological decay.

A total of 246 mice were used in the experiment. The mean output constant was 0.28 and the biological half life was 2.5 days. Genetic variances attributed to sire and dam have been obtained with theoretical fractions of the various components due to different gene actions. The estimate of heritability in the narrow sense with its sampling error was 0.10 ± 0.017. An average genetic correlation of about 0.35 between random individuals in this generation indicates the reduction of heritability in this population relative to a random-bred population—a population from which the inbred strains are assumed to have been derived.

REFERENCES

CHAI, C. K., AMIN, A. & REINEKE, E. P. (1957) Thyroidal iodine metabolisms in inbred and F_1 hybrid mice, *Am. J. Physiol.* **188,** 499–502.

CHAI, C. K. (1958) Endocrine variation: thyroid function in inbred and F_1 hybrid mice, *J. Heredity* **49,** 143–148.

COMSTOCK, R. E. (1955) Theory of quantitative genetics, *Synthesis Cold Spring Harbor Symposia Quant. Biol.* **20,** 93–102.

OSBORNE, R., & PATERSON, W. S. B. (1952) On the sampling variance of heritability estimates derived from variance analysis. *Proc. Roy. Soc. Edinburgh*, B **LXIV**, 456–461.
WRIGHT, S. (1921) System of mating II. The effect of inbreeding on the genetic composition of a population, *Genetics* **6**, 124–143.

APPENDIX

The diagram given in Fig. 2 illustrates the relationship between zygotes and gametes in the breeding system. a and b are path coefficients between mice in any two generations. G is the correlation between gametes and M is the correlation between zygotes. According to Wright (1921), the basic formulae for the path coefficients and correlations are:

$$a = \sqrt{\left[\frac{1}{2(1+G)}\right]}$$

$$b = \sqrt{\left[\frac{(1+G)}{2}\right]}$$

$$G = \{(\tfrac{1}{2})^n(1+G_A)\}$$

$$M = \{(\tfrac{1}{2})^{n-1}(1+G_A)\}/\sqrt{[(1+G_x)(1+G_y)]}$$

G_A refers to the inbreeding coefficient of the common ancestor.

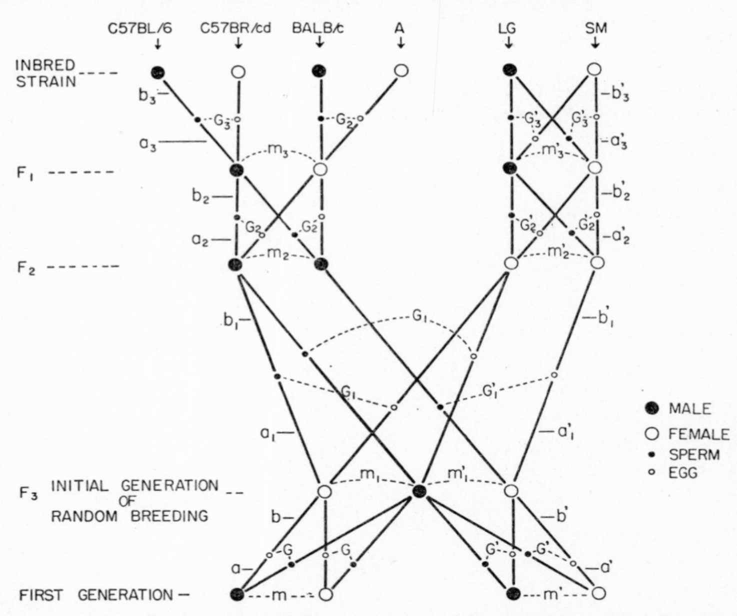

FIG. 2. A path coefficient diagram showing the relationships between individuals and gametes in the different generations. See Appendix for explanation of symbols and computations of the coefficients.

The mouse strains are assumed to be isogenic and the uniting gametes of any two strains are considered uncorrelated as far as this trait is concerned. Based on the above equations, the following path and correlation coefficients are obtained:

$a_3 = a'_3 = \sqrt{\frac{1}{2}}$	$a_2 = \sqrt{\frac{1}{2}}$
$b_3 = b'_3 = \sqrt{\frac{1}{2}}$	$a'_2 = \sqrt{(1/3)}$
$M_3 = 0$	$b_2 = b'_1 = \sqrt{\frac{1}{2}}$
$M'_3 = 1$	$M_2 = \frac{1}{2}$
$G_3 = G'_3 = 0$	$M'_2 = 2/3$
	$G_2 = 0$
	$G'_2 = \frac{1}{2}$
$a_1 = a'_1 = \sqrt{\frac{1}{2}}$	$a = \sqrt{(8/21)}$
$b_1 = \sqrt{\frac{1}{2}}$	$a' = \sqrt{(8/19)}$
$b'_1 = \sqrt{(3/4)}$	$b = b' = \sqrt{\frac{1}{2}}$
$M_1 = 5/8$ (full-sib)	$M = 13/21$
$M'_1 = 3/8$ (half-sib)	$M' = 11/19$
$G_1 = G'_1 = 0$	

In calculation of M it is easier to go back to the parents instead of using the above formula and consider the correlations between the four pairs only. For example:

$$m'_2 = 2(a'_2 b'_2 m'_1 b'_2 a'_2) + 2a'_2 b'_2 b'_2 a'_2 = 2/3.$$

The values for the other M's can be similarly calculated.

Correlations between sibs in the first generation with respective frequencies are as follows:

	frequency	M
Sibs from sibs (m)	1/8	13/21 = 0.6191
Sibs from non-sibs (m')	7/8	11/19 = 0.5790
Average		0.5840

The average correlation between random individuals in the first generation is too complicated to calculate, but can be obtained to a close approximation with the help of the average correlation between F_3 mates. The correlation between F_3 mates are:

	frequency	M
Sibs	1/8	5/8 = 0.6250
Non-sibs	7/8	3/8 = 0.3750
Average		0.4063

The connecting paths and correlations between gametes and individuals of different relationships are illustrated in Fig. 3. M_1 is the average correlation between the F_3 individuals. All the G's, b's and a's have the same coefficients. The value of each is as follows:

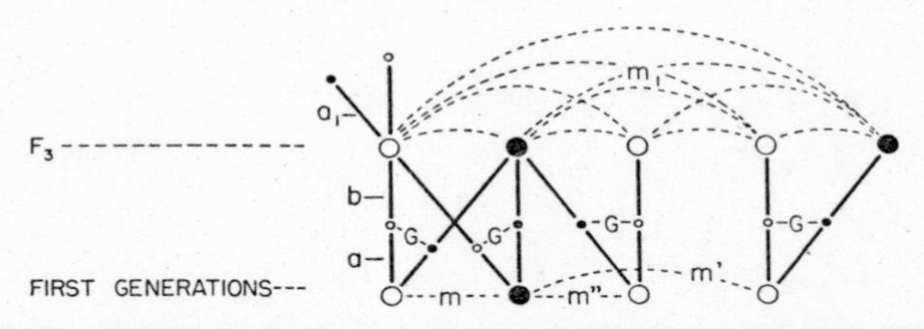

FIG. 3. A path coefficient diagram illustrating relationships between full-sibs, half-sibs and non-sibs in the first generation based on an average correlation of 0.4063 between animals in the F_3 generation. See Appendix for the computation of correlation and path coefficients.

$$M_1 = 0.4003$$
$$b = \sqrt{\tfrac{1}{2}}$$
$$a = \sqrt{(32/77)}$$
$$G = 13/64.$$

Using these values, we can compute the correlation coefficients between sibs, half-sibs and non-sibs. These values with respective frequencies are given as follows:

	Frequency	M
Sibs (m)	1/19	90/154 = 0.5844
Half-sibs (m')	1/19	71/154 = 0.4611
Non-sibs (m')	17/19	52/154 = 0.3377
Average		0.3572

AUTHOR INDEX

Page numbers in parentheses indicate entry is contained in references

INDEX

Page numbers in parentheses indicate entry is contained in references